Graduate Texts in Mathematics 234

Graduate Texts in Mathematics

(continued after index)

Palle E.T. Jorgensen

Analysis and Probability
Wavelets, Signals, Fractals

With graphics by Brian Treadway
58 figures and illustrations

 Springer

Palle E.T. Jorgensen
Mathematics Department
The University of Iowa
Iowa City, IA 52242
USA
jorgen@math.uiowa.edu

Mathematics Subject Classification (2000): 41A15, 42C20, 42A16, 42A65, 43A65, 46L55, 47C15, 60J15, 94A11

ISBN 978-1-4419-2126-0
e-ISBN 978-0-387-33082-2   e-ISBN: 0-387-33082-8
Printed on acid-free paper.

springer.com

Dedicated to the memory of Shizuo Kakutani

About the cover figure

The figure in the lower right-hand corner of the book cover illustrates the three themes from inside the book, *wavelets, signals, and fractals*: Firstly, this graph is one of the functions which are generated with the use of four magic numbers. Specifically, these same numbers also start an algorithmic generation of Daubechies wavelet functions, and the reader is referred to Figures 7.5 and 7.16 on pages 120–121 and 134 for more images, for mathematical background and explanations, more figures, as well as for theory and exercises in Chapter 7 itself.

To the experts: Figure 7.5 includes the cover figure, and it represents the progression of functions which starts with one of the four-tap cases, and which is governed by the so-called pyramid algorithm. The pyramid algorithm in turn is a delicate design used in the generation of sequences of basis functions. These functions are then further scaled and used in the representation of *wavelet packets*. And the representations and the choices leads to new bases, selections from "libraries of bases" and based on entropy considerations; hence probability!

More probability: The random-walk approach to the analysis of pyramid algorithms in turn is where the calculus of probability comes into the mix. And signals: To begin with, the use of four magic numbers is by adaptation from an algorithmic design which was first used by engineers, and which is fundamental in signal processing; now more recently adapted to image processing as well. But the particular function on the cover also represents the kind of sound signals that feature a beat. A quick glimpse of the figure finally reveals its fractal nature: By this we mean that shapes in a picture are repeated at different scales up to similarity; and which further display an underlying algorithm. Example: Large-scale shapes which envelop similar shapes at smaller scales!

Preface

If people do not believe that mathematics is simple, it is only because they do not realize how complicated life is.   —John von Neumann

While this is a course in analysis, our approach departs from the beaten path in some ways. Firstly, we emphasize a variety of connections to themes from neighboring fields, such as wavelets, fractals and signals; topics typically not included in a graduate analysis course. This in turn entails excursions into domains with a probabilistic flavor. Yet the diverse parts of the book follow a common underlying thread, and together they constitute a good blend; each part in the mix naturally complements the other.

In fact, there are now good reasons for taking a wider view of analysis, for example the fact that several applied trends have come to interact in new and exciting ways with traditional mathematical analysis—as it was taught in graduate classes for generations. One consequence of these impulses from "outside" is that conventional boundaries between core disciplines in mathematics have become more blurred.

Fortunately this branching out does not mean that students will need to start out with any different or additional prerequisites. In fact, the ideas involved in this book are intuitive, natural, many of them visual, and geometric. The required background is quite minimal and it does not go beyond what is typically required in most graduate programs.

We believe that now is a good time to slightly widen the horizons of the subject "analysis" as we teach it by stressing its relations to neighboring fields; in fact we believe that analysis is thereby enriched.

Despite the inclusion of themes from probability and even from engineering, the course still has an underlying core theme: A constructive approach to building bases in function spaces. The word "constructive" here refers to our use of recursive algorithms. As it turns out, the algorithmic ideas involved are commonly used in such diverse areas as wavelets, fractals, signal and image processing. And yet they share an underlying analysis core which we hope to bring to light.

Our inclusion here of some applied topics (bordering probability theory and engineering) we believe is not only useful in itself, but more importantly, core mathematics, and analysis in particular have benefited from their many interconnections to trends and influences from the "outside" world.

Yet our wider view of the topic analysis only entails a minor adjustment in course planning. Our branching out to some applications will be guided tours: to topics from probability theory (e.g., to certain random-walk models), and to signal and image processing. The ideas are presented from scratch, are easy to follow, and they do not require prior knowledge of probability or of engineering. But we will go a little beyond the more traditional dose of measure theory and matrix algebra that is otherwise standard or conventional fare in most first-year graduate courses.

For those reasons we believe the book may also be suitable for a "second analysis course," and that it leaves the instructor a variety of good options for covering a selection of neighboring disciplines and applications in more depth.

Iowa City,
June 2006

Palle E. T. Jorgensen

Contents

Drawing by the author, next page:
Wavelet algorithms are good for vast sets of numbers.
An engineering friend described the old approach to data mining as
"Just drop a computer down onto a gigantic set of unstructured numbers!"
*(*data mining: *see Section 6.2, pp. 102–105, and the Glossary, pp. xxiv–xxv).*

Getting started

From its shady beginnings devising gambling strategies and counting corp-
ses in medieval London, probability theory and statistical inference now
emerge as better foundations for scientific models, especially those of the
process of thinking and as essential ingredients of theoretical mathematics,
even the foundations of mathematics itself. —David Mumford

An apology

You ask: "Why all the fuss?" — Wavelets, signals, fractals? Isn't all of this merely a
fad? Or a transient popularity trend? And what's the *probability* part in the book all
about? And non-commuting operators? As for bases in linear spaces, what's wrong
with Gram–Schmidt?

You may think: "Fourier has served us well for ages; so why do we need all the
other basis functions?" — Wavelets and so on? — And why engineering topics in a
mathematics course? And the pictures? Are they really necessary?

And there are signal processing and image processing!? — Yes, technology is
lovely, but why not leave it to the engineers?

Response: The links between mathematics and engineering are much deeper than
the fact that we mathematicians teach service courses for engineers. Our bread and
butter!

Mathematics draws ideas and strengths from the outside world, and the connections to parts of engineering have been a boon to mathematics: From signal processing to wavelet analysis! That is true even if we forget about all of the practical applications emerging from these connections. Without inspiration from the neighboring
sciences, mathematics would in all likelihood become rather sterile, and overly for-
mal. I see opportunities at crossroads. In this book you will see the benefits mathematics is reaping from trends and topics in engineering. It is witnessed in a striking
way by exciting developments in wavelets. From wavelets we see how notions of

scale-similarity can be exploited in basis computations that use tricks devised for signal processing. Just open the book and glance at some of the wavelet functions. At the same time, the key notion of self-similarity, such as the scale-similarity used everywhere for wavelets, is essential to our understanding of fractals: Fern-like pictures that look the same at small and at large scales. One problem in the generation of wavelet bases is selecting the "nice" (here this means differentiable) wavelets among huge families of fractal-looking (non-smooth, or singular) functions. L^2-functions can be very "bad" indeed!! Computers generate the good and the bad, and we are left with the task of sorting them out and making selections. We will see (directly from large libraries of pictures) that mathematical wavelet machines are more likely to spit out bad functions unless they are told where to concentrate the search from the intrinsic mathematics.

These wavelets, signals, and fractals are things that have caught our attention in recent decades, but the mathematical part of this has roots back at least a hundred years, for example, to Alfred Haar and to Oliver Heaviside at the turn of the last century. From Haar we have the first wavelet basis, and with Heaviside we see the beginning of signal analysis. It is unlikely that either one knew about the other. Ironically, at the time (1909), Haar's paper had little impact and was hardly noticed, even on the small scale of "notice" that is usually applied to mathematics papers. Haar's wonderful wavelet only began to draw attention in the mid-nineteen-eighties when the connections to modern signal processing became much better understood. These connections certainly served as a main catalyst in what are now known as wavelet tools in pure and applied mathematics. But at the outset, the pioneers in wavelets had to "rediscover" a lot of stuff from signal processing: frequency bands, high-pass, low-pass, analysis and synthesis using down-sampling, and up-sampling, reconstruction of signals, resolution of images; all tools that have wonderful graphics representations in the engineering literature.

But still, why would we think that Fourier's basis, and his lovely integral decomposition, are not good enough? Many reasons: Fourier's method has computational drawbacks. This was less evident before computers became common and began to play important roles in applied and theoretical work. But expansion of functions or signals into basis decompositions (called "analysis" in signal processing) involves basis coefficients (Fourier coefficients, and so on), and if we are limited to Fourier bases, then the computation of the coefficients must by necessity rely on integration. "Computers can't integrate!" Hmmm! Well, not directly. The problem must first be discretized. And there is need for a more direct and algorithmic approach. Hence the wavelet algorithm! In any case, algorithms are central in mathematics even if you do not concern yourself with computers. And it is the engineering connections that inspired the most successful algorithms in our subject.

Glossary

function, random variable, signal, state, sequence (incl. vector-valued), random walk, time-series, measurement, nested subspaces, refinement, multiresolution, scales of visual resolutions, operator, process, black box, observable (if selfadjoint), Fourier dual pair, generating function, time/frequency, P/Q, convolution, filter, smearing, decomposition (e.g., Fourier coefficients in a Fourier expansion), analysis, frequency components, integrate (e.g., inverse Fourier transform), reconstruct, synthesis, superposition, subspace, resolution, (signals in a) frequency band, Cuntz relations, perfect reconstruction from subbands, subband decomposition, inner product, correlation, transition probability, probability of transition from one state to another, $f_{\mathbf{out}} = T f_{\mathbf{in}}$, input/output, transformation of states, fractal, conditional expectation, martingale, data mining (A translation guide!)

> *"The question is," said Alice, "whether you can make words mean so many different things."*   —Lewis Carroll

This *glossary* consists of a list of terms used inside the book in varied contexts of mathematics, probability, engineering, and on occasion physics. To clarify the seemingly confusing use of up to four different names for the same idea or concept, we have further added informal explanations spelling out the reasons behind the differences in current terminology from neighboring fields.

When sorting through the disparate variations of lingo in the sciences, the more mundane problems of plain and "ordinary" languages might seem minor: There is the variety of differences from Indo-European to the schizophrenia of Finno-Hungarian. And inside the same building on campus, there are even the variations in lingo that separate areas of mathematics: If you are a mathematician doing analysis in "plain English" you might well learn to understand the "Portuguese" spoken by your colleagues in algebra; but when it comes to the Hungarian of an engineer, or the Bantu of some physicists, you can get lost or confused. A former student just wrote me about the language gulf between domestic mathematics and the jungle of industry. He now works in a company and is doing applied wavelets. And he writes that the language of *implementation* is quite different from that of our standard mathematics books.

DISCLAIMER: This glossary has the structure of four columns. A number of terms are listed line by line, and each line is followed by explanation. Some "terms" have up to four separate (yet commonly accepted) names. The last four terms in the list, "fractal," "conditional expectation," "martingale," and "data mining," are the only ones where I could think of only one name.

It should be added that my "descriptions" for the various terms are meant to stress intuitive aspects, as opposed to mathematical definitions. One reason for stressing the intuition behind the concepts is that there is not quite agreement about the precise meaning of some of the terms in the four fields: in mathematics, in probability, in engineering, and in physics.

MATHEMATICS	PROBABILITY	ENGINEERING	PHYSICS
function (measurable)	**random variable**	**signal**	**state**

Mathematically, functions may map between any two sets, say, from X to Y; but if X is a probability space (typically called Ω), it comes with a σ-algebra $\mathcal{B}$ of measurable sets, and probability measure P. Elements E in $\mathcal{B}$ are called events, and P(E) the probability of E. Corresponding measurable functions with values in a vector space are called random variables, a terminology which suggests a stochastic viewpoint. The function values of a random variable may represent the outcomes of an experiment, for example "throwing of a die." In this simplest experiment, the range of the random variable is the set of integers from 1 to 6, the six possible measurements resulting from the experiment.

Yet, function theory is widely used also in engineering where functions are typically thought of as signal. In this case, X may be the real line for time, or $\mathbb{R}^d$. And I noticed that engineers visualize functions as signals. A particular signal may have a stochastic component, and this feature simply introduces an extra stochastic variable into the "signal," for example noise.

Turning to physics, in our present application, the physical functions will be typically be in some L^2-space, and L^2-functions with unit norm represent quantum mechanical "states."

sequence (incl. vector-valued)	**random walk**	**time-series**	**measurement**

Mathematically, a sequence is a function defined on the integers $\mathbb{Z}$ or on subsets of $\mathbb{Z}$, for example the natural numbers $\mathbb{N}$. Hence, if time is discrete, this to the engineer represents a time series, such as a speech signal, or any measurement which depends on time. But we will also allow functions on lattices such as $\mathbb{Z}^d$.

In the case $d = 2$, we may be considering the grayscale numbers which represent exposure in a digital camera. In this case, the function (grayscale) is defined on a subset of $\mathbb{Z}^2$, and is then simply a matrix.

A random walk on $\mathbb{Z}^d$ is an assignment of a sequential and random motion as a function of time. The randomness presupposes assigned probabilities. But we will use the term "random walk" also in connection with random walks on combinatorial trees.

nested subspaces	**refinement**	**multiresolution**	**scales of visual resolutions**

While finite or infinite families of nested subspaces are ubiquitous in mathematics, and have been popular in Hilbert-space theory for generations (at least since the 1930s), this idea was revived in a different guise in 1986 by Stéphane Mallat, then an engineering graduate student; see [Mal89]. In its adaptation to wavelets, the idea is now referred to as the multiresolution method.

What made the idea especially popular in the wavelet community was that it offered a skeleton on which various discrete algorithms in applied mathematics could be attached and turned into wavelet constructions in harmonic analysis. In fact what we now call multiresolutions have come to signify a crucial link between the world of discrete wavelet algorithms, which are popular in computational mathematics and in engineering (signal/image processing, data mining, etc.) on the one side, and on the other side continuous wavelet bases in function spaces, especially in $L^2(\mathbb{R}^d)$. Further, the multiresolution idea closely mimics how fractals are analyzed with the use of finite function systems.

But in mathematics, or more precisely in operator theory, the underlying idea dates back to work of John von Neumann, Norbert Wiener, and Herman Wold, where nested and closed subspaces in Hilbert space were used extensively in an axiomatic approach to stationary processes, especially for time series. Wold proved that any (stationary) time series can be decomposed into two different parts: The first (deterministic) part can be exactly described by a linear combination of its own past, while the second part is the opposite extreme; it is *unitary*, in the language of von Neumann.

von Neumann's version of the same theorem is a pillar in operator theory. It states that every isometry in a Hilbert space H is the unique sum of a shift isometry and a unitary operator, i.e., the initial Hilbert space H splits canonically as an orthogonal sum of two subspaces H_s and H_u in H, one which carries the shift operator, and the other H_u the unitary part. The shift isometry is defined from a nested scale of closed spaces V_n, such that the intersection of these spaces is H_u.

However, Stéphane Mallat was motivated instead by the notion of scales of resolutions in the sense of optics. This in turn is based on a certain "artificial-intelligence" approach to vision and optics, developed earlier by David Marr at MIT, an approach which imitates the mechanism of vision in the human eye.

The connection from these developments in the 1980s back to von Neumann is this: Each of the closed subspaces V_n corresponds to a level of resolution in such a way that a larger subspace represents a finer resolution. Resolutions are relative, not absolute! In this view, the relative complement of the smaller (or coarser) subspace in larger space then represents the visual

MATHEMATICS   PROBABILITY   ENGINEERING   PHYSICS

detail which is added in passing from a blurred image to a finer one, i.e., to a finer visual resolution.

This view became an instant hit in the wavelet community, as it offered a repository for the fundamental father and the mother functions, also called the scaling function φ, and the wavelet function ψ. Via a system of translation and scaling operators, these functions then generate nested subspaces, and we recover the scaling identities which initialize the appropriate algorithms. What results is now called the family of pyramid algorithms in wavelet analysis. The approach itself is called the multiresolution approach (MRA) to wavelets. And in the meantime various generalizations (GMRAs) have emerged.

In all of this, there was a second "accident" at play: As it turned out, pyramid algorithms in wavelet analysis now lend themselves via multiresolutions, or nested scales of closed subspaces, to an analysis based on frequency bands. Here we refer to bands of frequencies as they have already been used for a long time in signal processing.

Even though J. von Neumann and H. Wold had been using nested or scaled families of closed subspaces in representing past and future for time series, S. Mallat found that this same idea applies successfully to the representation of visual resolutions. And even more importantly, it offers a variety of powerful algorithms for processing of digital images.

Now parallel to all of this, pioneers in probability theory had in fact developed versions of the same refinement analysis. For example, in the theory of martingales, consistency relations may naturally be reformulated in the language of nested subspaces in Hilbert space.

One reason for the success in varied disciplines of the same geometric idea is perhaps that it is closely modeled on how we historically have represented numbers in the positional number system; see, e.g., [Knu81]. Analogies to the Euclidean algorithm seem especially compelling.

operator	process	black box	observable (if selfadjoint)

In linear algebra students are familiar with the distinctions between (linear) transformations T (here called "operators") and matrices. For a fixed operator $T: V \to W$, there is a variety of matrices, one for each choice of basis in V and in W. In many engineering applications, the transformations are not restricted to be linear, but instead represent some experiment ("black box," in Norbert Wiener's terminology), one with an input and an output, usually functions of time. The input could be an external voltage function, the black

MATHEMATICS   PROBABILITY   ENGINEERING   PHYSICS

box an electric circuit, and the output the resulting voltage in the circuit. (The output is a solution to a differential equation.)

This context is somewhat different from that of quantum mechanical (QM) operators $T: V \to V$ where V is a Hilbert space. In QM, selfadjoint operators represent observables such as position Q and momentum P, or time and energy.

Fourier dual pair	**generating function**	**time/frequency**	P/Q

The following dual pairs position Q/momentum P, and time/energy may be computed with the use of Fourier series or Fourier transforms; and in this sense they are examples of Fourier dual pairs. If for example time is discrete, then frequency may be represented by numbers in the interval $[\,0, 2\pi)$; or in $[\,0, 1)$ if we enter the number 2π into the Fourier exponential. Functions of the frequency are then periodic, so the two endpoints are identified. In the case of the interval $[\,0, 1)$, 0 on the left is identified with 1 on the right. So a low frequency band is an interval centered at 0, while a high frequency band is an interval centered at $1/2$. Let a function W on $[\,0, 1)$ represent a probability assignment. Such functions W are thought of as "filters" in signal processing. We say that W is low-pass if it is 1 at 0, or if it is near 1 for frequencies near 0. Low-pass filters pass signals with low frequencies, and block the others.

If instead some filter W is 1 at $1/2$, or takes values near 1 for frequencies near $1/2$, then we say that W is high-pass; it passes signals with high frequency.

convolution	—	**filter**	**smearing**

Pointwise multiplication of functions of frequencies corresponds in the Fourier dual time-domain to the operation of convolution (or of Cauchy product if the time-scale is discrete.) The process of modifying a signal with a fixed convolution is called a linear filter in signal processing. The corresponding Fourier dual frequency function is then referred to as "frequency response" or the "frequency response function."

More generally, in the continuous case, since convolution tends to improve smoothness of functions, physicists call it "smearing."

MATHEMATICS	PROBABILITY	ENGINEERING	PHYSICS
decomposition (e.g., Fourier coefficients in a Fourier expansion)	—	**analysis**	**frequency components**

Calculating the Fourier coefficients is "analysis," and adding up the pure frequencies (i.e., summing the Fourier series) is called synthesis. But this view carries over more generally to engineering where there are more operations involved on the two sides, e.g., breaking up a signal into its frequency bands, transforming further, and then adding up the "banded" functions in the end. If the signal out is the same as the signal in, we say that the analysis/synthesis yields perfect reconstruction.

MATHEMATICS	PROBABILITY	ENGINEERING	PHYSICS
integrate (e.g., inverse Fourier transform)	**reconstruct**	**synthesis**	**superposition**

Here the terms related to "synthesis" refer to the second half of the kind of signal-processing design outlined in the previous paragraph.

MATHEMATICS	PROBABILITY	ENGINEERING	PHYSICS
subspace	—	**resolution**	**(signals in a) frequency band**

For a space of functions (signals), the selection of certain frequencies serves as a way of selecting special signals. When the process of scaling is introduced into optics of a digital camera, we note that a nested family of subspaces corresponds to a grading of visual resolutions.

MATHEMATICS	PROBABILITY	ENGINEERING	PHYSICS
Cuntz relations	—	**perfect reconstruction from subbands**	**subband decomposition**

The operator relations of Joachim Cuntz described in detail in Chapter 7 serve to make precise the kind of signal-processing design outlined in the previous paragraph. Although anticipated by engineers, the Cuntz relations give a particularly elegant way for us to understand the geometry of iterated subdivision schemes which include a variety of models with perfect reconstruction from signal and image processing.

MATHEMATICS	PROBABILITY	ENGINEERING	PHYSICS
inner product	**correlation**	**transition probability**	**probability of transition from one state to another**

In many applications, a vector space with inner product captures perfectly the geometric and probabilistic features of the situation. This can be axiomatized in the language of Hilbert space; and the inner product is the most crucial ingredient in the familiar axiom system for Hilbert space.

$f_{\text{out}} = Tf_{\text{in}}$	—	**input/output**	**transformation of states**

Systems theory language for operators $T: V \to W$. Then vectors in V are input, and in the range of T output.

fractal	—	—	—

Intuitively, think of a fractal as reflecting similarity of scales such as is seen in fern-like images that look "roughly" the same at small and at large scales. While there may not be agreement about a rigorous mathematical definition, Mandelbrot originally defined *fractals* as sets whose Hausdorff–Besicovich dimension exceeded their topological dimension, but later accepted all self-similar, self-affine, or quasi-self-similar sets as fractals. Moreover, even more generally, the self-similarity could refer alternately to space, and to time. And further versatility was added, in that flexibility is allowed into the definition of "similar."

In this book, our focus is more narrowly on the self-affine variant (where computations are relatively simple); but in addition, we encounter the fractal concept in other contexts, e.g., for *measures*, and for probability processes (such as fractal Brownian motion). Further, we have stressed examples more than the general theory.

The fractal concept for measures is especially agreeable in the self-affine case, since affine maps act naturally on measures. So for each fractal dimension s, there is a corresponding s-fractal probability measure $\mu = \mu_s$ (see Chapter 4) which is the unique solution to a natural fixed-point equation, one which depends on s. Moreover, we may then recover this way the spatial fractal set itself as the support of this measure μ.

As for s-fractal Brownian motion (fBm), the "s-fractal" feature there refers to how the position X_t at time t of the fBm-process transforms under scaling of t: If time t scales by c, then the respective distributions before and after scaling are related by the power-law c^s. Specifically, for all t, the finite distributions calculated for X_{ct} and for $c^s X_t$ coincide.

MATHEMATICS   PROBABILITY   ENGINEERING   PHYSICS

—   **conditional**   —   —
                                 expectation

Let $(\Omega, \mathcal{A}, P)$ be a probability space.

Recall that a function $X: \Omega \to \mathbb{R}$ (the reals) is an $\mathcal{A}$-random variable if it is measurable with respect to the two σ-algebras on the domain and the target, i.e., $\mathcal{A}$ on Ω, and $\mathcal{B} :=$ the standard Borel σ-algebra on $\mathbb{R}$. For an $\mathcal{A}$-random variable X, let $E(X) := \int_\Omega X\, dP$, or simply $\langle X \rangle$ denote the corresponding mean (or expected value). If $\mathcal{D}$ is a sub-σ-algebra of $\mathcal{A}$, define a measure μ on $\mathcal{D}$ by $\mu(S) := \int_S X\, dP$ for $S \in \mathcal{D}$. Then denote by $E[X \mid \mathcal{D}]$ the Radon–Nikodym derivative of μ with respect to P.

Let Y be a second $\mathcal{A}$-random variable, and let $\mathcal{D} := \mathcal{D}_Y = Y^{-1}(\mathcal{B})$ be the smallest σ-algebra with respect to which Y is measurable. Then clearly $\mathcal{D}$ is a sub-σ-algebra of $\mathcal{A}$, and we set $E(X \mid Y) := E[X \mid \mathcal{D}] = \langle X \mid Y \rangle$. This extends naturally to the case when there is a finite family of $\mathcal{A}$-random variables in place of Y.

—   **martingale**   —   —

We use the term here only in its simplest form, the discrete case, called "discrete-time:" Let $(\Omega, \mathcal{A}, P)$ be a probability space. The following identity defines a martingale. Consider a sequence of $\mathcal{A}$-random variables X_0, $X_1, \ldots$ each with finite mean. We say it is a martingale if for each n, the conditional expectation of X_{n+1} given $X_0, X_1, \ldots, X_n$ is X_n, i.e., $\langle X_{n+1} \mid X_0, \ldots, X_n \rangle = X_n$ (see Feller's book [Fel71, p. 210]). The term was first used to describe a type of wagering in which the bet is doubled or halved after a loss or win, respectively. The concept of martingales is due to Lévy, and it was developed extensively by Doob [Doo94].

A random walk on the integers with each successive step left or right equally likely, i.e., with equal transition probabilities ($p_L = p_R = 1/2$), is an example of a martingale.

—   —   **data mining**   —

The problem of how to handle and make use of large volumes of data is a corollary of the digital revolution. As a result, the subject of data mining itself changes rapidly. Digitized information (data) is now easy to capture automatically and to store electronically [HuTK05]. In science, in commerce, and in industry, data represents collected observations and information: In business, there is data on markets, competitors, and customers [AgKu04a, AgKu04b]. In manufacturing, there is data for optimizing production opportunities, and for improving processes [Kus02, Kus05]. A tremendous

MATHEMATICS   PROBABILITY   ENGINEERING   PHYSICS

potential for data mining exists in medicine [KuLD01, KuDS05], genetics [ShKu04], and energy [KuBu05]. But raw data is not always directly usable, as is evident by inspection. A key to advances is our ability to *extract information and knowledge* from the data (hence "data mining"), and to understand the phenomena governing data sources. Data mining is now taught in a variety of forms in engineering departments, as well as in statistics and computer science departments.

One of the structures often hidden in data sets is some degree of *scale*. The goal is to detect and identify one or more natural global and local scales in the data. Once this is done, it is often possible to detect associated similarities of scale, much like the familiar scale-similarity from multidimensional wavelets, and from fractals. Indeed, various adaptations of wavelet-like algorithms have been shown to be useful. These algorithms themselves are useful in *detecting* scale-similarities, and are applicable to other types of pattern recognition. Hence, in this context, generalized multiresolutions offer another tool for discovering structures in large data sets, such as those stored in the resources of the Internet. Because of the sheer volume of data involved, a strictly manual analysis is out of the question. Instead, sophisticated query processors based on statistical and mathematical techniques are used in generating insights and extracting conclusions from data sets. But even such an approach breaks down as the quantity of data grows and the number of dimensions increases. Instead there is a new research area (knowledge discovery in databases (KDD)) which develops various tools for automated data analysis.

However, statistics is still at the heart of the problem of *inference* from the data. The widespread use of statistics, pattern recognition, and machine-learning algorithms is somewhat hindered in many areas by our ability to collect large volumes of data. The next limitation in the subject arises when the data is too large to fit in the main computer memory. As a result, we are faced with new issues, e.g., quality of data, creative data analysis, and data transformation [Kus01]. Theory and hypothesis formation now becomes critical in our task of deriving insights into underlying phenomena from the raw data. Various adaptations of wavelet-like algorithms have again proved useful in detecting scale-similarities, and in other types of pattern recognition. Hence in this context wavelet ideas offer another tool for discovering structures in vast data sets, such as those in the resources of the Internet. And there are now a variety of such effective Web mining tools in use.

Areas of data mining include problems of representation, search complexity, and automated use of prior knowledge to help in a data search. Thus we see the beginnings of a new science for efficient inference from massive data sets.

Multiresolutions

If you stop to think about it, it is really ironic that Haar's wavelet basis (Figures 1.2 and 7.4, pp. 13 and 118–119) was missed for so long. It is especially ironic since Haar's work in 1909–1910 had in it implicitly the key idea which got wavelet mathematics started on a roll 75 years later with Yves Meyer, Ingrid Daubechies, Stéphane Mallat, and others—namely the idea of a multiresolution. In that respect Haar was ahead of his time. In 1909, Haar's measure on non-abelian groups became much more widely known.

Yet, returning to wavelets, the word "multiresolution" suggests a connection to optics from physics. So that should have been a hint to mathematicians to take a closer look at trends in signal and image processing! Moreover, even staying within mathematics, it turns out that as a general notion this same idea of a "multiresolution" has long roots in mathematics, even in such modern and pure areas as operator theory and Hilbert-space geometry. And in probability theory and in dynamics, A.N. Kolmogorov and J. Doob had already long ago identified martingales, again close cousins of multiresolutions. Looking even closer at these interconnections, we can now recognize scales of subspaces (so-called multiresolutions) in classical algorithmic construction of orthogonal bases in inner-product spaces, now taught in lots of mathematics courses under the name of the Gram–Schmidt algorithm. Indeed, a closer look at good old Gram–Schmidt reveals that it is a matrix algorithm, Hence new mathematical tools involving non-commutativity! Obviously, function spaces are infinite-dimensional. Since Gram–Schmidt is recursive, it does not stop, at least not until we tell it to stop. We do that when the basis expansion has achieved a "good enough" approximation to the true function, or the true signal or image which is being analyzed.

Approximation? So we must retain the "significant" terms in an analysis expansion and throw out the other terms! To know which is "significant," thresholds must be assigned, and probabilities, and even entropy, from information theory must be used.

A Wiener process, carried to the limit, gives a nowhere differentiable continuous Brownian path, parametrized by time. This is *a model* for a physical Brownian trajectory of an actual particle. Actual Brownian particles do not follow paths that are *precisely* of this nature.

If the signal to be analyzed is an image, then why not select a fixed but suitable *resolution* (or a subspace of signals corresponding to a selected resolution), and then do the computations there? Of course, the selection of a fixed "resolution" is dictated by practical concerns. That idea was key in turning computation of wavelet coefficients into iterated matrix algorithms. As the matrix operations get large, the computation is carried out in a variety of paths arising from big matrix products. Such paths have been studied in probability since Kolmogorov in the 1930s, but paths are perhaps better known in their continuous variants. Yet, what we know about the continuous case is the result of limit considerations arising from the discrete case. The dichotomy, continuous vs. discrete, is quite familiar to engineers. The industrial engineers typically work with huge volumes of numbers.

Numbers! — So why wavelets? Well, what matters to the industrial engineer is not really the wavelets, but the fact that special wavelet functions serve as an efficient way to encode large data sets—I mean encode for computations. And the wavelet algorithms are computational. They work on numbers. Encoding numbers into pictures, images, or graphs of functions comes later, perhaps at the very end of the computation. But without the graphics, I doubt that we would understand any of this half as well as we do now. The same can be said for the many issues that relate to the crucial mathematical concept of self-similarity, as we know it from fractals, and more generally from recursive algorithms.

Prerequisites and cross-audience

I have used preliminary versions of this book in my courses. These courses fit the bill: "a second course in analysis," in one form or the other. Some of my courses were more traditional, and for mathematics students, while others served a quite mixed audience, including students from engineering. At my university, there is a serious demand for interdisciplinary mathematics courses, not only involving engineers, but also students from physics, statistics, computer science, finance, and more. And I expect that this is a national trend. However, we found that many traditional mathematics texts are too narrowly specialized and not well suited for cross-audiences. With that in mind, we have attempted a wider focus even within mathematics proper; specifically, we feel that a graduate text in analysis should be relevant to computational mathematics and to numerical analysis. Our present emphasis on wavelets, signals and fractals invites such a wider focus.

The students in my courses typically had some familiarity with function theory and measures. But their background was always diverse and varied. To accommodate diverse audiences (referring to the level of mathematical maturity, specialization, etc.), I included in my courses, and in the book, facts from a variety of topics.

How? Some of the exercises serve this purpose, assimilation. For example, Exercises 1.11 through 1.14 have the flavor of *tutorials*; they let students pick up on some quite basic but central points from Fourier series, inner-product spaces, linear transformations, matrices (finite and infinite), and Hilbert space. Working the exercises is the best way for students to learn and review fundamentals! In these multipart exercises, the reader is then guided step by step through the issues, but as they are needed in the text. As other basic topics are needed later in the book, there are then other multipart exercises that accomplish the same goal: e.g., Exercise 2.6 (integral operators), Exercises 2.7 through 2.10, and 9.8–9.9 (Brownian motion, including the fractional variant), Exercises 7.2 through 7.7 (matrix theory), and Exercises 7.9 through 7.11 (tensor product of Hilbert space, and product measure). An advantage of this approach is that students then see and learn these preliminaries precisely in the form in which they are used in the course.

When I was teaching mixed groups of students, the engineers in my class typically came from the following departments, EE (electrical engineers), electrical and computer engineering, communications, mechanical, industrial engineering, data mining, sensors—among others! Generally, the engineers looked for an agreeable mathematical presentation of central ideas from signal and image processing. ("Why then wavelets?" you may say. Reason: Wavelet *algorithms* share a lot in common with signal/image processing schemes! And they are *used* by engineers!)

Some of the engineers in my course worked at our University Hospital, a large teaching hospital. Their projects involve designing and improving technology in medical imaging.

I recently gave one of my thesis students (with a good background in mathematics and engineering) the following assignment: "Work out the mathematics used in the processing of color images in a digital camera!" Reason: This is actually lovely algorithmic matrix theory, and it is based directly on wavelet algorithms.

Challenge! There is a huge difference in jargon used by engineers and by mathematicians (not to mention the other disciplines!); and often there is a call for some serious translation of technical lingo before you discover that the two groups are talking about the same thing. At times, my course would begin with first overcoming the cultural and the communication barriers; hence the system of interrelated *appendices* on polyphase matrices in the back of the book, and the *list of names and discoveries* on pages xxx–xxxiii below.

Aim and scope

The aim of this book is to show how to use processes from probability, random walks on branches, and their path-space measures in the study of convergence questions from harmonic analysis, with particular emphasis on the infinite products that arise in the analysis of wavelets.

The focus is by nature interdisciplinary, and it is motivated by some new mathematical trends that are still somewhat in a state of flux. We outline how they combine diverse areas from mathematics and engineering in unexpected ways. As a result, we aim to address a diverse audience, perhaps unusually diverse, ranging from pure to applied (engineering and physics), from probability (random walk) to analysis (infinite products), from wavelets to fractals, from linear to non-linear, from function theory to non-abelian operator algebras, from Lebesgue to Hausdorff measure, and from classical (Fourier) to modern (wavelets and more generally scale-similarity in time and space). This diversity presents us with a challenge, and we have taken pains to articulate the interconnections, describe a coherent unity, and address the union (and not the intersection) of the various groups of readers who have an interest in this area of mathematics. Our exposition is designed to reach the beginning graduate student, having in mind both students and workers meeting at the crossroads in a variety of fields.

Self-similarity

The idea of self-similarity is common to the construction of wavelets, various fractals, and graph systems. These subjects may seem diverse, and they are often thought of as disparate. However, we hope to outline how the notion of self-similarity runs through these subjects as a red thread connecting central themes: themes from harmonic analysis, discrete mathematics, probability, and operator algebras. In addition, we list the two papers [BoNe03] and [Nek04] as sources that cover this from a somewhat different but related angle.

Indeed, the concept of self-similarity has proved ubiquitous as well as fundamental in mathematics and in diverse applications, perhaps because it serves to *renormalize* a rich variety of structures on nested families of scales (for example, similarity scales in time and/or in space). In wavelet theory, the scales may be represented in *resolutions* (a name deriving from optics) taking the form of nested systems of linear spaces. Similar such systems occur in fractal theory and in dynamics. And in quantum field theory [Nel73], the self-similarity idea underlies the notion of "renormalization group," while in C^*-algebra theory [Dav96], it gives rise to representations of algebras on relations and generators, such as operator algebras on infinite particle systems [PoSt70], or the algebras of Cuntz, or Cuntz–Krieger. In fact, the pioneering paper [Bat87] early on stressed a fascinating connection between the renormalization group in quantum physics on the one hand, and a certain fundamental wavelet construction on the other.

To help the reader better see the bigger picture which we wish to present, we have included a system of interrelated appendices outlining a certain geometric approach to subband filtering which is both more operator-theoretic and more general than is usual. Our appendices build a bridge between two ways of doing wavelet/fractal subdivision algorithms, one based on quadrature conditions and their generalizations, and the other based on unitary operator functions and on representations of a certain C^*-algebra.

Recent developments in operator theory, approximation theory, orthogonal expansions, and wavelets demonstrate the need for a combination of techniques from analysis and probability. Since the relevant tools and techniques for these new applications are often interdisciplinary, they are not always readily available in the standard textbook literature. Or if they are, they are scattered over a number of older books or papers which are written for other purposes and aimed at other applications. The analysis problems that we focus on here are typically not presented together with their counterparts from probability theory: random walk, path space, infinite products, martingales, Kolmogorov extension techniques in their classical form, and in some of their modern non-commutative versions.

This book aims to fill an apparent gap in the literature, or at least to help bridge a gap. It gives a rigorous treatment of a number of convergence questions, and it also includes some new results. Our use of analysis in this book relies heavily on probabilistic tools, and the book offers a presentation of them.

New issues, new tools

This book is primarily about wavelets, but it takes a new direction in the subject: While it is about convergence issues, the questions come from applications with a twist that is different from the one that has dominated the literature.

The aim of this book is broader. We wish to show how some methods from probability, operator algebras, and random-walk theory can be used to prove theorems in analysis. The ideas from probability that we will use include processes, random walk on branches, and path-space measures associated with them. The recurring theme will be the use of these ideas from probability in the study of convergence questions from harmonic analysis. Our emphasis is on the kinds of infinite products that arise in the analysis of wavelets and more generally in the harmonic analysis of iterated function systems, as well as in dynamical systems.

Many modern wavelet constructions from the past few years are by necessity frequency-localized; and because of that fact, the convergence issues and the tools that must be employed to resolve them are completely different from the more traditional ones that were developed and tailored in the 1980s to time-localized functions, i.e., the wavelets that have the scaling function (the father function) and the wavelet function (the mother function) both of compact support. Those are the wavelets where multiresolution tools have been especially successful.

By contrast, the frequency-localized wavelets have compact support only in the Fourier-dual variable, and their resolution subspaces are typically not singly generated, so the more traditional multiresolution methods have fallen short, at least in the form in which they originally were given.

What this means is that some of the fundamental issues concerning pointwise convergence in the theory must be attacked with quite different tools: in this case, with tools from random walk, probability, and the theory of diffusions, processes, and martingales.

So the book is on the interface and applications of probability, random walk, and path-space measures to convergence questions in harmonic analysis and dynamics.

List of names and discoveries

Many of the main discoveries summarized below are now lore, and they are often used inside the book without explicit mention of the pioneers by name. (For page numbers of the indicated chapters and figures, refer to Contents on pages ix–xiii above and Figures on pages xxxix–xlii below.)

1807 Jean Baptiste Joseph Fourier mathematics, physics (heat conduction)	Expressing functions as sums of sine and cosine waves of frequencies in arithmetic progession (now called Fourier series). Received somewhat late recognition for his work.	Section 6.2 [Zyg32]
1909 Alfred Haar mathematics	Discovered, while a student of David Hilbert, an orthonormal basis consisting of step functions, applicable both to functions on an interval, and functions on the whole real line. While it was not realized at the time, Haar's construction was a precursor of what is now known as the Mallat subdivision, and multiresolution method, as well as the subdivision wavelet algorithms.	Chapters 5, 6, 7, see also Figures 1.2, 6.1, 7.4 [Haa10, Waln02]
1946 Denes Gabor (Nobel Prize): physics (optics, holography)	Discovered basis expansions for what might now be called time-frequency wavelets, as opposed to time-scale wavelets, the subject of this book.	[JaMR01, Gro01]
1948 Claude Elwood Shannon mathematics, engineering (information theory)	A rigorous formula used by the phone company for sampling speech signals. Quantizing information, entropy, founder of what is now called the mathematical theory of communication.	Section 1.4 [Sha49, AlGr01]
1935 Andrei Nikolaevich Kolmogorov information theory, probability, statistics	Pioneered the use of probability theory in analysis, especially the use of measures on path space, the Kolmogorov consistency relation.	Chapters 1, 2, 5 [Kol77, Wil91, Nev65]
1976 Claude Garland, Daniel Esteban (both) signal processing	Discovered subband coding of digital transmission of speech signals over the telephone	Chapter 7, Figures 7.7, 7.14 [JaMR01, StNg96]

1981 Jean Morlet petroleum engineer	Suggested the term "ondelettes." J.M. decomposed reflected seismic signals into sums of "wavelets (Fr.: ondelettes) of constant shape," i.e., a decomposition of signals into wavelet shapes, selected from a library of such shapes (now called wavelet series). Received somewhat late recognition for his work. Due to contributions by A. Grossman and Y. Meyer, Morlet's discoveries have now come to play a central role in the theory.	Section 7.2 [JaMR01, GrMo84]
1984 Alex Grossman mathematics, quantum physics	Pioneered the theory of coherent (quantum-mechanical) states, precursors for dual wavelet systems. Mentor for, and coauthor with, J. Morlet and I. Daubechies.	Sections 8.1–8.2 [Dau92, MeCo97, GrMo84]
1985 Yves Meyer mathematics, applications	Mentor for A. Cohen, S. Mallat, and other of the wavelet pioneers, Y.M. discovered infinitely often differentiable wavelets.	[JaMR01, Mey89, MeCo97, Mey97]
1989 Albert Cohen mathematics (orthogonality relations), numerical analysis	Discovered the use of wavelet filters in the analysis of wavelets—the so-called Cohen condition for orthogonality.	Chapters 5, 6 [Coh90, Dau92, Law91a, Law91b]
1986 Stéphane Mallat mathematics, signal and image processing	While still a graduate student in engineering, working on vision, and on the Littlewood–Paley octaves, formalized and discovered what is now known as the subdivision, and multiresolution method, as well as the subdivision wavelet algorithms. This allowed the effective use of operators in the Hilbert space $L^2(\mathbb{R})$, and of the parallel computational use of recursive matrix algorithms.	Chapters 5, 6, 7 [Dau92, Mal89, Mal98]

1987 Ingrid Daubechies mathematics, physics, and communications	Discovered differentiable wavelets, with the number of derivatives roughly half the length of the support interval. Further found polynomial algorithmic for their construction (with coauthor Jeff Lagarias; joint spectral radius formulas).	Chapters 1, 7, see also Figures 7.16, 7.5 [Dau92]
1991 Wayne Lawton mathematics (the wavelet transfer operator)	Discovered the use of a transfer operator in the analysis of wavelets: orthogonality and smoothness.	Chapters 8, 9 [Law91a, Law91b, Dau92]
1999 Richard Gundy use of probability in the analysis of filters	Discovered the use of martingales and of Kolmogorov's 0–1 law for the rigorous analysis of wavelet filters in the analysis of wavelets—refined and corrected the so-called Cohen condition, orthogonality condition for wavelet filters.	Chapters 1, 5, 6 [Gun99, Gun04]
1992 The FBI using wavelet algo- rithms in digitizing and compressing fingerprints	C. Brislawn and his group at Los Alamos created the theory and the codes which allowed the compression of the enormous FBI fingerprint file, creating A/D, a new database of fingerprints.	Chapter 7 [Bri95, BrRo91, JaMR01]
2000 The International Standards Organization	A wavelet-based picture compression standard, called JPEG 2000, for digital encoding of images.	Chapters 3, 7, especially the figures [JaMR01]
1994 David Donoho statistics, mathematics	Pioneered the use of wavelet bases and tools from statistics to "denoise" images and signals.	Chapter 7 [DoJo94, JaMR01]

General theory

We consider a measurable space X with an endomorphism σ, mapping onto X, such that the inverse image of every point is of the same finite cardinality. The branches of the inverse are assigned probabilities by some positive function W, and we study the corresponding transition operator, also called the Perron–Frobenius–Ruelle operator $R = R_W$. By iteration, the branches determine a tree, and we study an associated random walk on this tree, and the transition measures indexed by the points in X.

While there is a considerable literature on this setup already, the various papers place some kind of regularity condition on W, or on the system, (X, σ), and the branches of the inverse. Our setting, assumptions and conclusions are in the measurable category. In contrast, when X is assumed to have a differentiable structure, and W is assumed Lipschitz, then, by Ruelle's theorem, there are solutions to the equations $\nu R = \nu$, $Rh = h$, and $\nu(h) = 1$, where ν is a Borel probability measure on X, and h is a non-negative measurable function on X.

While the measure ν may not exist in the general measurable setting, we develop formulas for solutions h to the equation $Rh = h$, the so-called R-harmonic functions, and we give applications to the case when R is the wavelet transition operator defined from some measurable low-pass filter. In that setting, there are existence questions, and we show that the random-walk properties determine a variety of notions of wavelet orthogonality properties.

A word about the graphics and the illustrations

We owe much to the professional skill of Brian Treadway in programming and creating the computer generated renditions of the numerous figures in this book. They are an essential part of the exposition. A list of our numbered figures, giving their captions and the page numbers where they appear, follows this "Getting started" section. This list includes the text for our figure captions. Readers are encouraged to preview the figures themselves to appreciate our use of trees, graphs, programming diagrams, subband-filtering schemes from engineering (signal/image processing), and a number of other visual tools and presentations. The author has himself found the figures, the graphs, and visualization of the algorithms exceptionally helpful in learning, teaching and discovering some of the material in this book; but more importantly, also in understanding the deeper connections in the subject.

The Mathematica program used in the production of Figure 7.5 (pp. 120–121) by Brian Treadway is given in full in the narrative in the "References and remarks" section at the end of Chapter 7 (pp. 152–153). The two figures 7.4–7.5 (pp. 118–121, each figure spanning two pages) serve to illustrate a particular aspect of the so-called pyramid algorithm for wavelets, i.e., the recursive algorithm which is used in among other things in the creation of wavelet packets; see, e.g., Figure 7.3 (p. 113). For this purpose, the algorithm is used in the two figures with two different initializations.

The first is the simpler one, the Haar scaling function (see Figure 7.4, pp. 118–119), and it makes the dyadic subdivision especially transparent. The second initializes with Daubechies' scaling function (see Figures 7.5 and 7.16, pp. 120–121 and 134). The reason for the name "wavelet packet" (which is the subject of Chapter 7) is especially transparent in Figure 7.5. Notice especially two aspects of the progression of functions in the sequence of graphs inside the respective figures: In moving from one graph to the next, the numerical frequency appears to increase with each subdivision-step. But in addition, an enveloping shadow emerges in the progression through the graphs, and a shape of a wave with a lower frequency (i.e., longer wavelength) appears to "capture" and group the functions themselves into packets, much like the enveloping "beats" from music composition. We mention these figures already now, as the geometry of the steps that go into the diverse recursive algorithms are especially transparent to the naked eye in Figures 7.4–7.5. See also the sequence of figures 7.6–7.13 (pp. 123–128) for the programming aspects of the same idea. Specifically, Figure 7.13 stresses the matrix steps that are indicated by the recursions.

We further stress that these figures play a central role in our presentation in this book: Some figures illustrate the kind of self-similarity in time and in space coordinates that is typical both in fractal analysis, and in the study of wavelets; while others illustrate decision trees; and yet others make clear the kinds of arrow-flow diagrams which are popular in building of recursive algorithms, and in programming more generally. See, e.g., [Knu84] as well as Knuth's monumental volumes [Knu81]. We mention Knuth's article [Knu84] as it emphasizes in a special case both the stochastic and the algorithmic features of the fundamental subdivision/filter algorithm.

For explanation of the cover figure, see "About the cover figure" at the front of the book (p. vi).

Special features of the book

A main aim of this book is to show how these ideas have proved fruitful in both the study of iterated function systems (IFS), see Chapter 4, and of wavelets, see Chapter 7. While the pyramid algorithm (in its diverse incarnations) is now typically identified with wavelets, it in fact has a long history in engineering, information theory [Sha49], and symbolic dynamics. The connection to signal and image processing from engineering was emphasized in our survey article [Jor03]; but see also [DoMSS03, Mal98, StNg96] for much more detail. The connections to symbolic dynamics are manifold, but we wish to especially recommend the beautiful and inspiring invitation [Rad99] addressed to students, and authored by Charles Radin.

The book contains four separate items which we hope will help readers reconcile current terminology used simultaneously in mathematics and in applications (especially in signal-processing engineering, and in physics—notably in optics!) These four elements are as follows: (i) a system of interrelated appendices (pp. 205–222), (ii) a list of comments for mathematicians on signal/image processing jargon ("Afterword," pp. 223–230), and (iii) a list of names (with historical comments) of mathematicians and scientists, both past and current era mathematicians/engineers/scientists who made pioneering contributions to the main ideas presented in the book (pp. xxx–xxxiii above).

Finally, in item (iv) we include a *glossary* consisting of a list of terms occurring in the book in varied contexts of mathematics, probability, engineering, and on occasion physics (pp. xvii–xxv above). To reduce the apparent confusion created by the same concept having up to four different names, the glossary includes informal explanations spelling out the reasons behind the differences in current terminology from neighboring fields.

In item (i) we attempt to translate the various engineering terms and constructs into mathematical formulas. This is a continuation of a theme we started in an AMS Notices article [Jor03]. For (iii), we apologize for the subjective nature of our comments; and we readily acknowledge the difficulties in writing history of events that are rather modern on a mathematical scale. All three concluding additions to the book are motivated by the nature of the subject at hand, specifically by the many connections between ideas from signal/image processing and the more mathematical themes from wavelets, fractals, and dynamics.

Exercises: Overview

The exercises are essential, and they serve several pedagogical purposes: They are there to help students and users practice the fundamental concepts in the book, and to test his/her hand at computations, and at sketching functions or iterative schemes. But they also serve to expand horizons! We hope students will acquire a hands-on feeling for the various basis functions already discussed in the book; and more importantly, get started at building bases of his/her own. Some readers might even want to begin with the exercises, and then read the text as they work along in the exercises. Indeed, in designing the exercises, I have been inspired, at least in part by books with a philosophy like this: "Learn Hilbert space by doing problems!" e.g., [Hal67]. Or: "Operator algebras by example!" e.g., [Dav96]. Finally, several of our exercises have been put in to expand on themes inside the text, pointing the reader to new developments in the subject, and especially stressing links to neighboring subjects and to applications; pointing to connections between modern trends and classical subjects, highlighting an especially powerful (and beautiful) idea, or even suggesting unorthodox applications.

One exercise in Chapter 7 is different from the others; it is a multipart exercise involving a search on the Internet. The student is asked to browse images (from image-processing engineering) on the web, and to follow visually how a certain (geometric and algorithmic) cascading process is made concrete. The mathematics of the cascade is worked out in Chapter 7 itself.

The exercises vary, with variation both within a given chapter, and variation from chapter to chapter. The longer chapters are supported by proportionally more exercises. Some of the exercises are short, and some are long. Some are conceptual, and others are computational. Some are hard, and a few are relatively easy. The latter are meant mainly for the student to practice the use of one definition or another. Yet others serve to extend material covered in the book, and again others are there to help the student review background. Then there is a sliding scale up to the more difficult exercises, but the reader will then find hints. Finally, some exercises are built up in steps as multipart exercises with many parts. So what is a single numbered exercise, for example Exercise 7.9, may have many parts, (a), (b), etc., and they progress in logical steps, often with one part building on the previous. In all, the exercises make up more than 40 pages.

We have presented the material so that different readers can select the parts of it that are closest to his/her own interests; and in particular, it is not necessary to begin with Chapter 1. In fact, for some it might be better to begin with the Appendices, or with the Afterword containing the special sections "Comments on signal/image processing terminology" and "Computational mathematics," or for some insight into the history of the subject, the "List of names and discoveries" on pages xxx–xxxiii above. While some chapters build on earlier ones, non-sequential reading is possible, especially with the use of two extensive index lists, an index of "Symbols" and a general "Index," which are the last items in the book. The following quote may be appropriate for interdisciplinary mathematics books.

> *Det er ganske sandt, hvad Philosophien siger, at Livet maa forstaaes baglænds. Men derover glemmer man den anden Sætning, at det maa leves forlænds. Hvilken Sætning, jo meer den gjennemtænkes, netop ender med, at Livet i Timeligheden aldrig ret bliver forstaaeligt, netop fordi jeg intet Øieblik kan faae fuldelig Ro til at indtage Stillingen: baglænds.*[1]

—Søren Kierkegaard

Iowa City,
June 2006

Palle E. T. Jorgensen

---

[1] "It is really true what philosophy tells us, that life must be understood backwards. But with this, one forgets the second proposition, that it must be lived forwards. A proposition which, the more it is subjected to careful thought, the more it ends up concluding precisely that life at any given moment cannot really ever be fully understood; exactly because there is no single moment where time stops completely in order for me to take position [to do this]: going backwards." Often shortened to "Life can only be understood backwards; but it must be lived forwards" (*Livet skal forstaas baglæns, men leves forlæns*).

Figures. *Read Me!*

Le plus court chemin entre deux vérités dans le domaine réel passe par le domaine complexe.
                                                        —Jacques Hadamard

Acknowledgments

—an apt comment on how science, and indeed the whole of civilization, is a series of incremental advances, each building on what went before.
                                                        —Stephen Hawking

While working on the book, we had numerous discussions with Dorin Dutkay, Wayne Lawton, Wai Shing Tang, and with the members of the 2004 Singapore Workshop on "Functional and harmonic analyses of wavelets and frames," 4–7 August 2004, at the National University of Singapore. In particular, Larry Baggett, Kathy Merrill, and Judy Packer made helpful suggestions.

We are pleased to acknowledge many helpful conversations with Roger Nussbaum and Richard Gundy while we visited Rutgers in May 2003. We had very helpful e-mail discussions in March 2004 with Richard Gundy. We also acknowledge numerous helpful discussions with Anilesh Mohari.

We are especially grateful to Brian Treadway. With his usual professionalism he produced this beautiful typeset text, provided numerous corrections, and created the figures and the graphics, including the graphic design and Mathematica programming of iterative algorithms. He also made a number of extremely helpful suggestions.

We had constructive conversations with the members of our NSF Focused Research Group (FRG), especially with Akram Aldroubi, Chris Heil, David Larson, and Gestur Ólafsson.

David Larson kindly read our final manuscript and offered encouragements and suggestions.

The key idea of using a transfer operator in the sense of random walks and of Perron, Frobenius and Ruelle for the analysis of wavelet basis systems was originally pioneered in the two papers [Law91a, Law91b] by Wayne Lawton. The reader will notice that this idea runs like a red thread through our present exposition. Indeed, the two papers of Lawton have influenced not only our present approach, but over the years, they have served to bring closer central ideas from probability and analysis in the study of classes of basis problems in function theory and in applications. These include the admittedly best-known such bases, the wavelets. By now, variants of the transfer operator, alias the Perron–Frobenius–Ruelle operator, serve as key tools in diverse areas of mathematics: in ergodic theory and dynamical systems, the analysis of fractals, iterated function systems (IFSs), and geometric spectral theory; see, e.g., [Bal00, BaCM02, Coh90, Coh03, Dau92, DaHRS03, DuJo06b, Dut02, Fal90, FaLa99, FeLa02, Gun99, Gun04, JiJS01, JoPe98, LaNg98, PaPo90, StNg96], which is but a partial list. Our present exposition in this book owes a great deal to Lawton's pioneering insight, and we are further pleased to acknowledge numerous discussions with him during the period of preparation of this book.

The author is also pleased to thank his colleagues and students at the University of Iowa; he benefited especially from our joint seminars and from helpful discussions with Tom Branson and Paul Muhly (in mathematics), and with Wayne Polyzou (in physics).

We thank our students in the course 22M:321, "Wavelets," taught in the spring of 2005, especially Myung-Sin Song, who was finishing her Ph.D. thesis in image processing at the time. We extend our thanks to Chris Brislawn of the Los Alamos National Laboratory for illuminating discussions and for guest lectures in 22M:321, and to two colleagues in the University of Iowa School of Engineering, Andrew Kusiak and Albert Ratner, of the Department of Mechanical and Industrial Engineering. We benefited enormously from many discussions with these colleagues, and with others, and we hope in the book to convey some of the excitement we experienced in communicating across disparate disciplines.

Several recent Springer authors have been generous with encouragement and with tips for preparation of the manuscript. We are pleased to thank William Arveson, Ward Cheney, Weimin Han, and Bruce Sagan.

A number of friends have been kind and generous with valuable advice. Here Peter Renz's wise suggestions stand out.

Finally, we thank Ann Kostant and the series editors for constructive suggestions. One notable suggestion which I took to heart: I was persuaded that it is poor taste for textbook authors to sprinkle the narrative with citations to journal articles and advanced books. The presentation of main ideas is self-contained from first principles and not distracted! Yet I want to assure researchers that their work does get cited. Be patient! Citations are concentrated in sections at the end of each chapter, "References and remarks;" and there is a "History" section at the end of Chapter 1. In addition, in the "Getting started" section above, we have a section called "List of names and discoveries" in which a number of pioneers in wavelets and signal processing are celebrated. Many undoubtedly have been omitted; and we apologize for that.

At least this principle of postponing citations has been followed within reason!

This material is based upon work supported by the U.S. National Science Foundation under Grant No. DMS-0139473 (FRG).

Analysis and Probability

The image collage on the next page illustrates central themes in the book: The three oscillatory graphs placed down diagonally in the collage represent the kind of functions generated algorithmically by tree-like, or so-called pyramid, algorithms. These recursive algorithms are structured around pyramid shapes as in the top right corner of the collage, and they come from successive repetitions of dyadic branching steps from the sketch in the lower left corner of the collage. See also "About the cover figure" (page vi).

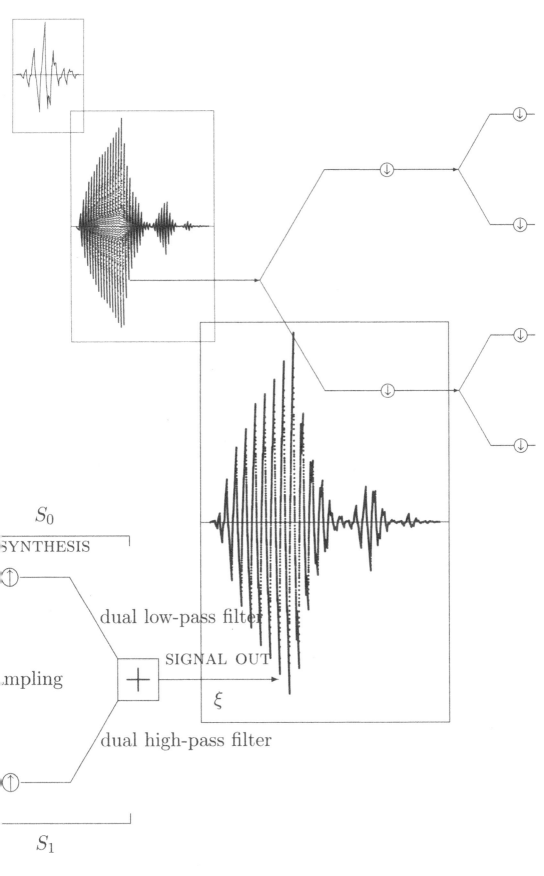

S_0

SYNTHESIS

dual low-pass filter

SIGNAL OUT

ξ

mpling

dual high-pass filter

S_1

Introduction: Measures on path space

*We believe that all curious people can enjoy and understand great mathe-
matical ideas without having to brush up on garden-variety school math or
relive their painful algebra daze.* —Edward B. Burger, Michael Starbird

PREREQUISITES: A sense of curiosity! Algebra of the integers and the real numbers; rudimentary facts about functions and measures; limits; compactness; Cantor;
matrices; inner-product spaces.

Question: "What if I don't have the prerequisites for reading the prerequisites?"
A: "Doesn't matter! Skip Chapter 1!"

Prelude

In the first section of this chapter, we introduce the fundamental concepts of wavelet
functions and wavelet constructions, but in a form which stresses *scale-similarity*.
This scale-similarity is a special case of a more general notion of *self-similarity*.
We will later see that the more general idea of self-similarity is needed for our understanding of fractals and symbolic dynamics.

One of the difficulties in moving from the traditional setting of wavelets to the
more general iterative models is the distinction between linear and non-linear: Recall
that wavelets are built in the *linear* space $\mathbb{R}^d$, which in turn comes equipped with its
canonical d-dimensional Lebesgue measure. By contrast, fractals are typically non-
linear structures, not even groups; and one of the first issues confronting us will be
that of finding a substitute for Lebesgue measure. As it turns out, such substitute measures exist, having certain intrinsic properties quite analogous to those of Lebesgue
measure; but the new measures depend on the particular fractal X under discussion.
Once a particular X is specified (by a finite system of affine mappings), we will
see that it acquires a natural and intrinsic fractal dimension (called the Hausdorff

dimension, say s), and a corresponding fractal measure called the Hausdorff measure. However, note that there is an s-dependence. Specifically, we have the existence of a Hausdorff measure μ_s on X for each value of s. And for the traditional case of $\mathbb{R}^d$, we have $s = d$. Later we shall outline iterative schemes which yield μ_s.

Further into the book, we will then extend both Fourier tools and wavelets to these fractals. The class of fractals we consider is somewhat restricted. But these are the fractal classes where a reasonable harmonic analysis is feasible.

To make the ideas more concrete, we concentrate initially on simple and very explicit fractals such as the middle-third Cantor set, and other Cantor sets on the line. But the various more general points and constructions will only emerge gradually as the subjects in the book progress in a natural order. Hence, Section 1.1 will include also a brief chapter-by-chapter outline of the central ideas in the book, stressing throughout how our random-walk model is used.

To help highlight wavelets, fractals, and signals, throughout the book, the narrative is illustrated with figures. Each figure is there to help students visualize main ideas, and many of the figures are created from recursive Mathematica programs, by Brian Treadway.

And in addition to the figures inside the text, each chapter contains little graphical ornaments or "dingbats." They should help readers navigate the book, and they also serve as reminders of the three themes. Some dingbats mark separation between the prelude sections and the rest of the chapter, while others are placed near the end of each chapter to mark the start of the exercises.

A closer inspection reveals that the dingbats that follow the chapter preludes are all different. Some dingbats represent certain selections from families of images. Within each family though, the dingbat images are different.

1.1 Wavelets

Wavelets are families of functions of one or several real variables, i.e., functions on $\mathbb{R}$ or on $\mathbb{R}^d$, satisfying three properties:

(i) They form a basis for $L^2(\mathbb{R})$ (or $L^2(\mathbb{R}^d)$ in the several-variable case) and have suitable orthogonality properties which we spell out below.

(ii) They are indexed by integer translations, i.e., by the operation $x \to x + k$, for $k \in \mathbb{Z}$, and by integer powers of a scaling. Often the scaling is dyadic, i.e., scaling is by powers 2^j, for $j \in \mathbb{Z}$.

(iii) There are two generating functions φ and ψ (called father and mother functions) for the whole double-indexed wavelet which relate the two operations of scaling and translation in the following way:

$$\varphi = \sum_k P_k \varphi(2 \cdot -k), \quad \psi = \sum_k Q_k \varphi(2 \cdot -k),$$

where the coefficients P_k and Q_k are carefully chosen.

Comments on (iii). The choice of the coefficients is essential, and it has both an algebraic and a geometric flavor. We will see that various admissible classes for the coefficient systems $\{P_i, Q_i\}$ may be thought of as quadratic varieties, and there are solutions both in finite and infinite dimensions. The two relations in (iii) above represent only the dyadic case of what is called *scaling relations*. The first is an equation for a function φ, and is called the *dyadic scaling equation*. The function φ is called a *scaling function*. The context and the ambient function space dictate choices for the P_i's, which in turn yield non-trivial solutions φ. Moreover, the possibilities for solutions φ are extremely sensitive to these choices, and we shall develop algorithms and discuss stability for solutions φ and ψ.

The coefficients P_i are called *masking coefficients*, and conditions on these coefficients must always be imposed. This is a crucial point which will be taken up in Section 1.3 below, and in more detail again within the book itself.

The context for solutions: Our context will include both standard Lebesgue measure and some classes of fractal measures as well. Specifically, we shall consider higher dimensions, such as $\mathbb{R}^d$, and more general scaling operations (e.g., matrix scaling). We will further introduce a variety of fractal structures which come with associated scaling relations. But in (iii) we have listed the simplest scaling relations only to illustrate the general idea. Special cases of classes of conditions for the coefficient systems $\{P_i, Q_i\}$ are known as *quadrature* conditions, or *quadrature-mirror conditions*. The ambient function space might be simply the familiar Hilbert space $L^2(\mathbb{R})$, or it may be a Hilbert space built on some affine fractal, which in turn is designed from a matrix scaling and an iterated function system of affine maps in $\mathbb{R}^d$ (definitions in Section 1.3 and Chapter 4). However, depending on the context, the admissibility conditions for the coefficients P_i are different.

The various problems connected with classes of scaling relations have traditionally been addressed with only standard tools from analysis. Here we will instead employ a suitable mix of analysis and path-space methods from probability.

In these problems, solutions are constructed from an algorithm which relates a certain function $\varphi(t)$, $t \in \mathbb{R}$, called a scaling function, to its scaled version $\varphi(Nt)$ where N is a fixed integer, 2 or more, or an expansive integral d-by-d matrix A if t is in $\mathbb{R}^d$.

For $d = 1$, the formula which determines φ is (1.3.1) below. It is called the *scaling identity*. (Note that the first relation in (iii) is a special case of (1.3.1).) It is not at all clear *a priori* that this identity should have L^2 solutions at all, or even solutions that are given by some kind of convergent algorithm. The coefficients in (1.3.1) are called masking coefficients, filters, or filter coefficients. For special values of the coefficients, it turns out that there is a normalized L^2 solution φ, and that pointwise convergence of a good approximation can be established in a meaningful way. Moreover, we show that the convergence behavior is dictated by properties of an associated transfer operator R, or Ruelle operator.

The expression on the right-hand side in equation (1.3.1) is also called a *subdivision* because of the function values $\varphi(Nt - k)$. An iteration of the operations on the right-hand side in (1.3.1) on some initial function is called a cascade approximation. This approximation is one approach to the function φ, and the other is the infinite product formula (1.3.5) for the Fourier transform of φ.

The relation between φ and its scaled refinement is well understood when we pass from the time domain to the frequency domain via the Fourier transform. In that case the relation is multiplicative, and involves a certain periodic matrix function m, called the low-pass filter. For further details, see formula (1.3.4) below.

The study of the filters m is part of signal processing (see, e.g., [Jor03, StNg96]). But by a "mathematical miracle," they have become one of the most useful tools in wavelet constructions; and at the same time, they have pointed to a host of exciting applications of wavelet mathematics. To get a path-space measure for some of the wavelet problems, we use the quadrature-mirror properties, or their generalizations, which are assumed for the filter function m, also called a frequency response function. It is periodic, in one or several variables. In $\mathbb{R}^d$, there is a variety of choices of a period lattice for the problems at hand.

Since the first question is to decide when φ is in L^2, we iterate and get an infinite matrix product involving the matrix $W := m^*m$. Since W is positive semidefinite, we may create a positive path measure of a random walk starting at x in some period interval. In several dimensions, x starts in a fundamental domain D for some fixed lattice, for example $\mathbb{Z}^d$. The paths starting at x arise by iteration of the inverse branches of $x \rightarrow Ax$ mod $\mathbb{Z}^d$. There are $N = |\det A|$ distinct branches. These N branches may be viewed as endomorphisms of D.

We construct our random walks in a general framework which includes both wavelets, wavelet packets (see Chapter 7), and some of the other more classical problems. We further show how some of the classical questions may be phrased and solved with the use of path-space measures.

It is interesting to contrast our proposed approach with the more traditional one used in wavelet analysis: see, e.g., [Dau92]. Traditionally, some kind of Lipschitz or Dini regularity condition must be assumed for the filter. Then the corresponding infinite product may be made precise, and we can turn to the question of when the wavelet generators are in $L^2(\mathbb{R}^d)$. As it turns out, both of these issues have natural formulations and solutions in terms of the path-space measures. The results allow a wider generality. In a variety of wavelet questions for band-limited wavelets, it is just an unavoidable fact that the regularity conditions are not satisfied for the filters m that are dictated by the setting and the applications.

Before turning to the details, we sketch a brief outline. We resume the summary in more detail in Section 1.6 below. The remaining sections in this chapter contain more definitions, motivation and examples, which will be used in the overview at the conclusion of Chapter 1.

In Section 1.2, we introduce the basic concept of a probability space built on covering mappings with a fixed number of branches. These systems give rise to random walks on trees, paths, and transition probabilities. We discuss these notions in Section 1.2.

In Section 1.3, we illustrate the relevance of the path-space measures to some questions in wavelets, and in Section 1.4, to sampling theory. To make the questions more concrete, we outline four examples at the end of Section 1.3, two variants of Haar's wavelet construction, Daubechies' wavelet, and finally we sketch an analogous harmonic analysis question for the middle-third Cantor set.

In Section 1.5, we prove a theorem on pointwise convergence of a class of infinite products. Our theorem uses the transition probabilities which are associated with the random walks that we introduce in Section 1.2 below.

Chapter 2 develops general theory, transition probabilities, branching processes, and corresponding probability spaces. This material has a more technical flavor.

In Chapter 3 we specialize the measures, constructed in a general framework in Chapter 2, to the concrete context of wavelets in the Hilbert space $L^2(\mathbb{R})$. In Chapter 2, we introduced transition probabilities P_x on a probability space Ω; and in the wavelet application, we outline how the group of integers $\mathbb{Z}$ is naturally embedded in Ω. And we show that the orthogonality issue for wavelets is equivalent to $\mathbb{Z}$ having full measure in Ω.

In Chapter 4 we turn to a class of affine fractals, iterated function systems (IFS) by affine maps, but with focus on certain Cantor sets, mainly the middle-quarter Cantor set. For the affine IFSs we show that a natural basis question is equivalent to the natural numbers $\mathbb{N}_0$ having full measure in Ω. For this formulation we outline a conjugate system of Cantor sets.

Chapter 5 addresses the general case of measurable systems constructed from a given N-to-one mapping. In this general context, we give a sufficient condition for $\mathbb{Z}$ having full measure in Ω.

In Chapter 6 we resume the discussion of wavelets, but in a non-commutative setting motivated by multiwavelets.

In Chapters 7 and 8 we turn to two measure-theoretic issues from the general framework of Chapter 5: There is a class of representations of two familiar C^*-algebras which produce IFSs in the measure category, the Cuntz algebra, and the algebra of the canonical anticommutation relations. Among other things, we show that the determinantal measures studied by Russell Lyons and others in combinatorial probability theory are special cases of this.

Chapter 8 contains some examples of wavelet packets and permutative representations. We give a systematic presentation of this subject, and we show that the concrete examples fit within a general measure-theoretic framework. While the examples have been studied in research papers, they have so far not found a unified formulation. In Chapter 9 we show that the underlying geometric questions for these examples may be phrased in the context of operators in Hilbert space.

Our selection in Chapters 8–9 and in the appendices includes certain geometric topics from operator algebras and Hilbert space. They have been carefully selected with a view to overlapping with signal and image processing, and keeping in mind the kind of scale-similarity relations that are used in the analysis of wavelets, fractals, and discrete dynamics. For example, we stress how problems in "fractal noise," in images, and more generally in higher dimension may be unified with the use of operators, tensor products of Hilbert space, and states on C^*-algebras.

A case in point is the serendipity involved in the observation (see [Jor03]) to the effect that representations of the so-called Cuntz relations and Cuntz algebras from C^*-algebra theory have been extensively used in the early days of signal processing (before they were "discovered" in C^*-algebras!), and that they continue to be relevant to the kind of recursive algorithms still used to this day in wireless communication and in image processing.

1.2 Path space

A well-tested tool in analysis and mathematical physics centers around the application of path-space measures. This tool is used in attacking a variety of singular convergence, or approximation, problems. We will adopt this viewpoint in our study of wavelet approximations. Traditionally, the setting for wavelet questions has included assumptions concerning continuity, or some kind of differentiability. In contrast, we shall work almost entirely in the measurable category. One advantage of this approach is that we stay in the measurable category when addressing problems from multiresolution analysis (MRA). Earlier work on the use of probability in wavelets includes that of R.F. Gundy et al.

Our present viewpoint is more general than [DoGH00], and it starts with the random walks naturally associated with a measure space $(X, \mathcal{B})$ and a given measurable onto map $\sigma : X \to X$ such that $\#\sigma^{-1}(\{x\}) = N$ for all $x \in X$, where N, $2 \le N < \infty$, is fixed. Iteration of the branches

$$\sigma^{-1}(\{x\}) := \{ y \in X \mid \sigma(y) = x \} \tag{1.2.1}$$

then yields a combinatorial tree. If

$$\omega = (\omega_1, \omega_2, \dots) \in \Omega := \{0, 1, \dots, N-1\}^{\mathbb{N}},$$

an associated path may be thought of as an infinite extension of the finite walks

$$\tau_{\omega_n} \cdots \tau_{\omega_2} \tau_{\omega_1} x$$

starting at x, where (τ_i), $i = 0, 1, \ldots, N - 1$, is a system of inverses, i.e., where

$$\sigma \circ \tau_i = \mathrm{id}_X, \qquad 0 \leq i < N. \tag{1.2.2}$$

We now turn to the path-space measures P_x alluded to above, but for now only in a special case. More general cases emerge later on, especially in Chapters 2, 5, and 7. These will be different applications, and Chapters 7 and 9 will even be in a non-commutative setting. The definition of P_x which we give below is quite standard, but it may not look simple or natural to someone unfamiliar with infinite products, or with the present viewpoint. This should not be alarming. We believe that the fundamentals of P_x will allow the reader to already now see a number of quite familiar and basic wavelet constructions in a new light. This will be useful later, both for wavelets and for a class of similar fractal constructions given in Chapter 4, as well as for frequency-localized multiwavelets in Chapter 7. Each measure P_x depends on the initial point x and on a prescribed and fixed weight function W on X.

We shall think of P_x as a measure on (infinite) paths originating at x, but its construction rests on a fundamental idea of Kolmogorov which states that P_x is determined by its value on paths that are only fixed at a finite number n of places. It is prescribed for each n, and it extends to all paths, i.e., to Ω, if and only if there is consistency from n to $n + 1$ for all n. This consistency condition is defined from the given function W, in that W assigns the transition probabilities; see Lemma 2.5.1 (Kolmogorov consistency, p. 46) for precise details. Our probability space Ω will be the space of all infinite words ω, Ω will be given its standard Tychonoff infinite-product topology, and $C(\Omega)$ will denote the space of all continuous complex-valued functions on Ω.

If $W: X \to [0, 1]$ is a given measurable function such that

$$\sum_{y : \sigma(y) = x} W(y) = 1, \tag{1.2.3}$$

then an associated measure P_x on Ω may be defined as follows. Suppose some function $f \in C(\Omega)$ depends only on a finite number of coordinates, say $\omega_1, \ldots, \omega_n$; then set

$$\int_\Omega f \, dP_x = \sum_{(\omega_1, \ldots, \omega_n)} f(\omega_1, \ldots, \omega_n) \, W(\tau_{\omega_1} x) \, W(\tau_{\omega_2} \tau_{\omega_1} x) \cdots W(\tau_{\omega_n} \cdots \tau_{\omega_1} x). \tag{1.2.4}$$

Extensions of this formula to Ω can be done in a number of ways: see Chapter 2, Figure 1.1, and the cited references.

We shall need the concept of *random walk* in a slightly restricted context. Normally, the concept of random walk is confined to a lattice, i.e., $\mathbb{Z}^d$ for some d. The qualitative features of such a walk depend both on the lattice dimension d and on

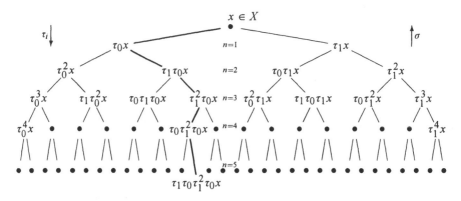

Fig. 1.1. $N = 2$, simple dyadic branch points; a function $W: X \rightarrow [0, 1]$ is given. A path in the random-walk model. Assignment of probability to a particular length-five path:
$$P_x^{(5)}\left(\{(0\ 1\ 1\ 0\ 1)\}\right) = W\left(\tau_0 x\right) W\left(\tau_1 \tau_0 x\right) W\left(\tau_1^2 \tau_0 x\right) W\left(\tau_0 \tau_1^2 \tau_0 x\right) W\left(\tau_1 \tau_0 \tau_1^2 \tau_0 x\right).$$

suitable transition probabilities. In our present context, we shall use a combinatorial tree (see Figures 1.1 and 2.1 (the Farey tree, p. 42)) in place of a lattice, and we shall use a given function W to prescribe transition probabilities. But the various paths within our tree can originate at points chosen from the set X. Here X is given (typically compact), and X carries a fixed finite-to-one endomorphism σ. Our construction is easier to visualize when a finite set of branches of the "inverse" for σ is assigned in concrete terms: hence the maps τ_ω. If we assume property (1.2.3) for the function W, and if x and y are points in X such that $\sigma(y) = x$, then the number $W(y)$ from (1.2.3) represents the probability of a transition from x to y. Figure 1.1 above illustrates how step-by-step conditional probabilities are then used in assigning probabilities to a finite path which originates at some chosen point in x.

What if the path is infinite? We shall see in Chapter 2 (Sections 2.4 and 2.5) how a fundamental idea of Kolmogorov then allows us to assign probabilities also to infinite paths.

In Section 1.1 above we already used this idea for the case when X is the circle, also called the one-torus, $\mathbb{T}$. For each N, we may then consider $\sigma(z) := z^N$. And in the context of wavelet constructions, we already noted how to concretely parametrize the branches of the inverse of z^N when z is complex and restricted to $\mathbb{T}$.

A special feature of this construction, which will be explored in this work, is that of attractive convergence properties for infinite products of the form

$$\prod_{n,\omega_1,\ldots,\omega_n} W\left(\tau_{\omega_1} x\right) \cdots W\left(\tau_{\omega_n} \cdots \tau_{\omega_1} x\right) \tag{1.2.5}$$

over certain subsets of Ω. As it turns out, these infinite products are determined by the measures $(P_x)_{x \in X}$, and by the Ruelle transition operator

$$(R_W g)(x) := \sum_{y:\sigma(y)=x} W(y) g(y), \qquad g \in L^\infty(X). \qquad (1.2.6)$$

The operator R in (1.2.6) is called the transition operator, the Ruelle operator, or the Ruelle–Perron–Frobenius operator, and it will play a major role in what follows.

Many problems in dynamics are governed by transition probabilities W, and P_x, and by an associated transition operator R_W as in (1.2.6). Wavelet theory is a case in point, and we show that fundamental convergence questions for wavelets and properties of the solutions to (1.3.1) depend on the positive solutions h to the eigenvalue problem $R_W(h) = h$. We refer to (1.3.10)–(1.3.11) below. The solutions h are called *harmonic*, and the function h in (1.3.10) is a special harmonic function which we will study in detail later in Chapter 3.

The nature of these solutions is a key to the link between the analysis and probability of path space. Since the early days when use of measures on infinite path space was first suggested for problems in mathematical analysis, a key question was: what is the *support* of the measure under discussion? And our use of the W-measures P_x for problems in wavelets and fractals is a case in point.

In particular applications of this viewpoint, the measures P_x are initially defined naturally in connection with certain random-walk models. And each P_x, for $x \in X$, is then a Borel measure on a certain rather large and unwieldy probability space Ω. But for computations it is essential to know that the measures are in fact supported on (or carried by) much smaller subsets of the initial space Ω. These smaller subsets in Ω can be made quite explicit, and they are closely related to dynamics and general classes of multiresolutions, as we proceed to describe.

1.3 Multiresolutions

All this time the Guard was looking at her, first through a telescope, then through a microscope, and then through an opera-glass.   —Lewis Carroll

The notion of *wavelet* refers to a specific basis construction in a function space which is fixed at the outset and which carries an inner product. This construction is popular, perhaps because it is so computationally attractive. It is based on a certain self-similarity (or scaling-similarity) which gives rise to a cascading or nested family of closed subspaces. These subspaces begin with a fixed resolution which is determined by a scaling equation such as (1.3.1) below; but as we will see, there are more general ways of identifying scaling-self-similarity.

The idea is that there is a scaling transformation which lets us move in discrete steps, up and down an associated scale of subspaces, hence the concept of a *multiresolution*, a concept derived from optics; see, e.g., [JaMR01], [Mal89], and the references given there. One end of the resolution scale refers to "coarse," and the other to "fine." Comparing two subspaces, the space of the coarse scale is contained in that of the fine resolution. The traditional wavelet multiresolutions are by now very nicely presented in the literature, and we especially recommend Daubechies' book [Dau92].

As noted for example in [Mey89] and [Mey97], a fixed scaling transformation is also the feature which most efficiently introduces such tools as Hilbert space, operator theory, martingales, conditional expectations, and computational algorithms into wavelet analysis. Since we are in Hilbert space, closed subspaces correspond in a one-to-one fashion to (orthogonal) projections, and the notion of multiresolution may thus be rewritten, as we will see (Chapter 7) in the language of projections. Thus the multiresolution structure, understood this way, offers a telescope for looking at functions or at signals in digitized form, and it makes a crucial link to signal and image processing. (See the appendices for further details!) We will meet a number of incarnations (some special, and some rather general) of multiresolutions in several chapters throughout the book, especially in Chapters 7–9; but they will always be based on the geometry of scaling projections in Hilbert space.

The multiresolution approach to wavelets involves functions on $\mathbb{R}$. It begins with the fixed-point problem

$$\varphi(t) = N \sum_{k \in \mathbb{Z}} a_k \varphi(Nt - k), \qquad t \in \mathbb{R}, \tag{1.3.1}$$

where a given sequence $(a_k)_{k \in \mathbb{Z}}$ is chosen with special filtering properties, e.g., quadrature-mirror filters; see [BrJo02b, Jor01a, DuJo06b]. The equation (1.3.1) is called the scaling identity, and the a_k's the response coefficients, or the masking coefficients. Introducing the Fourier series

$$m(x) = \sum_{k \in \mathbb{Z}} a_k e^{-i2\pi kx} \tag{1.3.2}$$

and Fourier transform

$$\hat{\varphi}(x) = \int_{\mathbb{R}} e^{-i2\pi tx} \varphi(t) \, dt, \tag{1.3.3}$$

we get the relation

$$\hat{\varphi}(x) = m\left(\frac{x}{N}\right) \hat{\varphi}\left(\frac{x}{N}\right), \qquad x \in \mathbb{R}, \tag{1.3.4}$$

which suggests a closer inspection of the infinite products

$$\prod_{n=1}^{\infty} m\left(\frac{x}{N^n}\right). \tag{1.3.5}$$

Since we want solutions φ to (1.3.1) which are in $L^2(\mathbb{R})$, (1.3.4)–(1.3.5) suggest the corresponding convergence questions for the function $W := |m|^2$.

When $(P_x)_{x\in[0,1]}$ is the family of measures on Ω corresponding to $W = |m|^2$, then the formal infinite product

$$|\hat{\varphi}(x)|^2 = \prod_{n=1}^{\infty} W\left(\frac{x}{N^n}\right)$$

is $P_x(\{(0, 0, 0, \dots)\})$, i.e., the measure of the singleton $(0, 0, \dots)$ (an infinite string of zeroes) in $\{0, \dots, N - 1\}^{\mathbb{N}}$. There is a natural way (based on Euclid's algorithm) of embedding $\mathbb{Z}$ into

$$\Omega = \{0, \dots, N - 1\}^{\mathbb{N}} \times \{0, \dots, N - 1\}^{\mathbb{N}} \tag{1.3.6}$$

such that

$$P_x(\mathbb{Z}) = \sum_{k\in\mathbb{Z}} |\hat{\varphi}(x + k)|^2. \tag{1.3.7}$$

Remark 1.3.1. Note that, in general, it is not at all clear that the measures (P_x), $x \in X$, on Ω should even have atoms. Typically, they do not have them! But if atoms exist, i.e., when there are points $\omega \in \Omega$ such that $P_x(\{\omega\}) > 0$, we note that this yields convergence of an associated infinite product. Let $\mathbb{N}_0 := \{0, 1, 2, \dots\} = \mathbb{N} \cup \{0\}$. Using Euclid, and the N-adic expansion

$$k = i_1 + i_2 N + \dots + i_n N^{n-1} \qquad \text{for } k \in \mathbb{N}_0, \tag{1.3.8}$$

we see that the points

$$\omega(k) = (i_1, \dots, i_n, \underbrace{0, 0, 0, \dots}_{\infty \text{ string of zeroes}})$$

represent a copy of $\mathbb{N}_0$ sitting in Ω. With the identification $k \leftrightarrow \omega(k)$, we set

$$P_x(\mathbb{N}_0) = \sum_{k=0}^{\infty} P_x(\{\omega(k)\}). \tag{1.3.9}$$

But in general, the function $P_x(\mathbb{N}_0)$ might be zero. Our first observation (Proposition 5.3.2) about

$$h(x) := P_x(\mathbb{N}_0), \qquad x \in X, \tag{1.3.10}$$

is that it solves the eigenvalue problem

$$R_W h = h. \tag{1.3.11}$$

We say that h is a minimal harmonic function relative to R_W. See Chapter 7 for the justification of the term "minimal". Note that $h = 0$ may happen!

Remark 1.3.2. Let X, $\mathcal{B}$, σ, τ_0, ..., τ_{N-1}, and W be as described above, and let $(P_x)_{x \in X}$ be the corresponding transition probabilities. Let

$$\mathbf{0} = \underbrace{(\ 0,\ 0,\ 0,\ \ldots\ )}_{\infty \text{ string of zeroes}} \in \Omega = \{0, 1, \ldots, N-1\}^{\mathbb{N}}.$$

While in general, often $P_x(\{\mathbf{0}\}) = 0$, the case when $P_x(\{\mathbf{0}\}) > 0$ is important. The condition $P_x(\{\mathbf{0}\}) > 0$ is a way of making precise sense of the infinite product

$$P_x(\{\mathbf{0}\}) = \prod_{n=1}^{\infty} W(\tau_0^n x). \tag{1.3.12}$$

If, for example, $\lim_{n \to \infty} W(\tau_0^n x) < 1$, then it is immediate from (1.3.12) that $P_x(\{\mathbf{0}\}) = 0$.

Suppose $P_x(\{\mathbf{0}\}) > 0$. Then it follows that

$$P_x(\{(i_1, \ldots, i_n, 0)\}) = W(\tau_{i_1} x) \cdots W(\tau_{i_n} \cdots \tau_{i_1} x) P_{\tau_{i_n} \cdots \tau_{i_1} x}(\{\mathbf{0}\}). \tag{1.3.13}$$

Using (1.3.8), we shall identify $k \in \mathbb{N}_0$ with the point $\omega(k) \in \Omega$, and write $P_x(\{k\})$ for the expression in (1.3.13).

Examples 1.3.3. Here are four examples of the equation (1.3.1) which may be understood with the use of transition probabilities for a certain random-walk model:

(a) $\varphi(t) = \varphi(2t) + \varphi(2t - 1)$, Haar's wavelet, Figure 1.2(a);
(b) $\varphi(t) = \varphi(2t) + \varphi(2t - 3)$, the stretched Haar wavelet, Figure 1.2(b);
(c) $\varphi(t) = \varphi(3t) + \varphi(3t - 2)$, Cantor's example;

and

(d) $\varphi(t) = \frac{1+\sqrt{3}}{4}\varphi(2t) + \frac{3+\sqrt{3}}{4}\varphi(2t - 1) + \frac{3-\sqrt{3}}{4}\varphi(2t - 2) + \frac{1-\sqrt{3}}{4}\varphi(2t - 3)$,
Daubechies' scaling function.

We shall be interested in solutions φ, called scaling functions, to (a)–(d) which satisfy the further *normalization*

$$\int \varphi(t)\, dt = 1. \tag{1.3.14}$$

A direct verification shows that (a) and (d) have normalized solutions $\varphi \in L^2(\mathbb{R})$.

We will meet several notions of "normalization," starting with (1.3.14). In addition to (1.3.14), we will consider L^2-normalization, defined by condition (1.3.24) below. L^2-normalization means "unit L^2-norm." The stretched function φ from example (b), henceforth denoted φ_b, i.e., the function in Figure 1.2(b), is L^1-normalized, but not L^2-normalized. Specifically, one checks that φ_b satisfies (1.3.14) but not (1.3.24).

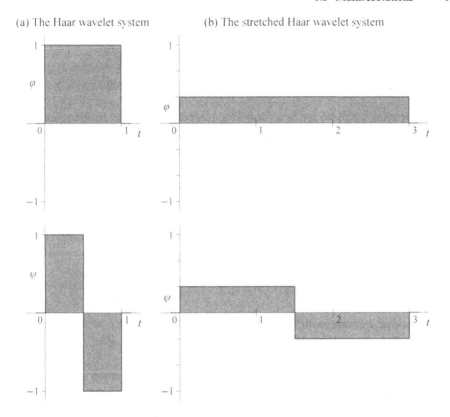

Fig. 1.2. Haar wavelets: The two functions φ and ψ are the father, resp., the mother functions for Haar's construction in cases (a) on the left, and the stretched Haar (b), on the right. In each case, we use ψ to create a double-indexed basis system (1.3.16). For (a) this system will be an orthonormal basis (ONB) in $L^2(\mathbb{R})$; but for (b), the functions (1.3.16) will only represent a Parseval frame, i.e., a function system which yields the Parseval identity (1.3.22) for every function in $L^2(\mathbb{R})$. As is apparent from (b), this Parseval system will not be an ONB for the stretched version. We resume the discussion of this in the text following Figure 6.1 (p. 103).

So the stretching, i.e., passing from (a) to (b) in Figure 1.2, leaves (1.3.14) stable, while the other two conditions (1.3.23) and (1.3.24) get lost. Specifically, the stretched scaling function φ_b also does not satisfy the orthogonality relations (1.3.23).

In contrast, the two distinct scaling functions

$$\varphi_a = \chi_{[0,1]} \qquad \text{(Haar)}$$

and

$$\varphi_d \qquad \text{(Daubechies)}$$

both satisfy all three conditions (1.3.14), (1.3.23), and (1.3.24).

For (a), we may take

$$\varphi = \varphi_a = \chi_{[0,1]},$$

and for (b),

$$\varphi = \varphi_b = \frac{1}{3}\chi_{[0,3]},$$

where χ denotes the indicator function of the respective intervals. Readers familiar with wavelets will recognize (d) as the scaling identity for the Daubechies wavelet: it has a normalized solution $\varphi = \varphi_d = \varphi_{\text{Dau}}$ in $L^2(\mathbb{R})$ which is supported in the compact interval $[0, 3]$, see Figure 7.16 (p. 134), and differentiable, see [Dau92]. The solution φ in (a) is the scaling function for the Haar wavelet; see Figure 1.2(a).

Equation (c) does not have any normalized solution φ in $L^2(\mathbb{R})$, but still $\varphi = \chi_{X_3}$ solves (c) when X_3 is the "middle-third Cantor set": see Chapter 4 and Figure 4.2 (p. 74). Moreover, there is a unique probability measure $\mu = \mu_3$ supported on X_3 such that

$$\int f(t)\, d\mu(t) = \frac{1}{2}\left(\int f\left(\frac{t}{3}\right) d\mu(t) + \int f\left(\frac{t+2}{3}\right) d\mu(t)\right) \qquad (1.3.15)$$

for all bounded continuous functions f on $\mathbb{R}$. The Cantor set X_3, with associated measure μ, is an example of an *iterated function system* (IFS) of *affine type*, and the harmonic analysis of these systems is the subject of Chapter 4.

Cantor's scaling identity, example (c), admits a normalized solution φ as follows. The Hilbert space will not be defined from Lebesgue measure, but rather from Hausdorff measure of fractal dimension s, in this case $s = \log_3(2)$. As our Hilbert space $\mathcal{H}_s$, we use in [DuJo06b] a separable L^2-space defined from the Hausdorff measure of fractal dimension $\log_3(2)$, and consisting of all L^2-functions on a certain set E_3, extending X_3, and built from X_3, using scaling in the large, and certain gap-filling steps; see [DuJo06b]. With this construction, the scaling function φ will be the indicator function of X_3, having unit norm in the Hilbert space $\mathcal{H}_s$.

The only reasonable solution to (c) is the indicator function of X_3, $\varphi = \chi_{X_3}$. This function is *not* normalized when referring to Lebesgue measure. The Lebesgue measure of X_3 is actually zero, while the Hausdorff measure h_s, $s = \log_3(2)$, of X_3 gives us the right normalization, $h_s(X_3) = 1$. Or stated differently, the analogues of the classical results are true if we modify the measure and the Hilbert space, using instead the Hilbert space $\mathcal{H}_s$ in place of $L^2(\mathbb{R})$. (Recall $L^2(\mathbb{R})$ is defined from Lebesgue measure.)

Rather, the new Hilbert space $\mathcal{H}_s$ is defined as an L^2 space with respect to Hausdorff measure h_s, $s = \log_3(2)$. For (c), we have the following true version of (1.3.14), which we can call $(1.3.14)_s$:

$$\int \varphi(t)\, dh_s(t) = 1, \qquad \varphi = \chi_{X_3} \text{ [indicator function].} \qquad (1.3.14)_s$$

As stated, when the integral in (1.3.14) is computed on the solution to (c), referring to Lebesgue measure, it is $= 0$.

The notion of "normalization" which is independent of the choice of Hilbert space involves the function h in (1.3.10). Of the four examples, (a)–(d), the three (a), (c), and (d) have $h = 1$, the constant function, while (b) has h non-constant, and h for this stretched wavelet is given by formula (6.2.17), $p = 3$, and sketched in Figure 6.2 (p. 107).

We postpone a full discussion of (c) to Chapter 4. This fractal case, i.e., the middle-third Cantor example, and a related much wider class of affine fractals, will be treated in detail and in a wider context in Sections 4.1 and 4.2; see also the paper [DuJo06b].

So in the list of four, (a)–(d) above, the only one that stands out as being different is the stretched Haar wavelet (b). Of course, all the fractal wavelets admit stretched versions. But we do not discuss those in the present book. However, it is true more generally that all the Cantor sets that arise as affine iterated function systems (IFSs) admit orthonormal wavelet bases; see [DuJo06b].

The fractal wavelets we treat in Chapters 4 and 6 are the ones that are orthonormal bases, and in particular, they are normalized.

As a result, the function h from (1.3.10), called the minimal eigenfunction, is the constant 1 in the examples from cases (a), (c), and (d), but not (b).

In the "stretched" example, case (b), we calculate the minimal eigenfunction h in (6.2.17) by a closed expression, the case $p = 3$; see also Figure 6.2 (p. 107).

An important question for dyadic wavelets in $L^2(\mathbb{R})$ is the issue of when these wavelets form *orthonormal bases* (ONBs). A dyadic wavelet function $\psi \in L^2(\mathbb{R})$ generates an ONB if the double-indexed family

$$\left\{ 2^{n/2} \psi \left(2^n t - k \right) \mid n, k \in \mathbb{Z} \right\} \tag{1.3.16}$$

satisfies (i) and (ii) below:

(i) $\displaystyle \int_{\mathbb{R}} \overline{\psi_{n,k}(t)}\, \psi_{m,l}(t)\, dt = \delta_{n,m}\delta_{k,l}$, with

$$\psi_{n,k}(t) := 2^{n/2} \psi \left(2^n t - k \right), \tag{1.3.17}$$

and

(ii) the closed linear span of $\left\{ \psi_{n,k} \mid n, k \in \mathbb{Z} \right\}$ is $L^2(\mathbb{R})$.

In our analysis of the scaling identity

$$\varphi(t) = 2 \sum_{k \in \mathbb{Z}} a_k \varphi(2t - k) \tag{1.3.18}$$

(a special case of (1.3.1)), we will be looking at two functions φ and ψ; the second one may be taken to be

$$\psi(t) = 2 \sum_{k \in \mathbb{Z}} (-1)^{k+1} \bar{a}_{1-k} \varphi(2t - k). \qquad (1.3.19)$$

This analysis is the approach to wavelets which goes under the name of *multiresolution analysis*. The function ψ which is used in (1.3.16)–(1.3.17) is the solution to (1.3.19). The two standing conditions which are placed on the numbers $(a_k)_{k \in \mathbb{Z}}$, called *masking coefficients*, are

$$\sum_{k \in \mathbb{Z}} \bar{a}_k a_{k+2n} = \frac{1}{2} \delta_{0,n}, \qquad n \in \mathbb{Z}, \qquad (1.3.20)$$

and

$$\sum_{k \in \mathbb{Z}} a_k = 1. \qquad (1.3.21)$$

These conditions in themselves do not imply orthonormality in (1.3.17), but only the following much weaker property:

$$\sum_{n,k \in \mathbb{Z}} |\langle \psi_{n,k} \mid f \rangle|^2 = \|f\|^2 = \int_{\mathbb{R}} |f(t)|^2 \, dt, \qquad f \in L^2(\mathbb{R}). \qquad (1.3.22)$$

A system of functions $(\psi_{n,k})$ satisfying (1.3.22) is called a *Parseval frame*, or a *normalized tight frame*.

It turns out that the ONB property for the wavelet is equivalent to either one of the following two conditions for the normalized scaling function φ:

$$\int_{\mathbb{R}} \overline{\varphi(t)} \varphi(t - k) \, dt = \delta_{0,k}, \qquad (1.3.23)$$

or

$$\|\varphi\|_{L^2(\mathbb{R})} = 1. \qquad (1.3.24)$$

Using this, the reader may check that the ONB property is satisfied for the two examples (a) and (d), but not for (b). However, the Parseval-frame property is evidently satisfied for example (b), i.e., for the stretched Haar wavelet. While in (b), $\varphi = \frac{1}{3} \chi_{[0,3]}$, the corresponding wavelet function ψ is

$$\psi(t) = \begin{cases} \dfrac{1}{3}, & 0 \le t < \dfrac{3}{2}, \\[2mm] -\dfrac{1}{3}, & \dfrac{3}{2} \le t < 3, \\[2mm] 0 & \text{otherwise;} \end{cases}$$

see Figure 1.2(b).

The relevance of random-walk probabilities for understanding of the distinction between Parseval frames and ONBs is treated systematically in Chapters 2 and 6.

Summary of the conclusions from Examples 1.3.3.

- Condition (1.3.14): yes for (a), (b), and (d). No for (c)!
- Condition (1.3.14)$_s$, $s = \log_3(2)$, yes for (c). The integral with respect to the Hausdorff measure h_s is ∞ for φ_a, φ_b, and φ_d.
- Condition (1.3.24): yes for (a), (d). No for (b) and (c)!
- Condition (1.3.24)$_s$, $s = \log_3(2)$, i.e., referring to the Hilbert space $\mathcal{H}_s$. Now yes for (c)! For $s = \log_3(2)$, the Hilbert $\mathcal{H}_s$-norm of φ_a, φ_b, and φ_d is ∞.
- Condition (1.3.23), orthogonality: Yes for (a), and (d); but no for (b).
- Condition (1.3.23)$_s$, $s = \log_3(2)$. Yes for (c), and no for the other three!

Remark 1.3.4. In an earlier textbook [BrJo02b], we consistently used the notational convention $m_0(0) = \sqrt{N}$ for the so-called frequency response function m_0; but in engineering, the alternative convention, $m_0(0) = 1$, is less confusing. This is because the convention $m_0(0) = 1$ captures the probabilistic meaning of "low-pass" better than the one from [BrJo02b]; see the "References and remarks" section at the end of Chapter 9 for a discussion of this point. (Here we have $W = |m_0|^2$.) Also notice that our current convention, $m_0(0) = 1$, is consistent with the pointwise convergence of the infinite products (1.3.5) and (1.3.12). Various versions of, and approaches to, these and related infinite products will play a central role in the next two sections, and in fact throughout the book.

1.4 Sampling

In this section and the next, we study an intriguing relationship between the following three problems:

(1) When does the scaling identity (1.3.1) have L^2 solutions?
(2) How may the transition probabilities P_x be used in *sampling* certain functions at the points $x + k$ as k runs over a set of integers?
(3) When is the infinite product (1.3.5) pointwise convergent?

In the wavelet applications, $X = [0, 1]$, and the system $\sigma, \tau_0, \ldots, \tau_{N-1}$ is as follows:

$$\begin{cases} \sigma(x) = Nx \bmod 1, \\ \tau_j(x) = \dfrac{x+j}{N}, & j = 0, 1, \ldots, N-1. \end{cases} \tag{1.4.1}$$

See also Figure 4.1 (p. 73) in Chapter 4.

Lemma 1.4.1. *Setting* $F(x) := P_x(\{0\})$ *and*

$$k = i_1 + i_2 N + \cdots + i_n N^{n-1} \qquad (\in \mathbb{N}_0), \tag{1.4.2}$$

we get the formula

$$P_x\left(\{k\}\right) = F\left(x+k\right), \tag{1.4.3}$$

where we have identified k with the point $\omega\left(k\right) := \left(i_1, \ldots, i_n, 0\right)$ in Ω.

Proof. To see this, identify functions on $[0, 1]$ with 1-periodic functions on $\mathbb{R}$, and note that the second formula in (1.4.1) yields $\tau_{i_n} \cdots \tau_{i_1}\left(x\right) = \left(x+k\right)/N^n$ where k is given by (1.4.2). Hence, if $1 \le s \le n$, then

$$W\left(\tau_{i_s} \cdots \tau_{i_1}\left(x\right)\right) = W\left(\frac{x + i_1 N + \cdots + i_s N^{s-1}}{N^s}\right) = W\left(\frac{x+k}{N^s}\right).$$

It follows that (1.4.3) is really just a rewrite of (1.3.13). The right-hand side of (1.3.13) yields

$$W\left(\frac{x+k}{N}\right) \cdots W\left(\frac{x+k}{N^n}\right) F\left(\frac{x+k}{N^n}\right) = F\left(x+k\right), \tag{1.4.4}$$

which is the desired conclusion. □

Remark 1.4.2. To extend $P_x\left(\cdot\right)$ from $\mathbb{N}_0$ to $\mathbb{Z}$, recall that $k \in \mathbb{N}_0$ is identified with the singleton $\omega\left(k\right) = \left(i_1, \ldots, i_n, 0\right)$ via (1.4.2). Now, if $-N^n \le k < 0$, then set

$$P_x\left(\{k\}\right) := P_x\left(\left\{\omega\left(N^{n+1} + k\right)\right\}\right). \tag{1.4.5}$$

To help the reader gain some intuitive feeling for the conclusion in Lemma 1.4.1, observe that the right-hand side of (1.4.3) represents a *sampling* of the function F at the integral translates on $\mathbb{R}$, starting at x, i.e., $x + k$. Obviously, different subsets of Ω would yield different sets of sampling points for F, including non-uniformly distributed sampling points; see [AlGr01].

Starting with Shannon [Sha49], the theory of sampling has emerged as a significant tool in signal processing; see, e.g., the beautifully written survey [AlGr01] as well as the references cited therein. Thus, in a general context, our formula (1.4.3) offers a probabilistic prescription for the sampling of functions on the real line, and at the same time it stresses the "random" feature of sampling.

1.5 A convergence theorem for infinite products

We now show how this viewpoint from sampling theory is closely related to some fundamental properties of the measures P_x. In particular, our Theorem 1.5.2 gives a necessary and sufficient condition for pointwise convergence of the infinite product (1.3.5), or more generally (1.2.5), with the condition for convergence stated in terms of the harmonic function h of (1.3.10). The relationship between h and the measure family P_x is studied more systematically in Sections 2.7 and 3.3 below.

Let $A \subset \mathbb{Z}$. Returning to (1.4.3), we set

$$P_x(A) := \sum_{k \in A} P_x(\{k\}) = \sum_{k \in A} F(x + k). \qquad (1.5.1)$$

As in Lemma 1.4.1, the number N, $N \geq 2$, and the function W are given. The measures P_x are constructed from these data using (1.2.4), and we have the two functions

$$F(x) := P_x(\{(\underbrace{0,\ 0,\ 0,\ \dots}_{\infty \text{ string of zeroes}})\}) \qquad (1.5.2)$$

and

$$h(x) := P_x(\mathbb{Z}), \qquad x \in \mathbb{R}. \qquad (1.5.3)$$

We shall meet this function h at several places later in the book. It is a distinguished non-negative eigenfunction (corresponding to eigenvalue 1) for the transfer operator R_W associated with the weight function W, and our next result, Theorem 1.5.2, shows that a property of h at points x determines the convergence of a crucial infinite product built from W at the same point x. The infinite products are studied systematically in Chapter 5, while Section 2.7 describes a wider class of eigenfunctions for R_W. We show in Theorem 2.7.1 that the 1-eigenspace $E_1(R_W)$ for R_W admits a boundary representation which mimics a classical boundary representation from harmonic analysis, and we outline the role h plays: It is characterized by a certain minimality property among functions in $E_1(R_W)$. This in turn is motivated by a certain Perron–Frobenius context for the operator R_W which is studied more generally in Chapter 6.

Finally, for $k \in \mathbb{N}$, set

$$N^k \mathbb{Z} := \left\{ N^k j \mid j \in \mathbb{Z} \right\}. \qquad (1.5.4)$$

Using (1.4.5), we see that $N^k \mathbb{Z}$ is represented in $\Omega = \{0, 1, \dots, N - 1\}^{\mathbb{N}}$ as

$$(\underbrace{0,\ \dots,\ 0,}_{k \text{ zeroes}}\ \underbrace{\omega_1,\ \omega_2,\ \dots,\ .,}_{\substack{\text{a finite string} \\ \text{of symbols} \\ \omega_i \in \{0,\dots,N-1\}}}\ \underbrace{0,\ 0,\ 0,\ \dots}_{\infty \text{ string of zeroes}}). \qquad (1.5.5)$$

An infinite string of zeroes will be denoted $\mathbf{0}$.

Lemma 1.5.1. *Let N, W, F, P_x, and h be as described above; see (1.5.2)–(1.5.3). Then h satisfies the following cocycle identity:*

$$h(x) W(x) = P_{Nx}(N\mathbb{Z}), \qquad x \in \mathbb{R}. \qquad (1.5.6)$$

In particular, if $h(x) \equiv 1$ a.e. $x \in \mathbb{R}$, then we recover the function W from the transition probabilities P_x, a.e. $x \in \mathbb{R}$.

Proof. We calculate the left-hand side in (1.5.6), using the earlier equations:

$$h(x) W(x) \underset{\substack{\text{by (1.4.3)}\\\text{and (1.5.3)}}}{=} W(x) \sum_{j\in\mathbb{Z}} F(x+j)$$

$$\underset{\text{by periodicity}}{=} \sum_{j\in\mathbb{Z}} W(x+j) F(x+j)$$

$$\underset{\text{by (1.4.4)}}{=} \sum_{j\in\mathbb{Z}} F(N(x+j))$$

$$= \sum_{j\in\mathbb{Z}} F(Nx+Nj)$$

$$\underset{\text{by (1.4.3)}}{=} \sum_{j\in\mathbb{Z}} P_{Nx}(\{Nj\})$$

$$\underset{\text{by (1.5.1)}}{=} P_{Nx}(N\mathbb{Z}).$$

This is the desired identity (1.5.6), and the proof is completed.   □

Theorem 1.5.2. *Let N, W, F, P_x, and h be as described above. Let $x \in \mathbb{R}$, and suppose that $P_x(\{0\}) > 0$. Then the following two conditions are equivalent.*

(a) *The limit on the right-hand side below exists, and*

$$F(x) = \lim_{n\to\infty} \prod_{k=1}^{n} W\left(\frac{x}{N^k}\right).$$

(b) *The limit on the left-hand side below exists, and*

$$\lim_{n\to\infty} h\left(\frac{x}{N^n}\right) = 1.$$

Proof. (a) $\Rightarrow$ (b). An iteration of the identity (1.5.6) in Lemma 1.5.1 above yields

$$P_x\left(N^k\mathbb{Z}\right) = \left(\prod_{j=1}^{k} W\left(\frac{x}{N^j}\right)\right) h\left(\frac{x}{N^k}\right). \tag{1.5.7}$$

Using (1.5.5), and working in Ω, we find that

$$\bigcap_{k\in\mathbb{N}} N^k\mathbb{Z} = \{0\}. \tag{1.5.8}$$

An application of a standard result in measure theory [Rud87, Theorem 1.19(e), p. 16] now yields existence of the following limit:

$$\lim_{k\to\infty} P_x\left(N^k\mathbb{Z}\right) = P_x(\{0\}) \underset{\text{by (1.5.2)}}{=} F(x). \tag{1.5.9}$$

Since (a) is assumed, and $F(x) > 0$, we conclude that the limit $h(x/N^k)$, for $k \to \infty$, must exist as well, and further that

$$F(x) = F(x) \lim_{k \to \infty} h\left(\frac{x}{N^k}\right).$$

Using again $F(x) > 0$, we finally conclude that (b) holds.

(b) $\Rightarrow$ (a). Recall that formula (1.5.7) holds in general. If (b) is assumed, we then conclude that the limit $\prod_{j=1}^{k} W\left(x/N^j\right)$ exists as $k \to \infty$. The limit on the left-hand side in (1.5.7) exists and is $F(x)$. The conclusion (a) follows as a result:

$$F(x) = \lim_{k \to \infty} \prod_{j=1}^{k} W\left(\frac{x}{N^j}\right) \lim_{k \to \infty} h\left(\frac{x}{N^k}\right) \underset{\text{using (b)}}{=} \lim_{k \to \infty} \prod_{j=1}^{k} W\left(\frac{x}{N^j}\right). \qquad \Box$$

1.6 A brief outline

In Chapter 2, we study random walk as a Markov process, and we compute the Markov transition measures P_x as x varies over the set X. The construction of P_x and the probability space Ω begins with a sequence of measures $P_x^{(n)}$, $n = 1, 2, \ldots$, corresponding to finite paths of length n. Then we show that the infinite-path-space measure, Lemma 2.4.1, results from an application of the Kolmogorov extension principle. Our technical analysis involves a certain transition operator R which generalizes Lawton's wavelet transition operator; see [Law91a, Law91b].

We already mentioned how the measures P_x serve to prescribe sampling of functions on the real line, Lemma 1.4.1. However, a deeper understanding of this sampling viewpoint is facilitated by the introduction of the Perron–Frobenius–Ruelle operator R, Definitions 2.3.1, and an associated family of harmonic functions. In fact, in Theorem 2.7.1, we make precise the concepts of boundary and of boundary values for these harmonic functions. Our proof of Theorem 2.7.1 uses the convergence theorem for martingales, and we outline the martingales associated with our general transition operator R.

In Chapter 3, a fundamental tightness condition for the random-walk model is introduced. The transition probabilities P_x live in a universal probability space Ω, but the essential convergence questions for the infinite products (see Chapter 2) depend on the the the P_x's being supported on a certain copy of $\mathbb{N}_0$ (the natural numbers), or of $\mathbb{Z}$ (the integers). This refers to the natural embedding of $\mathbb{Z}$ in Ω which we described above (and further in Chapter 2). These concepts and ideas are presented systematically in Chapter 3.

In Chapter 4, we study a family of examples of random walk on fractals, focusing on simple examples of affine iteration on the line, especially the middle-third Cantor set, X_3 (Figures 4.1 and 4.2), and its cousin X_4 (Figures 4.1 and 4.3) arising from quarter divisions. We recall from [JoPe98] that X_4 has a natural orthonormal Fourier basis, while X_3 has no such basis of Fourier frequencies. The difference between the two cases may be understood from an analysis of the random walks and the associated infinite products and transition probabilities.

We also recall from [DuJo06b] that both X_3 and a wider class of affine fractals have orthonormal wavelet bases, the so-called gap-filling wavelets.

For these fractal examples and also for the wavelet applications, the basis properties are determined by the size of the integers $\mathbb{Z}$ naturally embedded in our probability space Ω: the question is when $P_x(\mathbb{Z}) = 1$, i.e., when $\mathbb{Z}$ has full measure in Ω.

In Chapter 5, we prove a general theorem, Theorem 5.4.1, which captures all the examples. We prove that if a certain family of tail-sets in Ω is not negligible, then the condition $P_x(\mathbb{Z}) = 1$ is satisfied.

In general, the function $x \mapsto P_x(\mathbb{Z})$ is not constant. In fact, we show in Chapter 6 that this function is harmonic. Moreover, it is minimal in a sense we make precise.

In Chapters 7 and 8 we give a number of applications: wavelets, wavelet packets, generalized multiresolutions, wavelet filters that take matrix values, and we consider applications which depend on a certain family of infinite random products of matrix functions.

In Chapter 9, we study pairs of representations of the Cuntz algebras. While this is a subject from operator algebras, it turns out to apply to the examples from Sections 8.2, 8.3, and 8.4, i.e., to wavelet packets, and to the corresponding measure-theoretic issues.

1.7 From wavelets to fractals

The FBI has a database consisting of some 200 million fingerprint records ... As part of a modernization program, the FBI is digitizing these records as 8-bit grayscale images, with a spatial resolution of 500 dots per inch. This results in some 10 megabytes per card, making the current archive about 2,000 terabytes in size. —C.M. Brislawn 1995

One of the reasons wavelets have found so many uses and applications is that they are especially attractive from the computational point of view. Traditionally, scale/translation wavelet bases are used in function spaces on the real line, or on the Euclidean space $\mathbb{R}^d$. Since we have Lebesgue measure, the Hilbert space $L^2(\mathbb{R}^d)$ offers the natural setting for harmonic analysis with wavelet bases. These bases can be made orthonormal in $L^2(\mathbb{R}^d)$, and they involve only a fixed notion of scaling, for example by a given expansive d-by-d matrix A over $\mathbb{Z}$, and translation by the integer lattice $\mathbb{Z}^d$. But this presupposes an analysis that is localized in a chosen resolution subspace, say V_0 in $L^2(\mathbb{R}^d)$. That this is possible is one of the successes of wavelet computations. Indeed, it is a non-trivial fact that a rich variety of such subspaces V_0 exist; and further that they may be generated by one, or a finite set of functions φ in $L^2(\mathbb{R}^d)$ which satisfy a certain *scaling equation* [Dau92].

The determination of this equation might only involve a finite set of numbers (four-tap, six-tap, etc.), and it is of central importance for computation. The solutions to a scaling equation are called *scaling functions*, and are usually denoted φ. Specifically, the scaling equation relates in a well-known way the A-scaling of the function(s) φ to their $\mathbb{Z}^d$-translates.

The fact that there are solutions in $L^2(\mathbb{R}^d)$ is not at all obvious; see [Dau92]. In application to images, the subspace V_0 may represent a certain resolution, and hence there is a choice involved, but we know by standard theory, see, e.g., [Dau92], that under apropriate conditions such choices are possible. As a result there are extremely useful and computationally efficient wavelet bases in $L^2(\mathbb{R}^d)$. A resolution subspace V_0 within $L^2(\mathbb{R}^d)$ can be chosen to be arbitrarily fine: Finer resolutions correspond to larger subspaces.

As noted for example in [BrJo02b], a variant of the scaling equation is also used in computer graphics: there data is successively subdivided and the refined level of data is related to the previous level by prescribed masking coefficients. The latter coefficients in turn induce generating functions which are direct analogues of wavelet filters; see the discussion in Section 1.3, Chapters 7 and 9, and the Appendices.

One reason for the computational efficiency of wavelets lies in the fact that *wavelet coefficients* in *wavelet expansions* for functions in V_0 may be computed using matrix iteration rather than by a direct computation of inner products: the latter would involve integration over $\mathbb{R}^d$, and hence would be computationally inefficient, if feasible at all. The deeper reason why we can compute wavelet coefficients using matrix iteration is an important connection to the subband-filtering method from signal/image processing involving digital filters, down-sampling and up-sampling. In this setting, filters may be realized as functions m_0 on a d-torus, e.g., quadrature-mirror filters.

As emphasized for example in [Jor05] and [Bri95], because of down-sampling, the matrix iteration involved in the computation of wavelet coefficients involves so-called slanted Toeplitz matrices F from signal processing. The slanted matrices F are immediately available; they simply record the numbers (masking coefficients) from the φ-scaling equation. Further, these matrices have the computationally attractive property that the iterated powers F^k become sucessively more sparse as k increases, i.e., the matrix representation of F^k has mostly zeroes, and the non-zero terms have an especially attractive geometric configuration. In fact subband signal processing yields a finite family, F, G, etc., of such slanted matrices: for example, with L for "low frequency" and H for "high frequency,"

$$\varphi = \sum_k P_k \varphi(2 \cdot -k), \quad \psi = \sum_k Q_k \varphi(2 \cdot -k), \quad (1.7.1)$$

$$\begin{cases} F: \quad y_n^L = \dfrac{1}{\sqrt{2}} \sum_k P_{k-2n} x_k, \\[4mm] G: \quad y_n^H = \dfrac{1}{\sqrt{2}} \sum_k Q_{k-2n} x_k. \end{cases} \quad (1.7.2)$$

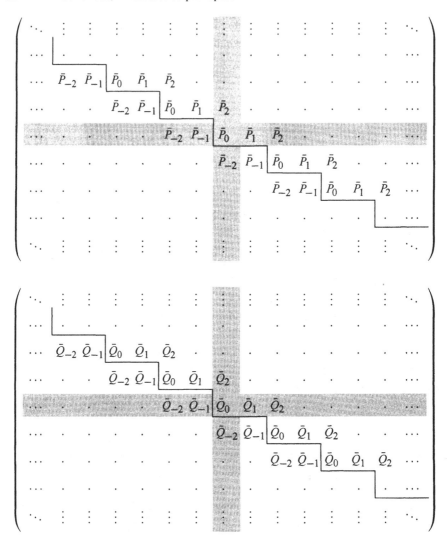

Fig. 1.3. The slanted matrices F and G of (1.7.2).

The associated pair of slanted matrices F and G are sketched in Figure 1.3.

Before getting to the theory behind the slanted matrices, we will need some preparation, and the matrices will then be motivated and studied systematically in Chapter 7 and again in Chapter 9.

In brief outline, the numbers P_i are entered into the rows of the matrix F via a specific slant-pattern. The placement is initiated in row/column position $0, 0$ as follows: The number P_0 is used in the row/column position 0, 0, and as we move to the next row one number down, the same row is simply repeated, but with a shift to the right by *two* places.

Similarly, we shift two places to the left for each one row-move up in the matrix. The resulting slanting is seen in Figure 1.3. Moreover, the matrix G is created from the numbers Q_i in exactly the same way.

The wavelet coefficients at scaling level k of a numerical signal s from V_0 are then simply the coordinates of $GF^k s$. By this we mean that a signal in V_0 is represented by a vector s via a fixed choice of scaling function; see [Dau92, BrJo02b, Jor03]. Then the matrix product GF^k is applied to s; and the matrices GF^k get more slanted as k increases.

Our approach begins with the observation that the computational feature of this engineering device can be said to begin with an endomorphism r_A of the d-torus $\mathbb{T}^d = \mathbb{R}^d/\mathbb{Z}^d$, an endomorphism which results from simply passing matrix multiplication by A on $\mathbb{R}^d$ to the quotient by $\mathbb{Z}^d$. It is then immediate that the inverse images $r_A^{-1}(x)$ are finite for all x in $\mathbb{T}^d$, in fact $\#r_A^{-1}(x) = |\det A|$. From this we recover the scaling identity, and we note that the wavelet scaling equation is a special case of a more general identity known in computational fractal theory and symbolic dynamics [Jor04a]. We show that wavelet algorithms and harmonic analysis naturally generalize to affine iterated function systems. Moreover, in this general context, we are able to build the ambient Hilbert spaces for a variety of dynamical systems which arise from the iterated dynamics of endomorphisms of compact spaces [DuJo06b].

As a consequence, the fact that the ambient Hilbert space in the traditional wavelet setting is the more familiar $L^2(\mathbb{R}^d)$ is merely an artifact of the choice of filters m_0. As we further show, by enlarging the class of admissible filters, there is a variety of other ambient Hilbert spaces possible with corresponding wavelet expansions: the most notable are those which arise from iterated function systems (IFSs) of fractal type, for example for the middle-third Cantor set and scaling by 3.

With examples, theorems, and graphics, we hope to bring these threads to light: The journey from wavelets to fractals via signal processing.

More generally (see Chapters 4 and 5), there is a variety of other natural dynamical settings (affine IFSs) that invite the same computational approach.

The two most striking examples which admit such a harmonic analysis are perhaps complex dynamics and subshifts. Both will be worked out in detail. In the first case, consider a given rational function $r(z)$ of one complex variable. We then get an endomorphism r acting on an associated Julia set X in the complex plane $\mathbb{C}$ as follows: This endomorphism $r: X \to X$ results by restriction to X [Bea91]. (Details: Recall that X is by definition the complement of the points in $\mathbb{C}$ where the sequence of iterations r^n is a normal family. Specifically, the Fatou set F of $r(z)$ is the largest open set in $\mathbb{C}$ where r^n is a normal sequence of functions, and we let X be the complement of F. Here r^n denotes the n'th iteration of the rational function $r(z)$.) The induced endomorphism r of X is then simply the restriction to X of $r(z)$.

If r then denotes the resulting endomorphism, $r: X \to X$, it is known [DuJo06a] that $\#r^{-1}(x) = $ degree of r, for every x in X (except for a finite set of singular points).

In the second case, for a particular one-sided subshift, we may take X as the corresponding state space, and again we have a naturally induced finite-to-one endomorphism of X of geometric and computational significance.

But in the general framework, there is no natural candidate for the ambient Hilbert space. That is good in one sense, as it means that the subband filters m_0 which are feasible will constitute a richer family of functions on X.

In all cases, the analysis is governed by a random-walk model with successive iterations where probabilities are assigned on the finite sets $\#r^{-1}(x)$ and are given by the function $W := |m_0|^2$. This leads to a *transfer operator R_W* (Section 2.3) which has features in common with the classical operator considered first by Perron and Frobenius for positive matrices; in particular, it has a Perron–Frobenius eigenvalue, and positive Perron–Frobenius eigenvectors, one on the right, a function, and one on the left, a measure; see [Rue89]. As we show in Chapters 2 and 6, this Perron–Frobenius measure, also sometimes called the Ruelle measure, is an essential ingredient for our construction of an ambient Hilbert space. All of this, we show, applies to a variety of examples, and as we show, has the more traditional wavelet setup as a special case, in fact the special case when the Ruelle measure on $\mathbb{T}^d$ is the Dirac mass corresponding to the point 0 in $\mathbb{T}^d$ (additive notation) representing zero frequency in the signal-processing setup.

There are two more ingredients entering in our construction of the ambient Hilbert space: a path-space measure governed by the W-probabilities, and certain finite cycles for the endomorphism r. For each x in X, we consider paths by infinite iterated tracing back with r^{-1} and recursively assigning probabilities with W. Hence we get a measure P_x on a space of paths for each x (Section 2.4). These measures are in turn integrated in x using the Ruelle measure on X. The resulting measure will now define the inner product in the ambient Hilbert space.

Our present harmonic analysis for these systems is governed by a certain class of geometric cycles for r, i.e., cycles under iteration by r. We need cycles where the function W attains its maximum, and we call them W-*cycles*. They are essential, and we include a discussion of W-cycles for particular examples, including their geometry, and a discussion of their significance for the computation in an orthogonal harmonic analysis; see especially Chapter 9. We give a necessary and sufficient condition for a certain class of affine fractals in $\mathbb{R}^d$ to have an orthonormal Fourier basis, and we even give a recipe for what these orthonormal bases look like. We believe that this throws new light on a rather fundamental question: which fractals admit complete sets of Fourier frequencies? Our results further extend earlier work by a number of authors, and in particular, clarify the scale-4 Cantor set on the line, considered earlier by the author and S. Pedersen [JoPe98], and also by R. Strichartz [Str00, Str05], and I. Laba and Y. Wang [ŁaWa02].

Exercises

Problems worthy
of attack
prove their worth
by hitting back.
—Piet Hein

1.1. Let $\mathbb{Z}_2 = \{0, 1\}$, and $\Omega := \prod_0^\infty \mathbb{Z}_2$.

(a) For $n \in \mathbb{N}$, $i_j \in \{0, 1\}$, $1 \le j \le n$, set

$$A(i_1, \ldots, i_n) := \{\omega \in \Omega \mid \omega_j = i_j, \ 1 \le j \le n\}.$$

Show that $\varnothing$ and these sets generate a topology $\mathcal{T}$ and a σ-algebra $\mathcal{B}$, and moreover that

$$\mathcal{T} \subsetneq \mathcal{B} \subsetneq \mathcal{P},$$

where $\mathcal{P}$ denotes the set of all subsets of Ω. We shall let $\mathcal{T}$ and $\mathcal{B}$ denote topology and σ-algebra, respectively, whenever continuity or measurability is needed, unless otherwise specified.

(b) Show that Ω is uncountable.

(c) Show that $(\Omega, \mathcal{T})$ is a compact space.

(d) Show that Ω and the Cantor set X_3 (with its usual topology) are homeomorphic.

(e) Show that the functions $\chi_{A(i_1,\ldots,i_n)}$ separate points in Ω.

(f) Using the Stone–Weierstraß theorem, show that the algebra generated by the constant function $\mathbb{1}$ on Ω and the functions $\chi_{A(i_1,\ldots,i_n)}$ is dense in $C(\Omega)$.

(g) Let $p \in (0, 1)$ be fixed, and set $L(\mathbb{1}) = 1$ and

$$L\left(\chi_{A(i_1,\ldots,i_n)}\right) = p^{\#\{j \mid i_j = 1\}} \cdot (1 - p)^{\#\{k \mid i_k = 0\}}.$$

Using (f), show that L extends uniquely by linearity to $C(\Omega)$, and that there is a measure $\mu = \mu_p$ on $\mathcal{B}$ such that

$$L(f) = \int_\Omega f \, d\mu \qquad \text{for all } f \in C(\Omega).$$

(The measure μ_p is called the p-Bernoulli-product measure.)

1.2. Let the measures μ_p be as in Exercise 1.1(g). Show that for $p \ne p'$, the two measures μ_p and $\mu_{p'}$ are mutually singular.

1.3. (a) Show that $\mathbb{Z}_2$ is an abelian group under addition mod 1 in $\mathbb{Z}$.

(b) Show that Ω in Exercise 1.1 becomes a compact abelian group under the infinite-"product" operation, i.e., with

$$(\omega_i) + (\omega_i') := (\omega_i + \omega_i'),$$

where $\omega_i + \omega_i'$ is the addition in $\mathbb{Z}_2$.

(c) The *Haar measure* μ of Ω is defined on $\mathcal{B}$ from Exercise 1.1(a) and satisfies:

- μ is a measure (σ-additive) defined on the σ-algebra $\mathcal{B}$;
- $\mu(\Omega) = 1$;
- $\mu(E + \omega) = \mu(E)$ for all $E \in \mathcal{B}$ and $\omega \in \Omega$, where $E + \omega := \{\xi + \omega \mid \xi \in E\}$.

Find the Haar measure μ of Ω. Explicit formula!

Hint: Take $p = 1/2$ in Exercise 1.1(g), and show that $\mu_{1/2}$ satisfies the three listed conditions. You may use the fact that Haar measure is unique subject to these conditions.

(d) Set

$$\Lambda := \left\{ \lambda = (\lambda_i)_{i \in \mathbb{N}_0} \mid \lambda_i \in \mathbb{Z}_2, \ \lambda_i = 0 \text{ except for a finite number of places} \right\},$$

and set

$$\chi_\lambda(\omega) := \prod_{k=0}^{\infty} e^{i\pi \lambda_k \omega_k},$$

and then show that χ_λ is a well-defined function on Ω for all $\lambda \in \Lambda$.

(e) Show that each χ_λ is continuous and satisfies:

- $\chi_0(\omega) = 1$ for all $\omega \in \Omega$;
- $\chi_\lambda(\omega + \omega') = \chi_\lambda(\omega) \chi_\lambda(\omega')$ for all $\lambda \in \Lambda$ and $\omega, \omega' \in \Omega$.

(**Note:** χ_λ is called a *character* on the group Ω.)

(f) Show that the linear span of the characters $\{\chi_\lambda \mid \lambda \in \Lambda\}$ is dense in $C(\Omega)$.

(g) Show that

$$\int_\Omega \overline{\chi_\lambda(\omega)} \, \chi_{\lambda'}(\omega) \, d\mu(\omega) = \delta_{\lambda, \lambda'}$$

for $\lambda, \lambda' \in \Lambda$, where μ is Haar measure.

1.4. Definition: An indexed family $\{h_\lambda \mid \lambda \in \Lambda\}$ in a Hilbert space $\mathcal{H}$ is said to be a *frame* (or a *frame basis*) if there are positive constants A and B such that

$$A \|f\|^2 \leq \sum_{\lambda \in \Lambda} |\langle h_\lambda \mid f \rangle|^2 \leq B \|f\|^2 \qquad \text{for all } f \in \mathcal{H}. \tag{1E.1}$$

Returning to the Cantor group Ω and its dual Λ, we examine the family

$$\{\chi_\lambda \mid \lambda \in \Lambda\}$$

in the Hilbert space $L^2(\Omega, \mu_p)$ for each p, $0 < p < 1$.

(a) Show that $\{\chi_\lambda \mid \lambda \in \Lambda\}$ is an orthonormal basis in $L^2(\Omega, \mu_p)$ if and only if $p = 1/2$.

(b) Show that $\{\chi_\lambda \mid \lambda \in \Lambda\}$ is *not* a frame basis in $L^2(\Omega, \mu_p)$ when $p \neq 1/2$.

Hint: For each n, consider the subset $\Lambda_n \subset \Lambda$ of points $\lambda = (\lambda_i)$ such that $\lambda_i = 0$ for $i > n$; and for each k, $0 \leq k \leq n$, the subset $\Lambda_n(k) \subset \Lambda_n$ consisting of $\lambda = (\lambda_i)$ in Λ_n such that $\# \{ i \mid \lambda_i = 1 \} = k$. Let f be the constant function $\mathbb{1}$, or equivalently, $f = \chi_0$. Using $\#\Lambda_n(k) = \binom{n}{k}$, justify the following calculation:

$$\sum_{\lambda \in \Lambda_n} |\langle \chi_\lambda \mid f \rangle|^2 = \sum_{k=0}^{n} \sum_{\lambda \in \Lambda_n(k)} |\langle \chi_\lambda \mid f \rangle|^2$$

$$= \sum_{k=0}^{n} \binom{n}{k} |1 - 2p|^{2k} = \left(1 + |1 - 2p|^2 \right)^n.$$

Since this limit is ∞ for $n \to \infty$ whenever $p \neq 1/2$, the conclusion follows.

(c) Is there a positive lower frame bound for $\{\chi_\lambda \mid \lambda \in \Lambda\}$ in the Hilbert space $L^2(\Omega, \mu_p)$, $p \neq 1/2$? In other words, is there some $A > 0$ such that the lower estimate in the relation (1E.1) is valid for all $f \in L^2(\Omega, \mu_p)$?

1.5. Using the idea from Exercise 1.1(a), show that there is a natural orthonormal basis (ONB) for $L^2(\Omega, \mu_{1/2})$.

1.6. Can you find a countable ONB for $L^2(\Omega, \mu_{1/2})$?

1.7. Let φ_a and φ_b denote the functions in the top part of Figure 1.2 (p. 13). Which of the two families of functions is orthogonal in $L^2(\mathbb{R})$,

$$\{\varphi_a(\cdot - k) \mid k \in \mathbb{Z}\} \quad \text{or} \quad \{\varphi_b(\cdot - k) \mid k \in \mathbb{Z}\}?$$

1.8. Let ψ_a and ψ_b denote the two functions in the bottom part of Figure 1.2 (p. 13).

(a) Which of the two families of functions

$$\left\{ 2^{j/2} \psi_a \left(2^j t - k \right) \mid j, k \in \mathbb{Z} \right\} \quad \text{or} \quad \left\{ 2^{j/2} \psi_b \left(2^j t - k \right) \mid j, k \in \mathbb{Z} \right\}$$

form ONBs in $L^2(\mathbb{R})$?

(b) Give a direct argument with pictures, showing that the double-indexed family of functions

$$\psi_{j,k}^{(a)}(t) = 2^{j/2} \psi_a \left(2^j t - k \right)$$

forms an ONB in $L^2(\mathbb{R})$.

(c) Give a direct argument with pictures, showing that the double-indexed family of functions

$$\psi_{j,k}^{(b)}(t) = 2^{j/2} \psi_b \left(2^j t - k \right)$$

satisfies

$$\|f\|_{L^2}^2 = \sum_{j,k \in \mathbb{Z}} \left| \langle \psi_{j,k}^{(b)} \mid f \rangle \right|^2$$

for all $f \in L^2(\mathbb{R})$.

1.9. Consider the four versions of the scaling identity on $\mathbb{R}$ listed in Section 1.3, Example 1.3.3, under (a), (b), (c), and (d).

Fill in the missing arguments and check that the conclusions listed in the summary at the end of Section 1.3 are correct.

1.10. Let $\varphi \in L^2(\mathbb{R})$, and consider the *ansatz*, for some operator $W = W_\varphi$,

$$W_\varphi \left(\sum_{k \in \mathbb{Z}} s_k \varphi \left(\cdot - k \right) \right) = (s_k),$$

where (s_k) is some sequence.

(a) Give a necessary and sufficient condition on the function φ for when W_φ defines a bounded linear operator from the natural closed subspace $V_\varphi \subset L^2(\mathbb{R})$ into $\ell^2 = \ell^2(\mathbb{Z})$.

(b) Give a necessary and sufficient condition on the function φ for when W_φ defines an invertible operator from V_φ onto ℓ^2.

(c) Give a necessary and sufficient condition on the function φ for when W_φ defines an isometric isomorphism of V_φ onto ℓ^2.

The remaining exercises in this chapter are most likely review for mathematics students: We hope that they make it easier for the reader to build up (or more likely review!) prerequisites that first-year grad students might need to refresh, as they move from one chapter to the next: Fourier, Hilbert, bases, a little on linear operators, etc. All standard material first year grad students have seen but perhaps might want to brush up on: Learning by doing!

1.11. Hilbert space (the separable case)

Definition (the list of axioms)

- $\mathcal{H}$: vector space over the complex field $\mathbb{C}$.

- $\langle \cdot \mid \cdot \rangle : \mathcal{H} \times \mathcal{H} \to \mathbb{C}$, satisfying
  (i) $x \mapsto \langle x \mid y \rangle$ is conjugate linear for all $y \in \mathcal{H}$,
  (ii) $y \mapsto \langle x \mid y \rangle$ is linear for all $x \in \mathcal{H}$,
  (iii) $\langle x \mid y \rangle = \overline{\langle y \mid x \rangle}, x, y \in \mathcal{H}$,
  (iv) $\langle x \mid x \rangle \geq 0$ for all $x \in \mathcal{H}$, and
  (v) $\langle x \mid x \rangle = 0 \Rightarrow x = 0$.

- Setting $\|x\| := \langle x \mid x \rangle^{1/2}$ turns $\mathcal{H}$ into a *complete normed space*, i.e., if some sequence $(x_n)_{n \in \mathbb{N}}$ satisfies $\|x_n - x_m\| \underset{n,m \to \infty}{\to} 0$, then there is some $x \in \mathcal{H}$ such that $\|x - x_n\| \underset{n \to \infty}{\to} 0$.

Review your real-variables book, and then show that the following are examples of Hilbert spaces:

- $\mathcal{H} := \mathbb{C}^k$ = the k-dimensional complex vector space with $x = (x_1, \ldots, x_k)$, $x_j \in \mathbb{C}$ for $1 \le j \le k$, and

$$\langle x \mid y \rangle := \sum_{j=1}^{k} \bar{x}_j y_j.$$

- $\mathcal{H} := \ell^2$ = all sequences $x = (x_j)_{j \in \mathbb{N}}$ such that $\sum_{j=1}^{\infty} |x_j|^2 < \infty$, where we set

$$\langle x \mid y \rangle := \sum_{j=1}^{\infty} \bar{x}_j y_j.$$

- $\mathcal{H} := \ell^2(A)$ where A is some fixed countable set = all functions $x: A \to \mathbb{C}$ satisfying $\sum_{a \in A} |x(a)|^2 < \infty$, and where we set

$$\langle x \mid y \rangle := \sum_{a \in A} \overline{x(a)}\, y(a).$$

Does this construction work also if A is not countable? What is $\ell^2(A)$ if A is not countable?

- Let $(X, \mathcal{B}, \mu)$ be a σ-finite measure space, and set $\mathcal{H} := L^2(X, \mathcal{B}, \mu)$, or $L^2(\mu)$ for short, i.e., all measurable functions f on X satisfying

$$\int_X |f(x)|^2\, d\mu(x) < \infty,$$

where we set

$$\langle f \mid g \rangle := \int_X \overline{f(x)}\, g(x)\, d\mu(x),$$

and where we identify two functions f_1 and f_2 if there is a subset S with $\mu(S) = 0$, and $f_1 = f_2$ on $X \setminus S$.

1.12. Give your own proof of the following basic facts about Hilbert space $\mathcal{H}$.

- $|\langle x \mid y \rangle| \le \|x\|\, \|y\|$, $x, y \in \mathcal{H}$ (Schwarz's inequality).

- A linear mapping $L: \mathcal{H} \to \mathbb{C}$ (functional) satisfies $|L(x)| \le \text{Const.}\, \|x\|$ if and only if it has the form $L(x) = \langle y \mid x \rangle$ for some $y \in \mathcal{H}$ (Riesz's theorem).

1.13. Operators

Let $\mathcal{H}_i$, $i = 1, 2$, be two Hilbert spaces and let $T: \mathcal{H}_1 \to \mathcal{H}_2$ be a linear transformation. Show that the following conditions are equivalent.

- T is continuous relative to the respective norms on $\mathcal{H}_1$ and $\mathcal{H}_2$.

- $\|Tx\|_2 \le C \|x\|_1 \ \forall x \in \mathcal{H}_1$ holds for some finite constant C.
- $|\langle Tx_1 \mid x_2 \rangle| \le C \|x_1\|_1 \|x_2\|_2 \ \forall x_i \in \mathcal{H}_i, i = 1, 2$, holds for some finite constant C.

Show that the best constant C is the same in the two estimates.

1.14. Fourier series

(a) We shall identify the interval $I = [0, 1)$ and $\mathbb{T} := \{z \in \mathbb{C} \mid |z| = 1\}$ via $z = e^{i2\pi t}$. Show that this identification respects the usual structures of topology and measurable subsets for I and for $\mathbb{T}$.

(b) Show that the restriction of the usual Lebesgue measure on $\mathbb{R}$ to I induces a unique normalized measure μ on $\mathbb{T}$, and that this measure satisfies

$$\mu(zE) = \mu(E)$$

whenever $z \in \mathbb{T}$ and E is a measurable subset of $\mathbb{T}$. (Here $zE := \{zw \mid w \in E\}$.)

(c) For $n \in \mathbb{Z}$, set $e_n(z) := z^n$. Show that the functions $\{e_n \mid n \in \mathbb{Z}\}$ on $\mathbb{T}$ are in $L^2(\mathbb{T})$, and satisfy the two conditions

- $\langle e_n \mid e_m \rangle = \delta_{n,m}, n, m \in \mathbb{Z}$; and
- $f \in L^2(\mathbb{T})$ & $\langle e_n \mid f \rangle = 0$ for all $n \in \mathbb{Z} \Rightarrow f = 0$.

(A system of functions with these properties is called an orthonormal basis (ONB).)

(d) If $f \in L^2(\mathbb{T})$, set

$$(Uf)(n) := \tilde{f}(n) := \langle e_n \mid f \rangle = \int_{\mathbb{T}} \bar{e}_n f \, d\mu,$$

and show that $U: L^2(\mathbb{T}) \to \ell^2(\mathbb{Z})$ is linear, isometric, and maps *onto* $\ell^2(\mathbb{Z})$.

(e) Deduce from (d) that the identity

$$\sum_{n \in \mathbb{Z}} \left|\tilde{f}(n)\right|^2 = \int_{\mathbb{T}} |f|^2 \, d\mu \qquad \text{(Parseval)}$$

holds for all $f \in L^2(\mathbb{T})$, and then make precise the following representation:

$$f(z) = \sum_{n \in \mathbb{Z}} \tilde{f}(n) z^n, \qquad z \in \mathbb{T}. \qquad (1E.2)$$

(f) Review your real-variables book and check that the last identity (1E.2) holds a.e. on $\mathbb{T}$, i.e., the series (1E.2) is convergent on $\mathbb{T}$ except possibly on a subset of measure zero. (This is a difficult theorem due to Lenard Carleson.)

History

Naturally infinite products have a rich history in mathematics and its applications; but in this book, the use of infinite products and applications to wavelet algorithms and harmonic analysis are emphasized. This serves as a modern key between analysis and probability: Perhaps somewhat surprisingly, the wavelet connection started with signal processing. In fact, the use of digital filters in wavelet theory dates from the 1980s, with the pioneering work of S. Mallat [Mal89], A. Cohen [Coh90], W. Lawton [Law91a, Law91b], among others. And fundamental ideas of Y. Meyer [Mey79] and I. Daubechies [Dau92] loom in the background. For this interdisciplinary connection, we further refer to the papers cited in [Dau92] and in [BrJo02b]. Another element is the transfer operator, or the wavelet transfer operator. It has many names, e.g., the Perron–Frobenius–Ruelle operator. Or by now this transfer operator is often called the Ruelle operator because of D. Ruelle's use of it in the 1960s on phase-transition problems in statistical mechanics [Rue69]. As we hope will become clear in the first two chapters below, the transfer operator (in any one of its many incarnations) serves as a crucial mathematical link connecting diverse interdisciplinary trends. The probability aspect of this endeavor was stressed by R. Gundy [Gun00] and others, e.g., [CoRa90]. Our presentation here relies in crucial ways on Gundy's viewpoint, as it seems to unify the different threads in the subject that came before it.

It turns out that the marriage of signal processing and wavelets inspired the generation of new algorithms that now go under the name of wavelet algorithms. The algorithms have further served to make wavelets useful to engineers and the medical community, among others.

Mathematically, the choice of closed subspaces (V_n) in Hilbert space to model resolutions is inspired by optics and image processing. So this inspiration came from physics, and from very practical applications. (And hence the terms resolution, pixels, and level of detail have now entered mathematics.) In the Hilbert-space context, the relative complement W_n of two successive spaces V_n from the nested scale of spaces represent a level of detail, and the reader may find it helpful to think of the elements in some space W_n as representing the detail level in an image. But at the same time, this is also the way to think of algorithms, much the same way we think of numerical algorithms based on the positional number system. The positional number representation closely mirrors the wavelet context. In the wavelet algorithm, there is a scaling operation which implements a kind of similarity (to be made precise in Chapter 5) between level n and the next level $n + 1$ in the finer scale of resolutions. Hence we have V_n realized as a subspace of V_{n+1}. The intersection of the spaces V_n is $\{0\}$ and the union is dense in $L^2(\mathbb{R})$.

Mathematically, this viewpoint has inspired the use of pyramid algorithms in wavelets (see Chapters 7, 8, and 9). The viewpoint is versatile, and applies equally well to one and several dimensions, as we shall see.

Infinite products have played a central role in a number of classical problems for more than a hundred years. Recall some very familiar cases:

(1) The factorization over the primes of the Riemann zeta function [Edw01], and its many generalizations in dynamics [May91, Rue02, Rue94, SeCh67].
(2) The solution of second order differential equations with the use of a 2×2 propagator matrix [PaPo90].
(3) Complex dynamics, iterated substitution of rational functions [Sch1871, FrLM83].
(4) Symbolic dynamics: Iterated substitution from words to letters, random products of Perron–Frobenius matrices [Jor01a, Per07, Wal01, Bal00, Rad99].
(5) Statistical mechanics and phase-transition problems [Rue69, Bal00].
(6) The solution of diffusion equations using Wiener's path measure [Sim79].
(7) Analytic continuation of Wiener's solution in (6) to the solution of Schrödinger's equation; again based on path measures, but now the (ill-defined) Feynman measure [Nel64, Nel69].

More recent applications of infinite random products include:

(8) piecewise linear iterated function systems (IFS) [BrJo99a, DeSh04, Shu04, Shu05], fractals and chaos [Rue94]; and
(9) wavelets [Dau92, BrJo02b, CoHR97, CoRa90, Gun00, DoGH00, GuKa00, Gun04, PaSW99].

Even though general methods from probability, random walk, transition probabilities, and path space have a long history in analysis and in applications, their use in wavelet analysis is of rather more recent vintage.

Ubiquitous to our present approach is a certain "transfer operator" R, see [Bal00] and [BrJo02b]. This operator in fact has many incarnations (and many names). It has emerged and re-emerged, over the years, in a variety of applications. The underlying idea behind it is clear from matrix theory, in the guise of a positive matrix P and the familiar Perron–Frobenius theorem on the spectrum of P. But we now address an infinite-dimensional setting.

Our approach is motivated by David Ruelle's use of an infinite-dimensional variant of R in the 1960s. Ruelle used R in his study of phase-transition problems of quantum statistical mechanics. Since then, other variants of R have re-emerged in a variety of different applications: in dynamics, continuous and discrete, experimental and symbolic; and in our (limited) understanding of fractals and other attractors! The operator R is used in such applications as wavelets and fractals, as well as in pure mathematics (zeta functions, trace formulas, etc.).

This book is actually focused around (9) from the list of topics above, i.e., the kind of random-walk problems (see, e.g., [Spi76, DiFr99]) that are associated with analysis of wavelets [Dau92, BrJo02b] and with iterative algorithms for wavelet packets [Wic93, Wic94].

References and remarks

Historically the meeting ground of probability and mathematical analysis has been in the areas of potential theory and stochastic differential equations; see, e.g., [Bas95], [Bas03], [Doo94], and [Doo01]. A classic textbook in probability theory for the beginner is Feller's [Fel71], and it is still a pleasure to read.

Recent papers which build on the interconnections between wavelets and fractals on the one side and probability and signals on the other include [HeJL04], [Jor01a], [DuJo06b], [BaJMP04], and [Gun66, Gun99, Gun00, DoGH00, GuKa00, Gun04].

In contrast to traditional textbooks and research articles, there is now a new information system, Wikipedia, which offers a delightful and student-friendly invitation to some fundamental wavelet ideas and wavelet packets. One of the entries from Wikipedia for the keyword "wavelet" [WWW/wiki], also available as the paper [ViMu95], contains both delightful exposition and Mathematica do-it-yourself procedures. In addition it reaches out to applications (e.g., to hands-on experiments with thresholding), and to neighboring fields such as probability. The reader is likely to find other helpful and relevant material in [WWW/wiki]. Since it is a "community site," not everything is up to date; but if used with care, it can be really helpful—and free!

Turning to some fundamentals of probability theory, the novice might find the lovely survey article [Stro96] helpful. It is a bird's-eye view on path-space measures from the Gaussian viewpoint and their applications. See also [Stro00]. Both treatments include many useful and modern references. Further, the same author D.W. Stroock has an attractive new book [Stro05] giving a concise introduction to Markov processes.

Our present focus is different: We stress certain algorithmic and potential-theoretic features of the theory of wavelets, fractals, and iterated function systems (IFS). Our emphasis is more on the discrete side and on developments that have taken place in the past two decades, but they have been motivated by the more classical approaches to continuous martingales and stochastic analysis that grew out of probabilistic methods for the heat equation and its cousins in applied mathematics. One approach to discrete harmonic analysis is via quadratic forms and resistance inequalities; see, e.g., [Kig01]. Our viewpoint is related to this, but different in that it is based on the analysis of a certain transfer operator rather than on energy forms as in [Kig01], i.e., on certain quadratic forms with resistance numbers relating transitions between states on a graph configuration.

As outlined in Section 1.3 in this chapter, Mallat's approach to multiresolutions [Mal89] involves three mathematical tools: Fourier transform, infinite products, and the analysis of periodic functions. In several variables, i.e., functions on $\mathbb{R}^d$ this last step in turn relies on classical Fourier duality between the familiar rank-d lattice $\mathbb{Z}^d$ on the (multi)frequency side and the compact torus $\mathbb{R}^d/\mathbb{Z}^d$ on the other. Now the quotient $\mathbb{R}^d/\mathbb{Z}^d$ may be represented as the d-torus $\mathbb{T}^d$, but also in a variety of other ways as well. Specifically, we may represent it as a suitably selected subset of $\mathbb{R}^d$, for example as the usual d-cube $\mathbb{D}$. The other choices for $\mathbb{D}$ are called *fundamental domains* for the lattice $\mathbb{Z}^d$. Whichever the choice of fundamental domain, we arrive at the Hilbert space $L^2(\mathbb{D})$ and the following fact: The functions $e_\lambda(x) := e^{i2\pi x \cdot \lambda}$ with the vector index λ in $\mathbb{Z}^d$ form an orthogonal basis for the Hilbert space $L^2(\mathbb{D})$; i.e., an ONB when normalized.

There is a variation of this theme which starts with the observation that the pair of sets $(\mathbb{D}, \mathbb{Z}^d)$ is a *spectral pair* in the sense of [JoPe93]. Specifically, consider two subsets $\mathbb{D}$ and Λ of $\mathbb{R}^d$ with $\mathbb{D}$ having positive and finite Lebesgue measure. We say that it is a *spectral pair* if the functions $\{e_\lambda(x) := e^{i2\pi x \cdot \lambda} \mid \lambda \in \Lambda\}$ form an orthogonal basis for $L^2(\mathbb{D})$. The e_λ functions are restricted to $\mathbb{D}$, and $L^2(\mathbb{D})$ is defined relative to Lebesgue measure, but there are important variations of the definition (see, e.g., [JoPe96]) when other measures are used, and we shall return to this theme in Chapter 4.

The joint papers by S. Pedersen and the present author, e.g., [JoPe92], were motivated in part by an influential paper by B. Fuglede [Fug74]. An important observation in [Fug74] is that the spectral pairs $(\mathbb{D}, \Lambda)$ for which Λ is a group are precisely those when $\mathbb{D}$ *is* necessarily a fundamental domain for a rank-d lattice Γ. In that case, Λ may be taken to be the lattice which is dual to Γ.

There are a number of other papers which follow up on this general theme. Of these perhaps [ACM04] and [CaHM04] and the references cited therein are especially relevant.

In a series of papers (starting with [GaNa98b]) J.-P. Gabardo and his coauthors have taken up the idea of using spectral pairs as the basis for wavelet constructions which are then based on "non-uniform multiresolutions." The main theme in this approach is the use of general spectral pairs (possibly with irregularities, and with inhomogeneities) in the same way Mallat's traditional multiresolution approach uses Fourier's spectral pair (d-cube, $\mathbb{Z}^d$). This theory follows the general theme in this book, but the details are outside the scope of a moderate-size book; so interested readers are referred to [GaNa98b, GaYu05]. Here we only emphasize that the approach is especially well suited to the analysis of fractals with multiresolutions. They are taken up in Chapters 8 and 9.

Before embarking on the details in the chapters to follow, the reader may want to first consult some relevant references (books and papers) covering measures [Bil99, Jor04b, FrLM83], probability theory [Kol77] [Wil91], sampling [Sha49, AlGr01], and wavelets [AyTa03, Coh90, BrJo02a, BrJo02b, Dau92, Jor05], and [CoRa90].

As for the general theory of random processes, we recommend the reader study the books by Skorohod [Sko61, Sko65]. A more modern approach, stressing martingales, may be found in the two books by J. Neveu [Nev75, Nev65]. A (small) sample of the rich variety of applications includes the papers [Hug95, GlZu80, Mon64].

The function h in (1.3.10) and variations of it depend on the chosen space X and the given weight function W. We outlined this function above, and it will again play a central role in Chapter 3. Here we stress its connection to Kolmogorov's zero-one law [Sat99, Theorem 1.14]. Recall that Kolmogorov's 0–1 law applies to a given probability space $(\Omega, P, \mathcal{F})$ where P is a probability measure defined on a σ-algebra $\mathcal{F}$ in Ω: Let $(\mathcal{F}_n)$ be an independent and countable family of sub-σ-algebras in Ω, and let A be a subset of Ω. If, for each n, A belongs to the tail-σ-algebra generated by $\mathcal{F}_n, \mathcal{F}_{n+1}, \mathcal{F}_{n+2}, \ldots$, then it follows that $P(A)$ must be zero, or one.

There are three features of this:

(1) We view the integers $\mathbb{Z}$ as canonically embedded in the probability space Ω of (1.3.6).
(2) When our weight function W is given, we then get an associated family of measures P_x on Ω. (In our applications to wavelets, W will be $|m_0|^2$ where m_0 is some low-pass wavelet filter.)
(3) For every x in X, we may apply the zero-one law of Kolmogorov to the probability space (Ω, P_x). Let x be given. If there is an independent and countable family of σ-algebras $(\mathcal{F}_n)$ on Ω such that $\mathbb{Z}$ belongs to all the tail-σ-algebras of $(\mathcal{F}_n)$, then it follows that $h(x) = P_x(\mathbb{Z})$ must be zero or one.

We now turn to a closer study of the measures P_x in Chapter 2, and we outline their dependence on the prescribed weight function W.

In addition to the papers and books on wavelets, sampling, and signal processing, cited inside Chapter 1, readers might wish to consult one or more of the following treatments. They serve to supplement, in one way or the other, the point of view taken in this book: [Gro01, HeWe96, JaMe96, JaMR01, Mal98, MeCo97, StNg96, Waln02].

In the chapters to follow, we will stress *interconnections* between several trends in the subject, i.e., we emphasize how tools from analysis (including operator theory and operator algebras) and probability theory are used in wavelets, fractals, and dynamics. The part of operator algebras that we have in mind is often called *non-commutative probability*, and it is concerned with representations of algebraic structures by operators in Hilbert space: indeed, this is the key to their usefulness in wavelets, fractals, dynamics, and other areas as well.

In the non-commutative setting, the analogue of a standard probability measure is called a *state*. In mathematical terms, *a state is a positive linear functional on an algebra of operators*. A normalization condition is usually added to the definition. This viewpoint (see especially Chapter 9) is of course motivated by Riesz's theorem, see [Rud87], and quantum physics. Getting a concrete problem represented in Hilbert space is the key to the use of such tools as spectral theory; see, for example, the following papers where the present author has had a hand: [BaJMP06, DuJo05b, DuJo05a, BrJO04, Jor04a, BaJMP05, JoKr03, Jor01c, Jor01b, BrEJ00, BrJKW00, BrJo99b, Jor99, BrJo97]. But, as will become clear later, each of our themes will have its connection to Hilbert space in one form or another, and more citations will follow.

Transition probabilities: Random walk

The Cat only grinned when it saw Alice. . . .

"Cheshire Puss," she began, rather timidly, as she did not at all know whether it would like the name: however, it only grinned a little wider. "Come, it's pleased so far," thought Alice, and she went on. "Would you tell me, please, which way I ought to go from here?"

"That depends a good deal on where you want to get to," said the Cat.

"I don't much care where—" said Alice.

"Then it doesn't matter which way you go," said the Cat.

"—so long as I get somewhere," Alice added as an explanation.

"Oh, you're sure to do that," said the Cat, "if you only walk long enough."   —Lewis Carroll

PREREQUISITES: Curiosity about an idea of Kolmogorov; a vague recollection of the Stone–Weierstraß theorem; a rough idea about probabilities, and measurable sets; comparing measures; having encountered the spectral theorem in its simplest form.

Prelude

A key link between wavelets and fractals on the analysis side and random walk on the probability side is to be found in the use of filters from signal processing. For the standard dyadic wavelets on the real line, we already sketched this approach in Chapter 1. Stepping back and taking a more general and systematic view of the underlying idea, one sees that in a real sense it is (almost) ubiquitous in both pure and applied mathematics.

Originally "filters" were introduced in their most primitive form by Norbert Wiener and Andrei Kolmogorov in the 1930s and 1940s for use in a variety of applied problems involving information and time series. Since then and up to the present, this has been further refined into an art form by engineers with a view to transmission of speech signals. The first step in the refinement is an identification of so-called frequency bands, for example a subdivision into two bands, say high or low, or more generally, a subdivision of the whole frequency range into a fixed finite number of bands, say N bands.

In image processing (as used in digital cameras), the same idea, suitably modified, yields instead arrays of visual resolutions. Then it is natural to use four filters, i.e., $N = 4$, corresponding to recursive and iterated subdivision of squares (called pixels).

One approach to the analysis of the signal/image at hand may be understood via a *random-walk* model, i.e., random walk on a combinatorial tree with a suitable N-fold branching. Thought about this way, one sees that the basic idea is indeed ubiquitous, and in particular that it is further relevant for the kind of geometric self-similarity notions which go into our understanding of fractals.

We will adopt this view here, and note that these more general filters are then prescribed by certain functions which "assign probabilities" to branch points, or the bands, i.e., assign probabilities to the N "choices" at each step in the "walk." In the case of speech, the good filters from engineering are those that produce perfect reconstruction of output signals from a synthesis of subbands. Surprisingly, these carefully designed subband filters are the very same ones which may be adapted successfully to mathematics problems, and which, among other things, produce efficient wavelets. If there are only two bands, the filters are known as quadrature-mirror filters. It is intriguing to take an even wider view and to compare the subband study of wavelets and fractals to the familiar positional number system dating back to the Arabs of ancient time: We all know that the expansion of a number in base N amounts to specifying a string of "digits," in this case the "digits" are selected from the possibilities $0, 1, \ldots, N - 1$. In the most elementary case, that of the natural numbers, this is accomplished by a repeated application of Euclid's algorithm; and we are here attempting to imitate the idea, now with a probabilistic twist, and in a varied array of applications, ranging from wavelets to fractals and from speech signals to image processing.

2.1 Standing assumptions

We now turn to the construction of the random walk and the transition probabilities in the general context of a measure space $(X, \mathcal{B})$ and a fixed N-to-1 measurable mapping σ.

Let X be a set, and let $\mathcal{B}$ be a fixed σ-algebra of subsets of X. Let

$$\sigma: X \to X$$

be an onto mapping which is assumed $\mathcal{B}$-measurable, i.e., for all $B \in \mathcal{B}$, the inverse image

$$\sigma^{-1}(B) := \{x \in X \mid \sigma(x) \in B\}$$

is again in $\mathcal{B}$. Let μ be a probability measure defined on $\mathcal{B}$. We shall assume that the singletons $\{x\}$, for $x \in X$, are in $\mathcal{B}$, but the measure μ need not be atomic. We shall further assume that

$$\text{for all } x \in X, \quad \#\sigma^{-1}(\{x\}) = N, \tag{2.1.1}$$

where $N \geq 2$ is fixed (and finite).

Let $W: X \to [0, \infty)$ be given, and assume that

(i) W is measurable, i.e., that $W^{-1}(J) \in \mathcal{B}$ for all intervals J in $[0, \infty)$,

and further that

(ii) $\displaystyle\sum_{y \in X, \sigma(y) = x} W(y) \leq 1, \mu$ a.e. $x \in X$.

In view of (2.1.1), the sets $\sigma^{-1}(\{x\})$ may be labeled by

$$\mathbb{Z}_N = \{0, 1, \ldots, N-1\} = \mathbb{Z}/N\mathbb{Z}.$$

Since the singletons are in $\mathcal{B}$, we may pick measurable branches of the (set-theoretic) inverse σ^{-1}, i.e., measurable maps $\tau_i: X \to X$, $i = 0, 1, \ldots, N-1$, such that

$$\sigma \circ \tau_i = \mathrm{id}_X, \qquad i = 0, 1, \ldots, N-1. \tag{2.1.2}$$

Using W, we may then define a probability of a transition, or walk, from x to one of the points $(\tau_i(x))_{0 \leq i < N}$ in $\sigma^{-1}(x)$, by

$$P(x, \tau_i(x)) := W(\tau_i(x)). \tag{2.1.3}$$

Note that by assumption (ii),

$$\sum_i P(x, \tau_i(x)) = \sum_{\sigma(y) = x} W(y) \leq 1.$$

The fact that we allow "$\leq$" rather than "$=$" in (ii) is a way of including the possibility of dissipation in our random-walk model. For details, see Remark 2.8.3 below.

2.2 An example

Example 2.2.1. Farey trees. Let $X = \bigcup_{n=1}^{\infty} X_n$ where X_n is the set of monotonically increasing sequences of those continued fractions

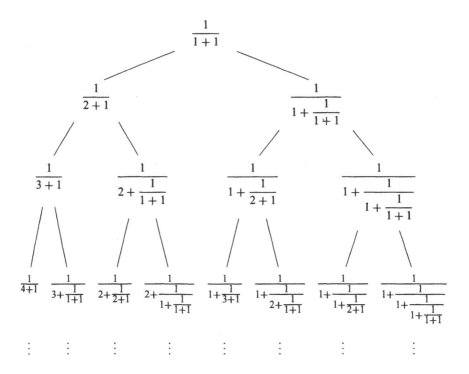

Fig. 2.1. The Farey tree.

$$[a_1, a_2, \ldots, a_k] = \cfrac{1}{a_1 + \cfrac{1}{a_2 + \cfrac{1}{\cdots \cfrac{1}{a_k}}}}$$

between 0 and 1 such that $a_i \in \mathbb{N}$ for $1 \leq i < k$, $a_k \geq 2$, and $\sum_{i=1}^{k} a_i = n + 2$. The number of terms in X_n is 2^n, and two branches τ_0 and τ_1 are defined by

$$\begin{cases} \tau_0\,([\ldots, a]) = [\ldots, a - 1, 2], \\ \tau_1\,([\ldots, a]) = [\ldots, a + 1]. \end{cases}$$

Note that each τ_j maps X_n into X_{n+1}. If $x \in X$, we say that $\tau_0 x$ and $\tau_1 x$ are the two daughters in the binary tree. As an example, consider Figure 2.1. These systems define random walks, and are studied in connection with circle maps, dynamics, and gap labeling in statistical mechanics; see [Hal83] and [CvSS85].

2.3 Some definitions: The Ruelle operator, harmonic functions, cocycles

The next definitions prepare us for the statements and proofs of Lemma 2.4.1, giving the existence and uniqueness of the measures P_x, and Theorem 2.7.1, giving cocycles as boundary values of bounded harmonic functions.

Definitions 2.3.1. (a) The *Ruelle operator* $R = R_W$ is defined by

$$(Rf)(x) = \sum_{y \in X, \, \sigma(y)=x} W(y) f(y), \qquad x \in X, \ f \in L^\infty(X), \qquad (2.3.1)$$

and maps $L^\infty(X)$ into itself.

(b) Let Ω be the compact Cartesian product

$$\Omega = \mathbb{Z}_N^{\mathbb{N}} = \{0, \ldots, N-1\}^{\mathbb{N}} = \prod_1^\infty \{0, \ldots, N-1\}. \qquad (2.3.2)$$

(c) A bounded measurable function $V: X \times \Omega \to \mathbb{C}$ is said to be a *cocycle* if

$$V(x, (\omega_1, \omega_2, \ldots)) = V\left(\tau_{\omega_1}(x), (\omega_2, \omega_3, \ldots)\right) \qquad (2.3.3)$$

for all $\omega = (\omega_1, \omega_2, \ldots) \in \Omega$.

(d) A function $h: X \to \mathbb{C}$ is said to be *harmonic*, or R_W-*harmonic*, if

$$R_W h = h. \qquad (2.3.4)$$

(e) Let $n \in \mathbb{N}$, and let $i_1, \ldots, i_n \in \mathbb{Z}_N$. Then the subset

$$A(i_1, \ldots, i_n) := \{ w \in \Omega \mid \omega_1 = i_1, \ \ldots, \ \omega_n = i_n \} \qquad (2.3.5)$$

is called a *cylinder set*.

2.4 Existence of the measures P_x

The cylinder sets generate the topology of Ω and its Borel σ-algebra. In determining Radon measures on Ω, it is therefore convenient to first specify them on cylinder sets. This approach was initiated by Kolmogorov [Kol77]; see also Nelson [Nel69]. Recall that Ω is compact in the Tychonoff topology, and that we may use the Stone–Weierstraß theorem on $C(\Omega) =$ the algebra of all continuous functions on Ω.

Lemma 2.4.1. *Let* X, $\mathcal{B}$, μ, σ, τ_0, $\ldots$, τ_{N-1}, *and* W *be given as described above. We make the following more restrictive assumption on* W:

$$\sum_{y \in X, \, \sigma(y)=x} W(y) = 1 \qquad \text{a.e. } x \in X. \qquad (2.4.1)$$

Then for every $x \in X$ there is a unique positive Radon probability measure P_x on Ω such that

$$P_x (A (i_1, \ldots, i_n)) = W (\tau_{i_1} x) W (\tau_{i_2} \tau_{i_1} x) \cdots W (\tau_{i_n} \cdots \tau_{i_1} x). \qquad (2.4.2)$$

Remark 2.4.2. It turns out that the general case $\sum_y \cdots \leq 1$ (assumption (ii) above) may be reduced to (2.4.1). So (2.4.1) is not really a restriction. This is discussed in Remark 2.8.3 below.

Proof of Lemma 2.4.1. If P is a Radon measure on Ω, we set

$$P [f] := \int_\Omega f (\omega) \, dP (\omega) \qquad \text{for all } f \in C (\Omega). \qquad (2.4.3)$$

Set

$$C_{\text{fin}} (\Omega) = \{ f \in C (\Omega) \mid \exists n \text{ such that } f (\omega) = f (\omega_1, \ldots, \omega_n), \qquad (2.4.4)$$

$$\text{i.e., } f \text{ depends only on the first } n \text{ coordinates in } \Omega \}$$

$$= \bigcup_{n=1}^{\infty} \mathfrak{A}_n.$$

Note that (2.4.4) defines $C_{\text{fin}} (\Omega)$, but may also be regarded as an implicit definition of $\mathfrak{A}_n$, functions depending only on the first n coordinates. The algebra $C_{\text{fin}} (\Omega)$ is defined as a union over n, which as such is independent of n, and the argument is that this union is dense in $C (\Omega)$. Considering $\mathfrak{A}_n$ in the definition (2.4.4) for increasing values of the index n, we get an ascending nest of subalgebras of $C (\Omega)$,

$$\mathfrak{A}_1 \subset \mathfrak{A}_2 \subset \cdots \subset \mathfrak{A}_n \subset \mathfrak{A}_{n+1} \subset \cdots . \qquad (2.4.5)$$

An immediate application of Stone–Weierstraß shows that $C_{\text{fin}} (\Omega)$ is uniformly dense in $C (\Omega)$, i.e.,

$$\overline{\bigcup_{n=1}^{\infty} \mathfrak{A}_n} = C (\Omega),$$

where $\overline{}$ stands for norm-closure. Let $x \in X$, and $f \in C_{\text{fin}} (\Omega)$. Suppose

$$f (\omega) = f (\omega_1, \ldots, \omega_n),$$

and set

$$P_x [f] = \sum_{(\omega_1, \ldots, \omega_n) \in \mathbb{Z}_N^n} W (\tau_{\omega_1} x) \cdots W (\tau_{\omega_n} \cdots \tau_{\omega_1} x) f (\omega_1, \ldots, \omega_n). \qquad (2.4.6)$$

Note that if there is some $h \in L^\infty (X)$ such that

$$f (\omega_1, \ldots, \omega_n) = h (\tau_{\omega_n} \cdots \tau_{\omega_1} x),$$

then

$$P_x[f] = \sum_{(\omega_1,\ldots,\omega_n)} W\left(\tau_{\omega_1}x\right)\cdots W\left(\tau_{\omega_n}\cdots\tau_{\omega_1}x\right) h\left(\tau_{\omega_n}\cdots\tau_{\omega_1}x\right) \tag{2.4.7}$$

$$= \sum_{y\in X,\, \sigma^n y = x} W\left(\sigma^{n-1}y\right)\cdots W\left(\sigma y\right) W\left(y\right) h\left(y\right)$$

$$= \left(R_W^n h\right)(x).$$

We now show that $P_x[f]$ is well defined. This is the Kolmogorov consistency: we must check that the number $P_x[f]$ is the same when some $f \in \mathfrak{A}_n$ ($\subset \mathfrak{A}_{n+1}$) is viewed also as an element in $\mathfrak{A}_{n+1}$. Then

$$f(\omega) = f(\omega_1,\ldots,\omega_n)$$
$$= f(\omega_1,\ldots,\omega_n,\omega_{n+1}),$$

and

$$P_x\left[f_{n+1}\right] = \sum_{\omega_1,\ldots,\omega_{n+1}} W\left(\tau_{\omega_1}x\right)\cdots W\left(\tau_{\omega_{n+1}}\cdots\tau_{\omega_1}x\right) f\left(\omega_1,\ldots,\omega_{n+1}\right)$$

$$= \sum_{\omega_1,\ldots,\omega_n} W\left(\tau_{\omega_1}x\right)\cdots W\left(\tau_{\omega_n}\cdots\tau_{\omega_1}x\right)$$

$$\cdot \underbrace{\left(\sum_{\omega_{n+1}} W\left(\tau_{\omega_{n+1}}\tau_{\omega_n}\cdots\tau_{\omega_1}x\right)\right)}_{=1 \text{ by } (2.4.1)} f\left(\omega_1,\ldots,\omega_n\right)$$

$$= \sum_{\omega_1,\ldots,\omega_n} W\left(\tau_{\omega_1}x\right)\cdots W\left(\tau_{\omega_n}\cdots\tau_{\omega_1}x\right) f\left(\omega_1,\ldots,\omega_n\right)$$

$$= P_x\left[f_n\right],$$

as claimed.

The consistency conditions may be stated differently in terms of conditional probabilities: for $f \in C(\Omega)$, set

$$P_x^{(n)}[f] = P_x[f \mid \mathfrak{A}_n] \tag{2.4.8}$$

$$= \sum_{(\omega_1,\ldots,\omega_n)} W\left(\tau_{\omega_1}x\right)\cdots W\left(\tau_{\omega_n}\cdots\tau_{\omega_1}x\right) f\left(\omega_1,\ldots,\omega_n\right).$$

We proved that

$$P_x^{(n)}[f] = P_x^{(n+1)}[f] \qquad \text{for all } f \in \mathfrak{A}_n.$$

Using now the theorems of Stone–Weierstraß and Riesz, we get the existence of the measure P_x on Ω. It is clear that it has the desired properties. In particular, the property (2.4.2) results from applying (2.4.6) to the function

$$f(\omega) := \delta_{i_1,\omega_1} \cdots \delta_{i_n,\omega_n}, \qquad \omega \in \Omega, \tag{2.4.9}$$

when the point $(i_1, \ldots, i_n)$ is fixed.

These functions, in turn, span a dense subalgebra in $C(\Omega)$ (by Stone–Weierstraß), so P_x is determined uniquely by (2.4.2). □

2.5 Kolmogorov's consistency condition

For general reference, we now make explicit the extension principle of Kolmogorov [Kol77] in its function-theoretic form.

Lemma 2.5.1. (Kolmogorov) *Let $N \geq 2$ be fixed, and let*

$$\Omega = \{0, 1, \ldots, N-1\}^{\mathbb{N}}.$$

For $n = 1, 2, \ldots$, let

$$P^{(n)}: \mathfrak{A}_n \to \mathbb{C}$$

be a sequence of linear functionals such that (i)–(iii) *hold:*

(i) $P^{(n)}[\mathbb{1}] = 1$, *where $\mathbb{1}$ denotes the constant function 1 on Ω,*
(ii) $f \in \mathfrak{A}_n$, $f \geq 0$ *pointwise* $\Rightarrow P^{(n)}[f] \geq 0$,

and

(iii) $P^{(n)}[f] = P^{(n+1)}[f]$ *for all $f \in \mathfrak{A}_n$.*

Then there is a unique Borel probability measure P on Ω such that

$$P[f] = P^{(n)}[f], \qquad f \in \mathfrak{A}_n. \tag{2.5.1}$$

Specifically, for P, we have the implication result

$$f \in C(\Omega), \; f \geq 0 \text{ pointwise} \Rightarrow P[f] \geq 0. \tag{2.5.2}$$

Remark 2.5.2. Here we have identified positive linear functionals P on $C(\Omega)$ with the corresponding Radon measures $\tilde{P}$ on Ω, i.e.,

$$P[f] = \int_\Omega f \, d\tilde{P}. \tag{2.5.3}$$

This identification $P \leftrightarrow \tilde{P}$ is based on an implicit application of Riesz's theorem; see [Rud87, Chapter 1].

Proof of Lemma 2.5.1. The proof of Kolmogorov's extension result may be given several forms, but we note that the argument we used above (in a special case), based on an application of the Stone–Weierstraß theorem, also works in general. □

2.6 The probability space Ω

We note that the probability space Ω itself carries mappings σ and τ_i, $i = 0, 1, \ldots,$ $N - 1$, satisfying the conditions (2.1.2): stressing the Ω-dependence, we write

$$\sigma^{\Omega} (\omega) = (\omega_2, \omega_3, \ldots) \quad \text{and} \quad \tau_i^{\Omega} (\omega) = (i, \omega_1, \omega_2, \ldots) \tag{2.6.1}$$

for $\omega = (\omega_1, \omega_2, \ldots) \in \Omega$.

Remark 2.6.1. The connection between the cylinder sets in (2.3.5) and the iterated function systems (IFS) $(X, \sigma, \tau_0, \ldots, \tau_{N-1})$ may be spelled out as follows: the cylinder sets in Ω generate the σ-algebra of measurable subsets of Ω, and similarly the subsets $\tau_{i_1} \cdots \tau_{i_n} (X) \subset X$ generate a σ-algebra of measurable subsets of X. When nothing further is specified, these will be the σ-algebras which we refer to when discussing the measurable functions on Ω and X. In particular, we will denote by $M (\Omega)$ and $M (X)$ the respective algebras of all bounded measurable functiond on Ω, respectively X.

Note that if $X = [0, 1]$ and

$$\tau_i x = \frac{x + i}{N}, \qquad 0 \le i \le N - 1,$$

then we recover the familiar N-adic subintervals:

$$\tau_{i_1} \cdots \tau_{i_n} (X) = \left[\frac{i_1}{N} + \cdots + \frac{i_n}{N^n}, \frac{i_1}{N} + \cdots + \frac{i_n}{N^n} + \frac{1}{N^n} \right]. \tag{2.6.2}$$

Lemma 2.6.2. *There is a unique mapping $\rho: M (\Omega) \to M (X)$ which satisfies*

$$\rho (fg) = \rho (f) \rho (g) \tag{2.6.3}$$

and

$$\rho \left(\chi_{A(i_1,\ldots,i_n)} \right) = \chi_{\tau_{i_1} \cdots \tau_{i_n} (X)}. \tag{2.6.4}$$

The mapping ρ is an isomorphism of $M (\Omega)$ onto $M (X)$.

Proof. Recalling (2.4.9), we note that

$$\chi_{A(i_1,\ldots,i_n)} (\omega) = \delta_{i_1,\omega_1} \cdots \delta_{i_n,\omega_n}, \qquad \omega \in \Omega.$$

As a result,

$$\chi_{A(i_1,\ldots,i_n)} \chi_{A(j_1,\ldots,j_n)} = \delta_{i_1,j_1} \cdots \delta_{i_n,j_n} \chi_{A(i_1,\ldots,i_n)}. \tag{2.6.5}$$

We then define ρ first on $\mathfrak{A}_n$ by

$$\rho \left(\sum_{i_1,\ldots,i_n} a_{i_1,\ldots,i_n} \chi_{A(i_1,\ldots,i_n)} \right) = \sum_{i_1,\ldots,i_n} a_{i_1,\ldots,i_n} \chi_{\tau_{i_1} \cdots \tau_{i_n} (X)},$$

where $a_{i_1,\dots,i_n} \in \mathbb{C}$, and note that (2.6.3) is satisfied.

It is easy to check that the extension of ρ from $\mathfrak{A}_n$ to $\mathfrak{A}_{n+1}$ is consistent. The final extension from $\bigcup_n \mathfrak{A}_n$ to $M(\Omega)$ is done by Kolmogorov's lemma, and it can be checked that ρ has the properties stated in the conclusion of the present lemma.   □

Lemma 2.6.3. *Let X, W, and N be as described in the beginning of this chapter, and let $\{ P_x \mid x \in X \}$ be the process obtained in the conclusion of Lemma 2.4.1. Then*

$$\sum_{i=0}^{N-1} W(\tau_i x) P_{\tau_i x} [f(i, \cdot)] = P_x[f] \qquad \text{for all } f \in C(\Omega). \qquad (2.6.6)$$

Remark 2.6.4. Stated informally, formula (2.6.6) is an assertion about the random walk: it says that if the walk starts at x, then with probability one, it makes a transition to one of the N points $\tau_0(x), \dots, \tau_{N-1}(x)$. The probability of the move $x \mapsto \tau_i x$ is $W(\tau_i x)$. Recall (2.4.1) asserts that $\sum_i W(\tau_i x) = 1$.

Proof of Lemma 2.6.3. It follows from (2.4.6) and the arguments in the proof of Lemma 2.4.1 that it is enough to verify (2.6.6) for $f \in C_{\text{fin}}(\Omega)$, or for $f \in \mathfrak{A}_n$. Let $f \in \mathfrak{A}_n$. Then

$$\sum_i W(\tau_i x) P_{\tau_i x}[f(i, \cdot)]$$

$$= \sum_i \sum_{\omega_1,\dots,\omega_n} W(\tau_i x) W(\tau_{\omega_1} \tau_i x) \cdots W(\tau_{\omega_n} \cdots \tau_{\omega_1} \tau_i x) f(i, \omega_1, \dots, \omega_n)$$

$$\underset{\text{by } (2.4.6)}{=} P_x[f],$$

which is the desired conclusion. Recall $C_{\text{fin}}(\Omega)$ is norm-dense in $C(\Omega)$.   □

Remark 2.6.5. Note that the formula (2.6.6) generalizes the familiar notion of self-similarity for measures introduced by Hutchinson in [Hut81]; see also (4.1.4) below. In fact, (2.6.6) may be restated as

$$\sum_{i=0}^{N-1} W(\tau_i x) P_{\tau_i x} \circ (\tau_i^\Omega)^{-1} = P_x. \qquad (2.6.7)$$

2.7 A boundary representation for harmonic functions

The next result, Theorem 2.7.1, is a variant of the classical Fatou–Primalov theorem. But in the present context, it has cocycles as boundary values of certain bounded harmonic functions—the notion "harmonic" is here defined from the Ruelle operator R of Definition 2.3.1(a). We obtain our cocycles as an application of the familiar convergence theorem for bounded martingales.

We then resume our study of harmonic functions in Chapter 6 below.

Theorem 2.7.1. *Let X, W, and N be as described in the beginning of this chapter, and suppose in addition that (2.4.1) is satisfied. Let $R = R_W$ be the Ruelle operator on $L^\infty(X)$, and let $\{ P_x \mid x \in X \}$ be the process on Ω from Lemma 2.4.1. Then there is a 1–1 correspondence between the bounded harmonic functions h and the cocycles V as follows: If*

$$V: X \times \Omega \to \mathbb{C}$$

is a cocycle (bounded and measurable), then

$$h(x) = h_V(x) = P_x [V(x, \cdot)] \tag{2.7.1}$$

is harmonic, i.e.,

$$Rh = h. \tag{2.7.2}$$

Conversely, V may be recovered from h as a martingale limit.

Proof. $(2.7.1) \Rightarrow (2.7.2)$. This follows by Lemma 2.6.3 and the cocycle property. Let V be a cocycle, and define $h = h_V$ by (2.7.1). Then for $x \in X$,

$$(Rh)(x) = \sum_i W(\tau_i x) h(\tau_i x) = \sum_i W(\tau_i x) P_{\tau_i x} [V(\tau_i x, \cdot)]$$

$$\underset{\text{(the cocycle property)}}{=} \sum_i W(\tau_i x) P_{\tau_i x} [V(x, i \cdot)]$$

$$\underset{\text{by (2.6.6)}}{=} P_x [V(x, \cdot)] \underset{\text{by (2.7.1)}}{=} h(x),$$

where the summations are over $i \in \mathbb{Z}_N$. This proves (2.7.2).

The converse, $(2.7.2) \Rightarrow (2.7.1)$. Let h be a given harmonic function on X. Let $n \in \mathbb{N}$, and define

$$L_x[f] = \int_\Omega f(\omega) h(\tau_{\omega_n} \cdots \tau_{\omega_1} x) \, dP_x(\omega), \qquad f \in \mathfrak{A}_n. \tag{2.7.3}$$

An application of (2.7.2) and the argument above show that L_x is consistent, i.e., using $f(\omega) = f(\omega_1, \ldots, \omega_n) = f(\omega_1, \ldots, \omega_n, \omega_{n+1})$, we get

$$\int_\Omega f(\omega) h(\tau_{\omega_{n+1}} \cdots \tau_{\omega_1} x) \, dP_x(\omega)$$

$$= \int_\Omega f(\omega) (Rh)(\tau_{\omega_n} \cdots \tau_{\omega_1} x) \, dP_x(\omega)$$

$$\underset{\text{by (2.7.2)}}{=} \int_\Omega f(\omega) h(\tau_{\omega_n} \cdots \tau_{\omega_1} x) \, dP_x(\omega) = L_x[f],$$

which shows that Kolmogorov's consistency condition holds.

Hence there is a Radon measure on Ω, also denoted L_x, such that

$$L_x(f) = \int_\Omega f \, dL_x, \qquad f \in C(\Omega). \tag{2.7.4}$$

Absolute continuity is immediate, i.e.,

$$dL_x \ll dP_x.$$

Let $V(x, \cdot)$ be the Radon–Nikodym derivative, i.e.,

$$V(x, \cdot) = \frac{dL_x}{dP_x} \qquad \text{on } \Omega. \tag{2.7.5}$$

It then follows from (2.7.3) and (2.7.4) that V is a cocycle, i.e., that it satisfies the conditions in Definition 2.3.1(c). □

Remark 2.7.2. It is useful to think of Theorem 2.7.1 as an analogue of the classical Fatou–Primalov theorem [Rud87, Chapter 11] about the existence of boundary functions for bounded harmonic functions. Recall that every bounded harmonic function h in the disk $X = \{ x \in \mathbb{C} \mid |x| < 1 \}$ is the Poisson integral of a function v on the boundary of X, viz., the circle $S = \{ x \in \mathbb{C} \mid |x| = 1 \}$. Specifically, if P_x for $x \in X$ denotes the Poisson measure, then the analogue of (2.7.1) is

$$h(x) = P_x[v],$$

or

$$h(x) = \int_S v(\omega) \, dP_x(\omega),$$

or more explicitly in polar coordinates,

$$h\left(re^{i\theta}\right) = \frac{1}{2\pi} \int_{-\pi}^{\pi} v\left(e^{i\omega}\right) \frac{\left(1 - r^2\right) d\omega}{1 - 2r \cos(\theta - \omega) + r^2},$$

where $v\left(e^{i\theta}\right) = \lim_{r \to 1} h\left(re^{i\theta}\right)$ a.e. θ.

Moreover, see [Rud87, Theorem 11.22], $v(\omega)$ is the non-tangential limit of the given harmonic function, for points x tending non-tangentially to ω.

Hence in the present analogy, our probability space Ω is the analogue of the boundary, and our cocycle V is the analogue of the limit function v.

Using the notion of martingales, see [Wil91], we may recover V from h the following way. Let

$$X_k(\omega) = \omega_k \qquad \text{for } \omega \in \Omega,$$

and set

$$Z_n(x, \omega) = \tau_{X_n(\omega)} \cdots \tau_{X_1(\omega)} x$$
$$= \tau_{\omega_n} \cdots \tau_{\omega_1} x,$$

and note that Z_n is a Markov chain with transition probability P_x at x. If h satisfies (2.7.2), i.e., is R-harmonic, then $h(Z_n(x, \cdot))$, $n = 1, 2, \ldots$, is a bounded martingale, and so it converges pointwise P_x-a.e. on Ω, i.e., the limit

$$V(x, \cdot) := \lim_{n \to \infty} h(Z_n(x, \cdot)) \qquad \text{on } \Omega \tag{2.7.6}$$

is well defined. It is immediate from (2.4.7) that this V is a cocycle, and that it satisfies (2.7.1).

A good reference on the standard facts about martingales, including the martingale convergence theorem, is [RoWi00, II.48, pp. 146–148]. The martingale property for $h(Z_n(x, \omega))$ amounts to the identity

$$P_x(h(Z_n(x, \cdot)) \mid \mathfrak{A}_{n-1}) = h(Z_{n-1}(x, \cdot)). \tag{2.7.7}$$

This is the defining property of a martingale, and to verify it we proceed as follows. Using the identity $R_W h = h$, we get

$$P_x(h(Z_n(x, \cdot)) \mid \mathfrak{A}_{n-1}) = \sum_{\omega_n} W(\tau_{\omega_n} x) \, h(\tau_{\omega_n} \tau_{\omega_{n-1}} \cdots \tau_{\omega_1} x)$$

$$= (R_W h)(\tau_{\omega_{n-1}} \cdots \tau_{\omega_1} x)$$

$$= h(\tau_{\omega_{n-1}} \cdots \tau_{\omega_1} x) = h(Z_{n-1}(x, \cdot)),$$

which is the desired identity (2.7.7).

Corollary 2.7.3. *The 1–1 correspondence between the harmonic functions h in Theorem 2.7.1 and the cocycles V is an order-isomorphism when the ordering of both families of functions is defined in the pointwise sense.*

Proof. We noted that when V is a given cocycle, then the corresponding function h is defined by (2.7.1); and conversely, V may be computed from h via the formula (2.7.6).

Since each P_x is a positive measure, (2.7.1) yields the implication

$$V_1 \le V_2 \Rightarrow h_{V_1} \le h_{V_2}.$$

Conversely, if h_1, h_2 are given harmonic functions and V_1, V_2 are the corresponding cocycles, then

$$0 \le h_1 \le h_2 \Rightarrow V_1 \le V_2.$$

This second implication is immediate from (2.7.6).   □

Corollary 2.7.4. *Let $v: \Omega \to \mathbb{C}$ be a bounded measurable function, and let X, W, and $R = R_W$ be as stated in the theorem. Then*

$$V(x, \omega) := v(\omega), \qquad \omega \in \Omega, \tag{2.7.8}$$

is a cocycle if and only if v is invariant, i.e.,

$$v \circ \sigma^{\Omega} = v. \tag{2.7.9}$$

In particular, if v is invariant under the one-sided shift on Ω, then

$$h(x) = P_x[v] \qquad (2.7.10)$$

is harmonic.

Proof. Let $v: \Omega \to \mathbb{C}$ be given, and suppose V in (2.7.8) is a cocycle. Then

$$v(\omega) = V(x, \omega) = V\left(\tau_{\omega_1} x, (\omega_2, \omega_3, \dots)\right) = v(\omega_2, \omega_3, \dots) = v\left(\sigma^\Omega(\omega)\right),$$

which is the desired conclusion (2.7.9). The converse implication is immediate.

If h is defined by (2.7.10) for some shift-invariant v, then it follows from Theorem 2.7.1 that h is harmonic; see the proof of (2.7.1) $\Rightarrow$ (2.7.2). $\qquad \square$

Definition 2.7.5. We say that a subset $E \subset \Omega$ is *shift-invariant* if $\left(\sigma^\Omega\right)^{-1} E = E$. In view of (2.6.1),

$$\left(\sigma^\Omega\right)^{-1} E = \bigcup_{i=0}^{N-1} \tau_i^\Omega(E),$$

so shift-invariant sets E satisfy $\mathbb{Z}_N \times E = E$. For example,

$$E := \bigcup_n \underbrace{(\mathbb{Z}_N \times \cdots \times \mathbb{Z}_N}_{n \text{ times}} \times \{0\})$$

is shift-invariant. Recall that there is a canonical bijection, see (1.3.8), between this set E and the natural numbers $\mathbb{N}_0 = \{0, 1, \dots\}$.

Corollary 2.7.6. *Let $E \subset \Omega$, and let X, σ, τ_i, N, and W be as described in the beginning of the chapter. Set*

$$h_{\dot{E}}(x) := P_x\left[\chi_E\right], \qquad (2.7.11)$$

where χ_E denotes the indicator function of E.
  Then h_E is harmonic, i.e., satisfies $R_W h_E = h_E$ if and only if E is shift-invariant.

Proof. This follows directly from Corollary 2.7.4 above, if we note that

$$\chi_E \circ \sigma^\Omega = \chi_{(\sigma^\Omega)^{-1} E}. \qquad \square$$

2.8 Invariant measures

Definition 2.8.1. One of the uses of the functions h from (2.7.2), i.e., the harmonic functions, is that they determine invariant measures v on X, i.e., measures on X invariant under the endomorphism $\sigma: X \to X$. We say that v is *σ-invariant*, or simply *invariant*, if $v \circ \sigma^{-1} = v$, or

$$v\left(\sigma^{-1}(B)\right) = v(B), \qquad B \in \mathcal{B}. \qquad (2.8.1)$$

We say that v is *R-invariant* if

$$\int_X Rf \, dv = \int_X f \, dv \qquad (2.8.2)$$

for all bounded measurable functions f on X.

Proposition 2.8.2. *Let v be R-invariant, and let h satisfy $Rh = h$. Then the measure*

$$dv_h := h \, dv \qquad (2.8.3)$$

is invariant.

  Conversely, if v_1 is a B-measure on X which is assumed σ-invariant, and if $v_1 \ll v$, then the Radon–Nikodym derivative $h = \dfrac{dv_1}{dv}$ satisfies

$$Rh = h \qquad v\text{-a.e. on } X. \qquad (2.8.4)$$

Proof. (Part one!)

$$\int f \circ \sigma \, dv_h = \int f \circ \sigma \, h \, dv$$
$$= \int R(f \circ \sigma \, h) \, dv = \int f \, Rh \, dv$$
$$= \int f \, h \, dv = \int f \, dv_h,$$

which implies that v_h is σ-invariant.

  To prove (2.8.4) under the assumptions in the second part of the proposition, let f be a bounded B-measurable function on X. Then

$$\int f \, Rh \, dv = \int R[(f \circ \sigma) h] \, dv = \int (f \circ \sigma) h \, dv$$
$$= \int (f \circ \sigma) \, dv_1 = \int f \, dv_1 = \int f \, h \, dv,$$

where all integrals are over X. As f is arbitrary, the conclusion (2.8.4) follows.   □

Remark 2.8.3. Suppose there is some probability measure v on X satisfying

$$v \, R_W = v. \qquad (2.8.5)$$

Then the assumption (ii),

$$\sum_{\sigma(y)=x} W(y) \le 1, \qquad (2.8.6)$$

may be reduced to the special normalization (2.4.1) by the following argument. Assuming (2.8.6), then the sequence

$$h_n(x) := \sum_{\sigma^n(y)=x} W\left(\sigma^{n-1}(y)\right) \cdots W(\sigma(y)) W(y) \qquad (2.8.7)$$

is monotone decreasing. If a probability measure v exists satisfying (2.8.5), then

$$v(h_n) = \int_X h_n \, dv = 1 \qquad \text{for all } n,$$

and the limit function

$$h(x) := \inf_n h_n(x) = \lim_{n \to \infty} h_n(x)$$

is measurable, and satisfies

$$v(h) = 1 \qquad \text{and} \qquad R_W h = h. \qquad (2.8.8)$$

Since $W(x) h(x) \le h(\sigma(x))$, it follows that the modified W-function

$$W_h(x) := \frac{W(x) h(x)}{h(\sigma(x))}, \qquad x \in X, \qquad (2.8.9)$$

is well defined, and satisfies the special normalization rule (2.4.1), i.e.,

$$\sum_{y \in X, \, \sigma(y)=x} W(y) = 1 \qquad \text{a.e. } x \in X.$$

To see this, recall that

$$\sum_{\sigma(y)=x} W_h(y) = \sum_{\sigma(y)=x} \frac{W(y) h(y)}{h(\sigma(y))}$$

$$= \frac{1}{h(x)} \sum_{\sigma(y)=x} W(y) h(y)$$

$$= \frac{1}{h(x)} h(x) = 1,$$

which is the desired identity.

Exercises

2.1. Verify the details in the argument in the proof of Lemma 2.4.1 for why $\bigcup_n \mathfrak{A}_n$ is an algebra of continuous functions, and for why it is dense in $C(\Omega)$.

2.2. Give a direct and geometric argument for the identity (2.6.7) in Remark 2.6.5.

2.3. Give three different ways to see that a cocycle $V = V_h$ may be obtained from every solution h as specified by (2.7.2) in Theorem 2.7.1.

2.4. Can the assumption in Theorem 2.7.1 of boundedness on the harmonic function h be omitted?

2.5. Give a version of Theorem 2.7.1 which holds when h is not assumed bounded.

2.6. Compact operators

Let $I := [0, 1]$, and let $R: I \times I \to \mathbb{C}$ be a continuous function. Suppose that

$$\sum_i \sum_j \bar{\xi}_i \, R\left(x_i, x_j\right) \xi_j \geq 0 \qquad (2E.1)$$

holds for all finite sequences (ξ_i) and all point configurations $x_1, x_2, \ldots$ in I.

(a) Then show that there is a monotone sequence $\lambda_1, \lambda_2, \ldots, 0 \leq \lambda_{n+1} \leq \lambda_n \leq \cdots \leq \lambda_1$, such that $\lambda_n \to 0$; and an ONB (g_n) in $L^2(I)$, with Lebesgue measure, satisfying

$$\int_0^1 R(x, y) \, g_n(y) \, dy = \lambda_n g_n(x).$$

(b) **The spectral theorem:** Show that the operator T_R, defined as

$$(T_R f)(x) := \int_0^1 R(x, y) \, f(y) \, dy$$

in $L^2(I)$, satisfies

$$T_R = \sum_{n=1}^{\infty} \lambda_n \, |g_n\rangle \langle g_n|,$$

where $|g_n\rangle \langle g_n|$ is Dirac notation for the rank-one projection onto $\mathbb{C}g_n$. (We say that T_R is a *positive* (or *non-negative*) *compact operator*.)

2.7. Karhunen–Loève [Ash90]

Let $(\Omega, \mathcal{B}, \nu)$ be a probability space, i.e., with $\nu(\Omega) = 1$; and set

$$E(Y) := \int_\Omega Y(\omega) \, d\nu(\omega)$$

for random variables Y on Ω.

Let $X: I \to L^2(\Omega, \nu)$ be a random process with $X(x) := X(x, \cdot)$ varying continuously in $L^2(\Omega)$. Suppose the following two conditions hold:

(i) $E(X(x)) = 0$, for all $x \in I$, and
(ii) $R(x, y) := E\left(\overline{X(x)} X(y)\right)$ is continuous on $I \times I$.

(a) Then show that condition (2E.1) is satisfied, and let (g_n) be an associated ONB in $L^2(I)$.

(b) **Tensor product:** Show that there is a sequence (Y_n) such that

(i) $Y_n \in L^2(\Omega, \nu)$,

(ii) $X(x, \omega) = \sum_{n=1}^{\infty} g_n(x) Y_n(\omega)$ is convergent in $L^2(I) \otimes L^2(\Omega, \nu)$, and

(iii) $E(\bar{Y}_k Y_n) = \delta_{k,n} \lambda_k$.

Hint: Set

$$Y_k := \int_0^1 \overline{g_k(x)} X(x, \cdot) \, dx.$$

2.8. Brownian motion

Notation as in Exercises 2.6 and 2.7: $I = [0, 1]$, and $(\Omega, \mathcal{B}, \nu)$ is a fixed probability space.

Suppose $X: I \to L^2(\Omega)$ is given, and auppose also that it is Gaussian, that is, that the family $\{X(x) \mid x \in I\}$ of random variables has joint Gaussian distributions.

(a) Under the stated condition, prove that the random variables $\{Y_n \mid n \in \mathbb{N}\}$ in Exercise 2.7(b) are automatically *independent* Gaussian.

(b) Suppose in addition to the above condition on $\{X(x) \mid x \in I\}$ that $R(x, y) = \min(x, y)$ for $(x, y) \in I \times I$. Then show that $(X(x))$ is Brownian motion and has the following representation:

$$X(x, \omega) = \sqrt{2} \sum_{n=1}^{\infty} \frac{\sin\left(\left(n - \frac{1}{2}\right) \pi x\right)}{\left(n - \frac{1}{2}\right) \pi} Z_n(\omega) \qquad \text{for } x \in I, \ \omega \in \Omega, \qquad (2E.2)$$

where $\{Z_n \mid n \in \mathbb{N}\}$ is an orthonormal family of random variables in $L^2(\Omega)$. In particular, $E(Z_n) = 0$ and $E(Z_n^2) = 1$ holds for all $n \in \mathbb{N}$.

(c) With the same assumptions as in (b) above, prove that the expansion (2E.2) for a.e. $\omega \in \Omega$ in fact converges *uniformly* for $x \in I$.

(d) Show that $\sum_{n=1}^{\infty} \left(\left(n - \frac{1}{2}\right) \pi\right)^{-1} |Z_n(\cdot)|$ converges with probability 1.

2.9. Consider the setting in Exercise 2.8, i.e., $I = [0, 1]$, and $(\Omega, \mathcal{B}, \nu)$ a fixed probability space.

(a) Let $\chi_{[0,x)}$ denote the indicator function of the subinterval $[0, x) \subset I$. Show that

$$R(x, y) := \min(x, y) = \langle \chi_{[0,x)} \mid \chi_{[0,y)} \rangle_{L^2(I)} \qquad \text{for all } x, y \in I.$$

(b) Find the expansion of $\chi_{[0,x)}$ in the ONB $\left(\sqrt{2} \sin(n\pi t)\right)_{n \in \mathbb{N}}$, and use this to show that

$$X(x, \cdot) = \sqrt{2} \sum_{n=1}^{\infty} \frac{1 - \cos(n\pi x)}{n\pi} Z_n(\cdot)$$

where $(X(x))$ denotes the usual Brownian motion, and where $(Z_n)_{n\in\mathbb{N}}$ is an independent family of Gaussian random variables with $E(Z_n) = 0$ and $E(Z_n^2) = 1$; in particular, the random variables (Z_n) form an orthonormal family, different from the one in Exercise 2.8.

2.10. Fractional Brownian motion

Let $H \in (0, 1)$, and define

$$R_H(x, y) := \frac{1}{2}\left(x^{2H} + y^{2H} - |x - y|^{2H}\right) \qquad \text{for } x, y \in [0, \infty).$$

(a) Show that $R_H(\cdot, \cdot)$ is positive definite, i.e., that

$$\sum_n \sum_m \bar{\xi}_n R(x_n, x_m) \xi_m \geq 0 \qquad \text{(finite sum)}$$

for all $\xi_1, \xi_2, \ldots \in \mathbb{C}$, and all $x_1, x_2, \ldots \in [0, \infty)$.

(b) Show that $H = \frac{1}{2}$ reduces to the case of the standard Brownian motion considered in Exercises 2.8–2.9.

References and remarks

Readers who want to brush up on some of the tools used in this chapter might wish to consult one or more of the following references (books and papers), for example, covering path-space measures [Nel59, Nel64, Nel67, Nel69, Nel73, Sim79], random walk [BaNi70, HuMS82, Spi76, RoWi00, DiFr99], conditional expectations [Jam64, Rev84], and martingale theory [CoRa90, Gun66, HuSM81].

The idea of using the Kolmogorov extension principle in wavelet constructions was suggested in three papers by Dorin Dutkay [Dut02, Dut04b, Dut04a].

The use of the Ruelle operator R (alias the Perron–Frobenius–Ruelle operator) in wavelet analysis was first suggested by Lawton; see [Law91a, Law91b]. The idea is that the part of the spectrum of R lying on the circle $\{\lambda \in \mathbb{C} \mid |\lambda| = 1\}$ determines the wavelet orthogonality relations. This idea, and the results of Lawton, were extended by Bratteli and Jorgensen in [BrJo02b]. The papers by Jorgensen et al. [JoPe98, DuJo06b] and by Lau et al. [LaNg98, FaLa99, FeLa02] contain other applications of spectral theory of R to iterated function systems. The study of the transfer operator (alias Ruelle operator) R_W for the case when W is assumed to be in the Lipschitz class was initiated by C.T. Ionescu Tulcea et al. in the seminal Annals paper [IoMa50]. The results from [IoMa50] were extended in Chapters 4 and 5 of [BrJo02b].

—and within a week or two I saw that the noncommutation was really the dominant characteristic of Heisenberg's new theory.   —P.A.M. Dirac

While the Karhunen–Loève theorem in Exercise 2.7 (pp. 55–56) may be viewed as a result in probability theory, we will see in Chapters 8 and 9 that it is also a theorem in operator theory. In fact, it may be viewed as "pure" operator theory. A similar observation applies to our consideration of Schmidt's theorem (Exercise 7.11, p. 150) and to tensor products in general from Chapter 7. One reason for this double life is the familiar mathematical distinction between Hilbert spaces in their *concrete* form (say L^2-function spaces, or ℓ^2-sequence spaces) and in their *axiomatic* form. We will see that the use of operator theory in its more axiomatic form helps clarify the use of tensor products, and this in turn is vital for all the basis constructions we shall encounter, wavelets, fractals, and time series from signal analysis.

Abstract considerations of Hilbert space are facilitated by Dirac's elegant bra-ket notation, which we shall adopt. It is a terminology which makes basis considerations fit especially nicely into an operator-theoretic framework: If $\mathcal{H}$ is a (complex) Hilbert space with vectors x, y, z, etc., then we denote the inner product as a Dirac bra-ket, thus $\langle x \mid y \rangle \in \mathbb{C}$. In contrast, the rank-one operator defined by the two vectors x, y will be written as a ket-bra, thus $E = |x\rangle\langle y|$. Hence E is the operator in $\mathcal{H}$ which sends z into $\langle y \mid z \rangle x$.

The reader will notice from Exercise 2.6(b) that the conclusion of the spectral theorem for compact operators takes an especially nice form when expressed with Dirac's formalism.

3

$\mathbb{N}_0$ vs. $\mathbb{Z}$

Every axiomatic (abstract) theory admits, as is well known, an unlimited number of concrete *interpretations besides those from which it was derived. Thus we find applications in fields of science which have no relation to the concepts of random event and of probability in the precise meaning of these words.* —A.N. Kolmogorov 1933

PREREQUISITES: Periodic functions; power series; Fourier series; examples of bases in some function spaces, especially in L^2.

Prelude

The title of this chapter calls for an explanation: Given a base space X, an endomorphism σ of X, and a prescribed weight function W on X, we saw in Section 1.2 that there is an associated measure P_x on the space of infinite paths rooted at x; see Figure 1.1 (p. 8) for an illustration. As noted, the function W determines the transition probabilities that go into the probability measure P_x as follows: For two "successive" points y and z on such a path in X, a transition is possible if $\sigma(z) = y$, and the transition probability is then $W(z)$. If points on the path are further apart, we use a natural formula for conditional probabilities.

In the chapter that follows this prelude we will show that this construction is key to our understanding of both geometric and computational aspects of the kind of multiresolutions that can be built on X.

More generally, when path-space measures such as P_x are used in analysis, it is essential to have detailed knowledge about the "size" of their support. Typically path-space measures are supported on a rather "small" subset of the full space of all infinite paths. An example of this is illustrated by the canonical embedding of the real line $\mathbb{R}$ in the dyadic solenoid. Analogously, Section 1.5 shows that our P_x path space contains a copy of both $\mathbb{N}_0$ and $\mathbb{Z}$. This takes place via a specific encoding where $\mathbb{N}_0$ corresponds to the set of paths which after a finite number of bits finish with an infinite string of zeroes.

In the dyadic case, similarly $\mathbb{Z}$ corresponds to the paths which terminate with an infinite repetition of the pair 01, i.e., paths starting with an arbitrary finite bit-word followed by an infinite string $010101\ldots$. (A systematic study of the encodings into paths from general N-adic trees will be resumed in Chapter 8 below.)

Perhaps surprisingly, the measures P_x tend to have "small" support, and moreover their support properties are significant for the analysis of wavelets and fractals associated with systems (X, W, P_x). In this and the next two chapters, we will give conditions for when the support of P_x is $\mathbb{N}_0$ or $\mathbb{Z}$. And we will show that these cases of "small support" are "responsible" for a rather nice harmonic analysis.

In Chapters 1 and 2, we saw that the convergence of the infinite product (1.3.5) depends on the support of the measures P_x (see Lemma 2.4.1). In particular, the measure P_x applied to the two subsets $\mathbb{N}_0$ and $\mathbb{Z}$ in Ω is crucial. Recall from Remark 1.4.2 that the integers $\mathbb{Z}$ are naturally embedded in the probability space Ω. Hence, in this chapter, we will study the two functions $P_x(\mathbb{N}_0)$ and $P_x(\mathbb{Z})$.

3.1 Terminology

Let $N \in \mathbb{N}$, $N \geq 2$, be given. The cyclic group $\mathbb{Z}_N = \mathbb{Z}/N\mathbb{Z}$ will be identified with $\{0, 1, \ldots, N - 1\}$, and the operations of multiplication and addition are modulo N; or we use the fact that $\mathbb{Z}_N$ is a ring, and a cyclic group under addition.

Similarly, we will work with the circle, or one-torus, $\mathbb{T}$, as $\mathbb{R}/\mathbb{Z}$, and $\mathbb{R}$ will serve as a covering

$$\mathbb{R} \to \mathbb{R}/\mathbb{Z} \cong \mathbb{T}. \tag{3.1.1}$$

In this case, we can take advantage of Fourier duality and use the realization

$$\mathbb{R} \ni x \mapsto e^{i2\pi x} \in \mathbb{T}. \tag{3.1.2}$$

Functions on $\mathbb{T}$ may be viewed, or realized, in either one of the following equivalent ways (i)–(ii).

(i) Functions f on $\mathbb{R}$ which are 1-periodic, i.e.,

$$f(x + 1) = f(x), \qquad x \in \mathbb{R}. \tag{3.1.3}$$

If f is measurable, then (3.1.3) is understood to hold only a.e.

(ii) If f is absolutely integrable on $\mathbb{T} = \mathbb{R}/\mathbb{Z}$ with respect to Haar measure, then it has a Fourier expansion

$$f(x) = \sum_{k \in \mathbb{Z}} c_k e^{i2\pi kx}, \tag{3.1.4}$$

or

$$f(z) = \sum_{k \in \mathbb{Z}} c_k z^k, \qquad z = e^{i2\pi x}, \tag{3.1.5}$$

where

$$c_k = \int_0^1 f(x) e^{-i2\pi kx}\, dx = \int_{\mathbb{T}} f(z) z^{-k}\, d\mu(z); \tag{3.1.6}$$

the second formula uses (3.1.2), where $\mathbb{T}$ is taken to be

$$\mathbb{T} = \{ z \in \mathbb{C} \mid |z| = 1 \}, \tag{3.1.7}$$

and where (3.1.7) may serve to define the Haar measure μ on $\mathbb{T}$, i.e.,

$$d\mu\left(e^{i2\pi x}\right) \cong dx \qquad \text{on } [0, 1). \tag{3.1.8}$$

If W is a bounded measurable function on $\mathbb{T}$, then the corresponding Ruelle operator $R = R_W$ may be written in either one of the following equivalent forms:

(i_R)

$$(Rf)(x) = \sum_{k=0}^{N-1} W\left(\frac{x+k}{N}\right) f\left(\frac{x+k}{N}\right), \tag{3.1.9}$$

or

(ii_R)

$$(Rf)(z) = \sum_{w \in \mathbb{T},\, w^N = z} W(w) f(w), \qquad z \in \mathbb{T}, \tag{3.1.10}$$

where f is a bounded measurable function on $\mathbb{T}$. The function which is constant 1 on $\mathbb{T}$ will be denoted $\mathbf{1}$. Our normalization condition (1.2.3) may therefore be restated as

$$R_W \mathbf{1} = \mathbf{1}. \tag{3.1.11}$$

The equivalence of the two formulations (i) and (ii), or of (i_R) and (ii_R), also yields the following result.

Lemma 3.1.1. *Let W and f be bounded 1-periodic functions on $\mathbb{R}$. (If the two functions are measurable, they will be assumed only essentially bounded, and a.e. 1-periodic.)*

Then the function

$$\sum_{k=0}^{N-1} W\left(\frac{x+k}{N}\right) f\left(\frac{x+k}{N}\right) \tag{3.1.12}$$

is again bounded and 1-periodic.

Proof. Note that the expression in (3.1.12) is the right-hand side in (3.1.9), or equivalently in (3.1.10), and so it is the function $R_W f$. We now give the explicit argument as to why it is 1-periodic. Note that the individual terms in the sum (3.1.12) have period N and not 1. Let

$$g(x) = \sum_{k=0}^{N-1} W\left(\frac{x+k}{N}\right) f\left(\frac{x+k}{N}\right).$$

Then

$$g(x+1) = \sum_{k=0}^{N-1} W\left(\frac{x+1+k}{N}\right) f\left(\frac{x+1+k}{N}\right)$$

$$= \sum_{k=1}^{N-1} W\left(\frac{x+k}{N}\right) f\left(\frac{x+k}{N}\right) + \underbrace{W\left(\frac{x+N}{N}\right) f\left(\frac{x+N}{N}\right)}_{=W(\frac{x}{N})f(\frac{x}{N})}$$

$$= \sum_{k=0}^{N-1} W\left(\frac{x+k}{N}\right) f\left(\frac{x+k}{N}\right) = g(x). \qquad \square$$

3.2 The unit interval

As before, $N \geq 2$, $N \in \mathbb{N}$, is given and fixed throughout. We now revert to the setting of Chapter 2, but specializing to $X = [0, 1] =$ the unit interval. Then the mappings $\sigma, \tau_0, \ldots, \tau_{N-1}$ may be specified as follows.

$$\begin{cases} \sigma: x \mapsto Nx \bmod 1, \\ \tau_k: x \mapsto \dfrac{x+k}{N}, & k = 0, 1, \ldots, N-1, \end{cases} \tag{3.2.1}$$

or alternatively, in complex form,

$$\begin{cases} \sigma: z \mapsto z^N, & z \in \mathbb{T}, \\ \tau_k: z \mapsto \text{the } k\text{'th of the } N \text{ roots}, & k = 0, \ldots, N-1. \end{cases} \tag{3.2.2}$$

The second line in (3.2.2) may be spelled out as follows:

$$\tau_k: e^{i2\pi x} \mapsto e^{i2\pi(x+k)/N}. \tag{3.2.3}$$

Lemma 3.2.1. *Let* $W: [0, 1] \to [0, 1]$ *be a given measurable function and extend* W *from* $[0, 1]$ *to* $\mathbb{R}$ *by periodicity. Then the densities for the probabilities* P_x *in* (1.2.4) *are*

$$W\left(\tau_{\omega_1} x\right) \cdots W\left(\tau_{\omega_n} \cdots \tau_{\omega_1} x\right) = W\left(\frac{x+k}{N}\right) \cdots W\left(\frac{x+k}{N^n}\right), \tag{3.2.4}$$

where

$$k = \omega_1 + \omega_2 N + \cdots + \omega_n N^{n-1}, \qquad (3.2.5)$$

and $\omega_i \in \{0, 1, \ldots, N-1\}$, $1 \le i \le n$.

Proof. A direct calculation, using (3.2.1) and the periodicity of W, yields

$$W\left(\tau_{\omega_s} \tau_{\omega_{s-1}} \cdots \tau_{\omega_1} x\right) = W\left(\frac{x+k}{N^s}\right) \qquad \text{for } 1 \le s \le n.$$

It is understood that the integer $k \in \mathbb{N}_0$ is given by (3.2.5). Conversely, every $k \in \mathbb{N}_0$ has a unique such representation if we agree to let ω_n be the last (if any) non-zero term. The result (3.2.4) follows. □

If n is given, and $0 \le k \le N^n - 1$, then the terms $\omega_1, \ldots, \omega_n$ in (3.2.5) are determined. Let $k \in \mathbb{Z}$. Then determine $k', l \in \mathbb{Z}$ such that

$$0 \le k' \le N^n - 1 \qquad \text{and} \qquad k = k' + lN^n. \qquad (3.2.6)$$

This may be done with the Euclidean algorithm. If

$$k' = \omega_1 + \omega_2 N + \cdots + \omega_n N^{n-1},$$

it follows by Lemmas 1.4.1 and 3.1.1 that

$$W\left(\tau_{\omega_1} x\right) \cdots W\left(\tau_{\omega_n} \cdots \tau_{\omega_1} x\right) = W\left(\frac{x+k'}{N}\right) \cdots W\left(\frac{x+k'}{N^n}\right)$$
$$= W\left(\frac{x+k}{N}\right) \cdots W\left(\frac{x+k}{N^n}\right).$$

As a result, the probability densities $P_x^{(n)}(\{k\})$ are now defined for *all* $k \in \mathbb{Z}$, and not just for $0 \le k \le N^n - 1$.

Proposition 3.2.2. *Let N, $X = [0, 1]$, W, σ, $\tau_0, \ldots, \tau_{N-1}$, $\Omega = \{0, \ldots, N-1\}^{\mathbb{N}}$, and $P_x^{(n)}(\{k\})$ be as described above. In particular, assume that*

$$\sum_{k=0}^{N-1} W\left(\frac{x+k}{N}\right) = 1 \qquad \text{a.e. } x \in [0, 1). \qquad (3.2.7)$$

Then it follows that

$$\sum_{k=-N^n}^{(N-1)N^n - 1} P_x^{(n+1)}(\{k\}) = 1 \qquad \text{a.e. } x. \qquad (3.2.8)$$

Proof. We claim that

$$\sum_{k=-N^n}^{(N-1)N^n-1} P_x^{(n+1)}(\{k\}) = \sum_{k=-N^n}^{(N-1)N^n-1} P_x^{(n+1)}(\{k+N^n\}). \tag{3.2.9}$$

Once this is proved, the result follows since the sum on the right-hand side in (3.2.9) is

$$\sum_{k=0}^{N^{n+1}-1} P_x^{(n+1)}(\{k\}) = \sum_{(\omega_1,\omega_2,\dots,\omega_{n+1})} W\left(\tau_{\omega_1}x\right)\cdots W\left(\tau_{\omega_{n+1}}\cdots\tau_{\omega_1}x\right)$$

$$= \sum_{y\in X,\,\sigma^{n+1}(y)=x} W\left(\sigma^n y\right) W\left(\sigma^{n-1}y\right)\cdots W(y)$$

$$= R_W^{n+1}(\mathbb{1})(x) = \mathbb{1}(x) = 1,$$

where we used Lemmas 3.1.1 and 3.2.1, and formula (2.4.7).

We now prove (3.2.9) by induction. The case $n = 0$ reduces to the assumption (3.2.7). Suppose (3.2.9) holds up to $n-1$. Then the next term is

$$\sum_{k=-N^n}^{(N-1)N^n-1} W\left(\frac{x+k}{N}\right)\cdots W\left(\frac{x+k}{N^n}\right) W\left(\frac{x+k+N^n}{N^{n+1}}\right)$$

$$= R_W\left(\underbrace{\sum_{k=-N^{n-1}}^{(N-1)N^{n-1}-1} W\left(\frac{\cdot+k}{N}\right)\cdots W\left(\frac{\cdot+k}{N^n}\right)}_{=1 \text{ by the induction hypothesis}}\right)(x)$$

$$= R_W(\mathbb{1}) = 1,$$

and the induction step is completed. $\square$

3.3 A sufficient condition for $P_x(\mathbb{Z}) = 1$

In applications to wavelets, we noted in Chapter 1 that the scaling function φ of an N-scale wavelet satisfies

$$\left|\hat{\varphi}(x+k)\right|^2 = P_x(\{k\}). \tag{3.3.1}$$

It is well known that orthonormality of the corresponding N-adic wavelet system is equivalent to the normalization

$$\sum_{k\in\mathbb{Z}}\left|\hat{\varphi}(x+k)\right|^2 = 1 \qquad \text{a.e. } x \in [0,1]. \tag{3.3.2}$$

As a result, it is of interest to decide when the normalization property

$$P_x(\mathbb{Z}) = \sum_{k \in \mathbb{Z}} P_x(\{k\}) = 1$$

holds, or does not.

Recall [BrJo02b] that a scale-N orthonormal wavelet is a system

$$\psi_1, \ldots, \psi_{N-1} \in L^2(\mathbb{R})$$

such that

$$\left(N^{j/2} \psi_i \left(N^j x - k \right) \right)_{j,k \in \mathbb{Z}, \, i=1,\ldots,N-1}$$

is an orthonormal basis for $L^2(\mathbb{R})$.

Theorem 3.3.1. *Let N, $X = [0,1]$, W, σ, $\tau_0, \ldots, \tau_{N-1}$, and Ω be as in Proposition 3.2.2. In particular, we assume that $W : [0,1] \to [0,1]$ is measurable and satisfies (3.2.7). For $x \in [0,1]$, let P_x be the corresponding measure on Ω determined in Lemma 2.4.1.*

Suppose in addition that there are $n_0 \in \mathbb{N}$, $b \in \mathbb{R}_+$ such that

$$W\left(\frac{x+k}{N^{n_0}}\right) \cdots W\left(\frac{x+k}{N^{n_0+p+1}}\right) \geq b \qquad \text{for all } p \in \mathbb{N} \text{ and}$$

$$\text{all integers } k \text{ with } -N^{n_0+p} \leq k < (N-1) N^{n_0+p}. \quad (3.3.3)$$

Then it follows that

$$P_x(\mathbb{Z}) = 1;$$

i.e., that

$$\sum_{k \in \mathbb{Z}} P_x(\{k\}) = 1.$$

Proof. Let $x \in [0,1]$ be given. Suppose the numbers n_0 and b have been chosen such that (3.3.3) holds. Then set

$$f_n(k) = \chi_{[-N^n, (N-1)N^n)}(k) \, W\left(\frac{x+k}{N}\right) \cdots W\left(\frac{x+k}{N^{n+1}}\right).$$

Let P_x be the measures on Ω from Lemma 2.4.1. Then it follows from Proposition 3.2.2 that $\sum_{k \in \mathbb{Z}} f_n(k) = 1$. From Lemmas 2.4.1 and 3.2.1, we have

$$\lim_{n \to \infty} f_n(k) = P_x(\{k\})$$

and

$$\sum_{k \in \mathbb{Z}} P_x(\{k\}) = P_x(\mathbb{Z}) \leq 1.$$

But, using (3.3.3), we get

$$f_n(k) \leq b^{-1} P_x(\{k\}), \qquad n > n_0. \quad (3.3.4)$$

The conclusion $P_x(\mathbb{Z}) = 1$ now follows from the dominated convergence theorem, and a second application of Proposition 3.2.2. $\square$

Remarks 3.3.2. (a) If W is continuous near $x = 0$, and if $W(0) = 1$, then condition (3.3.3) will be satisfied provided W does not vanish on the dyadic rationals kN^{-n}, $n > n_0$.

(b) Even though W is initially only defined on $[0, 1]$, we extend it to $\mathbb{R}$ as a 1-periodic function. We already noted in Lemma 3.1.1 that R_W is acting on the 1-periodic functions on $\mathbb{R}$.

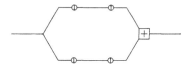

Exercises

3.1. Let N be a (fixed) natural number, $N > 1$. For $k \in \{0, 1, 2, \ldots, N-1\}$, let T_k denote the transformation $x \to Nx + k$, viewed as endomorphisms in $\mathbb{Z}$.

Set $C := \{0, -1\}$, and let D be the smallest subset of $\mathbb{Z}$ which contains C and is invariant under all the maps T_k.

(a) Show that $D = \mathbb{Z}$.

(b) What other two-element subsets C of $\mathbb{Z}$ have the property that the smallest subset of $\mathbb{Z}$ which contains C and is invariant under all the maps T_k is all of $\mathbb{Z}$?

(c) (Note that the transformations $T_k : x \to Nx + k$, for $k \in \{0, 1, 2, \ldots, N-1\}$, leave $\mathbb{N}_0$ invariant.) Show that the smallest subset of $\mathbb{N}_0$ which contains $\{0\}$ and is invariant under all the maps T_k is all of $\mathbb{N}_0$.

3.2. (a) Consider functions f and g as in (3.1.5):

$$f(z) = \sum_{k \in \mathbb{Z}} c_k z^k, \qquad g(z) = \sum_{k \in \mathbb{Z}} d_k z^k.$$

Show that

$$f(z) g(z) = \sum_k l_k z^k \qquad (3\text{E}.1)$$

where

$$l_k = \sum_{p \in \mathbb{Z}} c_p d_{k-p}. \qquad (3\text{E}.2)$$

(b) Show that if (c_k) and $(d_k) \in \ell^1$, then (l_k) in (3E.2) is also in ℓ^1.

(c) Is the conclusion in (b) valid if ℓ^1 is replaced with ℓ^2?

3.3. Let $(c_k) \in \ell^2$, and let a function f be defined by (3.1.5). Then show that $f \in L^2(\mathbb{T})$, where $\mathbb{T}$ is given the Haar measure; and moreover that the Parseval identity

$$\|c\|_{\ell^2} = \|f\|_{L^2(\mathbb{T})}$$

holds.

3.4. Let $f \in L^2(\mathbb{T})$ and consider the Fourier correspondence (3.1.5). Set

$$(Ff)(z) = \frac{1}{2} \sum_{\substack{w \in \mathbb{T} \\ w^2 = z}} f(w).$$

Show that $\lim_{n \to \infty} F^n f$ exists in $L^2(\mathbb{T})$.

3.5. Let $f \in L^2(\mathbb{T})$ be as in Exercise 3.4, and consider (3.1.5).
    (a) Show that then

$$(Ff)(z) = \sum_{k \in \mathbb{Z}} c_{2k} z^k.$$

    (b) Let $S = F^*$ be determined by

$$\langle Sf \mid g \rangle_{L^2} = \langle f \mid Fg \rangle_{L^2} \qquad \text{for all } f, g \in L^2.$$

Show that then

$$(Sf)(z) = f\left(z^2\right), \qquad z \in \mathbb{T},$$

and further that S is isometric in $L^2(\mathbb{T})$.
    (c) Show that

$$(Sf)(z) = \sum_{k \in \mathbb{Z}} c_k z^{2k}, \qquad z \in \mathbb{T}, \ f \in L^2(\mathbb{T}).$$

References and remarks

Some relevant references covering infinite products, as used in this chapter, are the books [Rud87, Zyg32], and papers which aim close to the present theme are [JoPe98, BeBK05, BeBe95, CvSS85].

The idea of using harmonic analysis of iterated function systems (IFS) and more general fractals in the study of similarity structures may originate with the paper [JoPe96] by Steen Pedersen and the author; see also [JoPe98], [BrJo99a], and [Str98].

The next chapter turns to harmonic analysis of affine IFSs. We will see that the kind of Fourier bases that can be devised for affine IFSs and wavelet bases have one thing in common: they are both better localized than Fourier waves. As a result (see [JoPe98], [Str05], and [Tao96]) both classes of the new bases have better convergence properties than traditional Fourier series; and the improvements come almost entirely from the fact that these new bases are better *localized*: if you try to adjust locally in a basis expansion with a Fourier wave, you get errors at far distances. Not so for localized bases!

A case study: Duality for Cantor sets

*Closer to this book and equally illuminating are the many problems trig-
gered by a sound or a picture. Only afterwards is a formula devised, and
then proclamed. . . .* —Benoit B. Mandelbrot

PREREQUISITES: The Euclidean algorithm, recursion; the positional number representation; rudimentary examples of abelian groups; spectrum; Lebesgue; Fatou;
Cantor.

Prelude

A well-known principle in Fourier series (reviewed in Section 3.1) for functions
on a finite interval states that an orthogonal trigonometric basis exists and will be
indexed by an arithmetic progression of (Fourier) frequencies, i.e., by integers times
the inverse wave length. Similarly, in higher dimensions d, we define periodicity
in terms of a lattice of rank d. The principle states that for d-periodic functions on
$\mathbb{R}^d$, the appropriate Fourier frequencies may then be realized by a certain dual rank-
d lattice. In this case, the inverse relation is formulated as a duality principle for
lattices; see, for example, [JoPe93] for a survey of this point.

The purpose of this chapter is to extend, in a self-contained presentation, this
duality principle to a class of *fractals*.

In order to capture the essence of the idea, we have restricted the exposition
here to those compact fractals that are realized by simple arithmetic on the real
line, and which were considered first by Cantor. Hence, the middle-third Cantor
set is an example. But in addition to scaling by 3, we shall consider more general
notions of scaling, including (later in the book) matrix scaling for the multivariable
case. Specifically, here we shall aim for compact Cantor constructions which take
place in $\mathbb{R}^d$.

Our first general observation is that a fixed such affine fractal X has an associated and canonical probability measure μ $(= \mu_X)$. We define (Section 4.1) our measure μ by a precise invariance property which is induced directly by the affine structure of X. The issue of the measure is a delicate one, as X, being a fractal, is a non-linear object and does not carry the structure of a group, or even anything close to that. (So no Haar measure!)

Nonetheless the measure μ allows us to formulate a natural Fourier principle, and to ask for "fractal" Fourier bases. Having μ, we may then imitate Fourier's construction, i.e., we may ask for an orthogonal Fourier basis for $L^2(X, \mu)$. But since X is constructed from recursively leaving out "fractions" (in $\mathbb{R}^d$), we will then expect that there is a dual "fractal-like" thinning of frequencies at infinity, i.e., a thinning relative to some rank-d lattice. Intuitively, we will expect a set Λ of Fourier frequencies to come from "fractals in the large." So we ask for the complex exponentials $e^{i\lambda \cdot x}$ indexed by $\lambda \in \Lambda$ to form an orthogonal basis for $L^2(X, \mu)$. We shall refer to such an orthogonal basis as a *Fourier basis*, or a complete orthogonal set of Fourier frequencies. (Our choice of complex exponentials, as opposed to Fourier's traditional wave-frames of sinusoids, is mainly convenience.)

In the context of affine fractals X, the surprise is that such orthogonal Fourier bases exist at all for *some* fractals, and not for others. In fact, it was previously believed that only asymptotic basis formulas were possible in the "fractal world."

If $d = 1$, we show that the basis principle works when Cantor's middle-interval construction is done with scale 4, but not with scale 3. So, surprisingly, the familiar middle-third Cantor set (the first example that comes to mind!) does *not* have a Fourier basis, but if it is modified a little, changing the scale number from 3 to 4, then we show that Fourier's basis principle holds.

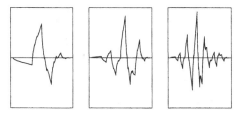

4.1 Affine iterated function systems: The general case

We considered in Chapter 2 a general class of iterated function systems (IFS) X with N branches, $N \geq 2$. They are defined in a general measure-theoretic category. We specified probabilities for random walks on the corresponding branches. They are determined by a fixed measurable function W on X and a normalization (see (1.2.3)). What results (Lemma 2.4.1) is a family of path-space measures P_x on the probability space $\Omega = \{0, 1, \ldots, N - 1\}^{\mathbb{N}}$, for $x \in X$.

In Chapter 3 we saw that both the natural numbers $\mathbb{N}_0$ and the integers $\mathbb{Z}$ embed naturally as subsets of Ω. As we saw in Chapter 1, the traditional integrability properties of wavelets in the Hilbert space $L^2(\mathbb{R})$ turn out to be closely related to the function $x \mapsto P_x(\mathbb{Z})$. For example, we proved that the orthonormal basis (ONB) property for the standard wavelets is equivalent to the identity

$$P_x(\mathbb{Z}) = 1 \qquad \text{a.e. } x \in X.$$

In other words, we are concerned with deciding when $\mathbb{Z}$ has full measure in Ω.

In this chapter, we consider instead a family of Cantor sets X, totally disconnected compact subsets of $\mathbb{R}$ of Hausdorff dimension s, $0 < s < 1$. As we show below, there is a natural basis question for these Cantor sets which is similarly related to the function $x \to P_x(\mathbb{N}_0)$, i.e., to the size of $\mathbb{N}_0$ in Ω.

Each Cantor set is an affine iterated function system (IFS), and it will have a natural realization X in $[0, 1]$, and a *conjugate* one $\bar{X}$ in $[-1, 0]$. We will refer to them as the right-handed, resp., the left-handed version of X.

The question we raise is when X has an ONB consisting of Fourier frequencies (see the definitions below). Let P_x, $x \in \bar{X}$, be the path-space measures. We then show (see also Theorem 5.4.1) that the ONB property for X is equivalent to the identity

$$P_x(\mathbb{N}_0) = 1, \qquad x \in \bar{X}.$$

In other words, in this case, the requirement is that $\mathbb{N}_0$ have full measure as a subset of Ω.

The function

$$W(x) := \cos^2(2\pi x) \tag{4.1.1}$$

came up in an earlier study by Jorgensen and Pedersen [JoPe98]. In that paper, we ask which Cantor sets have orthonormal bases (ONB) $\{e_\lambda \mid \lambda \in \Lambda\}$ for some $\Lambda \subset \mathbb{R}$. Here

$$e_\lambda(t) := e^{i2\pi\lambda t}, \qquad t \in \mathbb{R}. \tag{4.1.2}$$

While wavelets have fractal features, it turns out that a class of affine fractals, such as Cantor sets with division scale 3 or 4, have wavelet-like features. We illustrate this with two examples, and we then cover the general theory later in the chapter; see Sections 4.3–4.4.

One of the results in [JoPe98] states that a certain class of Cantor sets X do admit orthonormal bases of this form for suitable choices of sets Λ. If some X admits an ONB $\{e_\lambda \mid \lambda \in \Lambda\}$, we say that (X, Λ) is a *spectral pair* and that $(e_\lambda)_{\lambda \in \Lambda}$ is a Fourier basis.

The following two examples (Figure 4.1) illustrate this point: in Figure 4.1(a), we sketch the middle-third Cantor set X_3. It is constructed from

$$\sigma : x \mapsto 3x \bmod \mathbb{Z}$$

and the two branches of σ^{-1},

$$\tau_0(x) = \frac{x}{3} \quad \text{and} \quad \tau_1(x) = \frac{x+2}{3}.$$

The Cantor set X_4 in Figure 4.1b is constructed from

$$\sigma : x \mapsto 4x \bmod \mathbb{Z}$$

and the two branches of σ^{-1},

$$\tau_0(x) = \frac{x}{4} \quad \text{and} \quad \tau_1(x) = \frac{x+2}{4}. \tag{4.1.3}$$

We prove in [JoPe98] that X_3 does not have a Fourier basis, while X_4 does. Even so, Dutkay and Jorgensen showed in [DuJo06b] that all the affine IFS fractals X admit orthonormal wavelet bases. These wavelet bases are constructed from the ambient Hausdorff measure "$(dx)^s$" of dimension s (= the Hausdorff dimension of X), and they are realized in a separable Hilbert space built from $(dx)^s$. We call them "gap-filling wavelets." To help appreciate the examples, we recall the Hausdorff measure $(dx)^s$, $0 < s < 1$, and its restriction to the corresponding Cantor sets; see also [Fal85] and [Hut81].

Let $N \in \mathbb{N}$, $N \geq 2$, be given. Pick a subset $B \subset \mathbb{R}$ such that the points in B represent distinct residue classes in $\mathbb{Z}/N\mathbb{Z}$, i.e., such that N does not divide $b - b'$ when b and b' are distinct points in B. Then there is a unique measure $\mu = \mu_{(N,B)}$ on $\mathbb{R}$ such that

$$\mu = \frac{1}{\#(B)} \sum_{b \in B} \mu \circ \tau_b^{-1}, \tag{4.1.4}$$

where $\tau_b(z) := (x+b)/N$. Let $p := \#(B)$. Then the support of $\mu_{(N,B)}$ is a Cantor set $X_{(N,B)}$ of Hausdorff dimension $s = \ln p / \ln N = \log_N(p)$. Hence the Hausdorff dimension of X_3 is $\log_3(2)$, and for X_4 in Figure 4.1(b), it is $\log_4(2) = 1/2$.

For these fractals, the Hausdorff dimension equals the scaling dimension. We will not go into details here, but refer instead to [Fal85, Fal90]. The scaling dimension s is typically easier to compute; the formula is

$$s := \frac{\log(\text{number of replicas})}{\log(\text{magnification factor})}. \tag{4.1.5}$$

To be precise, we say that $X_{(N,B)}$ *has a Fourier basis* if, for some Λ, the family $\{e_\lambda \mid \lambda \in \Lambda\}$ is an ONB for $L^2\left(\mu_{(N,B)}\right)$.

4.2 The quarter Cantor set: The example $W(x) = \cos^2(2\pi x)$

Returning to X_4 in Figure 4.1(b), we recall the following lemma from [JoPe98].

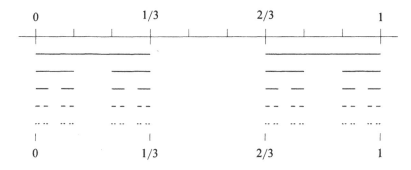

(a) X_3: middle-third Cantor set.

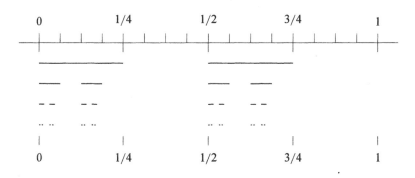

(b) X_4: the quarter Cantor set.

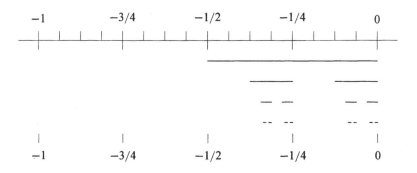

(c) $\bar{X}_4 := -\left\{ \sum_{i=1}^{\infty} \frac{l_i}{4^i} \,\middle|\, l_i \in \{0, 1\} \right\}$, the conjugate or
left-handed quarter Cantor set.

Fig. 4.1. Cantor sets.

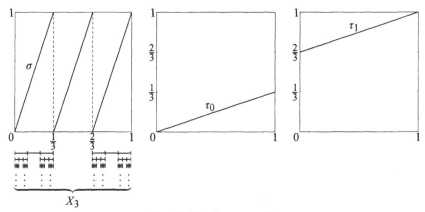

Fig. 4.2. The Cantor set X_3.

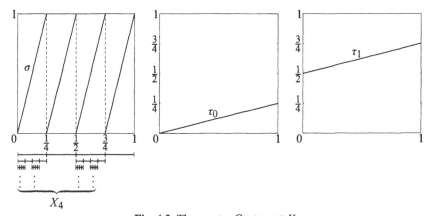

Fig. 4.3. The quarter Cantor set X_4.

Lemma 4.2.1. *Let the set X_4 with associated measure μ denote the Cantor construction of Figure* 4.1(b) *and* (4.1.3)–(4.1.4). *Specifically, μ is the Hausdorff measure on the fractal X_4 with Hausdorff dimension* $1/2$. *Let*

$$\Lambda = \Lambda_4 := \left\{ l_0 + l_1 4 + l_2 4^2 + \cdots \mid l_i \in \{0, 1\}, \text{ where the sums are finite} \right\}.$$

Then $\{ e_\lambda \mid \lambda \in \Lambda \}$ is orthonormal in $L^2(X_4, \mu)$. Equivalently, (X_4, Λ) is a spectral pair.

Remark 4.2.2. The main result in this chapter is that $\{ e_\lambda \mid \lambda \in \Lambda \}$ is in fact an ONB.

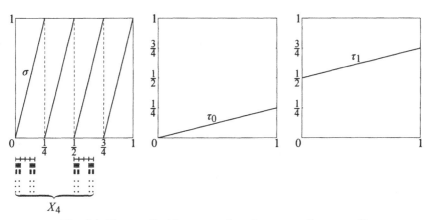

Fig. 4.4. Alternate limiting approach to the quarter Cantor set X_4.

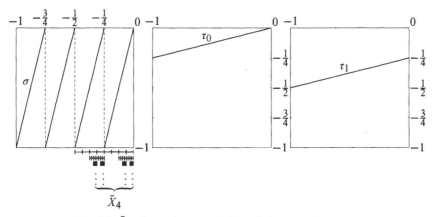

Fig. 4.5. $\bar{X}_4$, the conjugate or left-handed quarter Cantor set.

Proof of Lemma 4.2.1. Setting

$$C(\xi) := \int_{X_4} e_\xi(x)\, d\mu(x),\qquad\qquad (4.2.1)$$

we get the scaling relation

$$C(\xi) = \frac{1}{2}\left(1 + e^{i\pi\xi}\right) C\left(\frac{\xi}{4}\right),\qquad \xi \in \mathbb{R}. \qquad (4.2.2)$$

Since the inner products are

$$\langle e_\lambda \mid e_{\lambda'}\rangle_\mu = \int_{X_4} \overline{e_\lambda(x)}\, e_{\lambda'}(x)\, d\mu(x) = C(\lambda' - \lambda),\qquad (4.2.3)$$

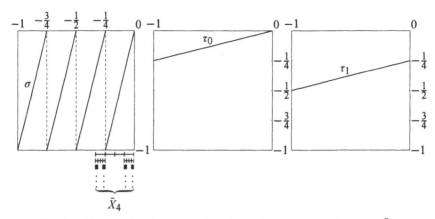

Fig. 4.6. Alternate limiting approach to the conjugate quarter Cantor set $\bar{X}_4$.

we need only show that, if $\lambda' \neq \lambda$ in Λ, then the product

$$\prod_{p=0}^{n} \cos\left(\frac{\pi\,(\lambda' - \lambda)}{2 \cdot 4^p}\right) \tag{4.2.4}$$

vanishes for some n. If $\lambda' \neq \lambda$, there is a first term where $l_i \neq l'_i$. If it is n, then $\lambda' - \lambda \in 4^n \cdot (\pm 1 + 4\mathbb{Z})$, and the last factor in (4.2.4) is then $\cos\left(\pm\frac{\pi \cdot 4^n}{2 \cdot 4^n}\right) = \cos\left(\pm\frac{\pi}{2}\right) = 0$. $\square$

4.3 The conjugate Cantor set, and a special harmonic function

Our next lemma is also from [JoPe98]. For an alternative to the argument from [JoPe98], see also an appendix to [JoPe98] written by R. Strichartz [Str98]. We state the lemma here without proof. The reader will easily be able to supply the details.

Lemma 4.3.1.

(a) *To verify the ONB property, it is enough to verify that the function*

$$h_\Lambda(x) := \sum_{\lambda \in \Lambda} |C\,(x - \lambda)|^2 \tag{4.3.1}$$

is constant and equal to 1, $x \in \mathbb{R}$.

(b) *Setting* $W(x) := \cos^2(2\pi x)$, *see* (4.1.1), *we get*

$$R_W h_\Lambda = h_\Lambda, \tag{4.3.2}$$

where

$$(R_W f)(x) := W\left(\frac{x}{4}\right) f\left(\frac{x}{4}\right) + W\left(\frac{x-1}{4}\right) f\left(\frac{x-1}{4}\right). \qquad (4.3.3)$$

Remark 4.3.2. We establish the fact that $\{e_\lambda \mid \lambda \in \Lambda\}$ is an ONB for $L^2(X_4, \mu)$ by showing that the eigenvalue problem (4.3.2) has only one solution h_Λ which satisfies $h_\Lambda(0) = 1$, and which is Lipschitz continuous.

We now turn to the random walk and the measures P_x on $\Omega = \{0, 1\}^\mathbb{N}$.

Now the measures P_x will be indexed by the conjugate fractal $\bar{X}_4$ in Figure 4.1(c), i.e., the one constructed from $\sigma : x \mapsto 4x \bmod \mathbb{Z}$, and the pair

$$\tau_0(x) = \frac{x}{4}, \qquad \tau_1(x) = \frac{x-1}{4}. \qquad (4.3.4)$$

We say that the Cantor set $\bar{X}_4$ in the interval $[-1, 0]$ constructed from the IFS (4.3.4), see Figures 4.5–4.6, is the *conjugate* of the quarter Cantor set X_4 from Figures 4.3–4.4. Both sets are affine fractals with Hausdorff dimension $1/2$: see formula (4.1.5).

Let X_4 be the Cantor set of Figures 4.3–4.4, i.e., based on (4.1.3). The Cantor set of the alternative system (4.3.4) will be denoted by $\bar{X}_4$, and we refer to it as the *conjugate* Cantor set to X_4. It is a little harder to visualize than the fractals in Figures 4.1(a) and 4.1(b). It is a little different from the fractals in Figures 4.1(a) and 4.1(b), in that the gap configuration appears to have less separation. However, that is just a "visual effect," as one can make the gaps appear the same size as in the first one by just plotting the image on $[-1/2, 0]$ instead of $[-1, 0]$. This fractal $\bar{X}_4$ in Figure 4.1(c) may be written as

$$\bar{X}_4 = -\left\{ \sum_{i=1}^{\infty} \frac{l_i}{4^i} \;\middle|\; l_i \in \{0, 1\} \right\}, \qquad (4.3.5)$$

and we call it the conjugate or left-handed quarter Cantor set (or the "back side" or "flip side" of the quarter Cantor set). It has the same Hausdorff dimension $s = 1/2$ as does X_4 from Figure 4.1(b).

Applying Lemma 2.4.1 to $W(x) = \cos^2(2\pi x)$ and the fractal $\bar{X}_4$ in (4.3.5), or Figure 4.1(c), we get the following formulas for the measure P_x on $\Omega = \{0, 1\}^\mathbb{N}$:

$$P_x(A(i_1, \ldots, i_n)) = \prod_{p=0}^{n-1} \cos^2\left(\frac{\pi(x-\lambda)}{2 \cdot 4^p}\right), \qquad (4.3.6)$$

and

$$P_x(\{\omega(\lambda)\}) = \prod_{p=0}^{\infty} \cos^2\left(\frac{\pi(x-\lambda)}{2 \cdot 4^p}\right) = |\langle e_x \mid e_\lambda \rangle_{L^2(X_4, \mu)}|^2, \qquad (4.3.7)$$

where $A(i_1, \ldots, i_n)$ denotes the cylinder set (2.3.5), and

$$\omega(\lambda) = (i_1, \ldots, i_n, \underbrace{0, 0, 0, \ldots}_{\infty \text{ string of zeroes}}) \tag{4.3.8}$$

for

$$\lambda = i_1 + i_2 4 + i_3 4^2 + \cdots + i_n 4^{n-1}. \tag{4.3.9}$$

In view of (4.3.8)–(4.3.9), we may identify $\mathbb{N}_0$ and Λ. Both are uniquely represented with points in Ω which terminate with an infinite string of zeroes, i.e., one of the form $(i_1, \ldots, i_n, \underbrace{0, 0, 0, \ldots}_{0})$ for some n.

It follows in particular that Λ, or equivalently $\mathbb{N}_0$, has measure 1 if and only if

$$P_x(\mathbb{N}_0) = h_\Lambda(x) = \sum_{\lambda \in \Lambda} \left| \langle e_x \mid e_\lambda \rangle_{L^2(X_4, \mu)} \right|^2 = 1 \qquad \text{for all } x \in X. \tag{4.3.10}$$

4.4 A sufficient condition for $P_x(\mathbb{N}_0) = 1$

Proposition 4.4.1. [JoPe98] *With the stated properties, we have $P_x(\mathbb{N}_0) = 1$ for all $x \in X$.*

Proof. Let

$$\chi_n(\lambda) = \begin{cases} 1 & \text{if } \lambda \in \Lambda \text{ and } \lambda < \dfrac{1}{3}(4^n - 1), \\ 0 & \text{otherwise}, \end{cases}$$

and set

$$F_x^{(n)}(\lambda) := \chi_n(\lambda) \prod_{p=0}^{n-1} \cos^2\left(\frac{\pi(x - \lambda)}{2 \cdot 4^p}\right).$$

Then we get

$$\sum_{\lambda \in \Lambda} F_x^{(n)}(\lambda) = 1. \tag{4.4.1}$$

It is clear from (4.3.7) that

$$\lim_{n \to \infty} F_x^{(n)}(\lambda) = P_x(\{\omega(\lambda)\}). \tag{4.4.2}$$

To prove that $P_x(\mathbb{N}_0) \equiv 1$, we must establish that the convergence in (4.4.2) is dominated.

For n large, the terms $\pi(x - \lambda)/(2 \cdot 4^p)$ are close to 0 for $p \geq n$; and we may pick some $b > 0$ and n_0 such that

$$\prod_{p=n_0}^{\infty} \cos^2\left(\frac{\pi(x - \lambda)}{2 \cdot 4^p}\right) \geq b. \tag{4.4.3}$$

We conclude that

$$F_x^{(n)}(\lambda) \leq b^{-1} P_x(\{\omega(\lambda)\}), \qquad n \geq n_0, \ \lambda \in \Lambda. \qquad (4.4.4)$$

This is the desired domination, and we therefore may apply the dominated convergence theorem to the sum $\sum_{\lambda \in \Lambda} \cdots$. The conclusion is

$$P_x(\mathbb{N}_0) = \sum_{\lambda \in \Lambda} |\langle e_x \mid e_\lambda \rangle_{L^2(X_4, \mu)}|^2 \equiv 1,$$

which is the desired result. $\qquad \qquad \qquad \qquad \qquad \qquad \square$

Remark 4.4.2. In the next chapter, we will prove a theorem, Theorem 5.4.1, for general path-space measures, which shows when $\mathbb{N}_0$ has full measure in Ω. As in the proof of Proposition 4.4.1 above, our reasoning there will be based on a domination argument.

Conclusions

When Lemma 4.3.1 and Proposition 4.4.1 are combined we conclude that the set $\{e_\lambda \mid \lambda \in \Lambda\}$ is an orthonormal basis (ONB) in the Hilbert space $L^2(X_4, \mu)$; i.e., that the Cantor set X_4 has a Fourier basis. The orthogonality of the functions e_λ is the easier part of the argument. It follows from (4.3.2) in the lemma. But only by also proving that the special function h_Λ in (4.3.1), the minimal R_W-harmonic function, is in fact the constant function 1 are we able to infer that the set $\{e_\lambda \mid \lambda \in \Lambda\}$ is total in $L^2(X_4, \mu)$, i.e., that it is an ONB.

However, this step is quite analogous to a key argument which we already encountered in Chapter 1 for wavelets. The argument for the L^2-density of the linear span of $\{e_\lambda \mid \lambda \in \Lambda\}$ hinges on (4.3.10) as follows: First use (4.3.10) to show that every e_x can be approximated in L^2 by functions in the span of the e_λ's. Then use Stone–Weierstraß to infer that the span of the e_λ's is dense in L^2.

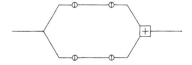

Exercises

4.1. Let τ_0 and τ_1 be the transformations in (4.1.3), and let X_4 be the quarter Cantor set X_4 in Figure 4.3 (p. 74). Show that

$$X_4 = \tau_0(X_4) \cup \tau_1(X_4).$$

4.2. Formulate and prove the analogous result for the usual middle-third Cantor set X_3.

4.3. Let τ_0, τ_1, and σ be the transformations of X_4 introduced in connection with (4.1.3).

(a) Compare the following two sets of Borel probability measures on X_4:

$$\mathcal{M}_\sigma = \left\{ \mu \mid \mu \circ \sigma^{-1} = \mu \right\} \quad \text{and} \quad \mathcal{M}_\tau = \left\{ \mu \mid \mu = \tfrac{1}{2}\left(\mu \circ \tau_0^{-1} + \mu \circ \tau_1^{-1} \right) \right\}.$$

(b) Estimate the cardinality of the two sets $\mathcal{M}_\sigma$ and $\mathcal{M}_\tau$ in (a).

4.4. Give a direct verification of the scaling law (4.2.2) in Lemma 4.2.1.

4.5. Try to carry out the arguments in Lemma 4.2.1 for the middle-third Cantor set X_3 in place of X_4, and check what goes wrong.

References and remarks

Readers not already familiar with fractals might wish to consult some relevant references covering analysis on affine fractals, e.g., the very readable books [Fal85, Fal90, Bal00], and/or the papers [LaNg98, FaLa99, LaNR01, FeLa02, BrMo75, Hut81, JoPe98, Hal83]. As for a student-friendly presentation of fractals in many parts of mathematics, we can recommend Devaney's lovely little book [Dev92].

The regularity issues that are the focus of this chapter are related to harmonic analysis questions from the theory of affine iterated function systems (IFS), and there is a substantial amount of work by Strichartz and others that spells out more connections to diverse areas of mathematics and applications. The treatment we gave above is especially inspired by [Str98], and [Str00]. In the context of our Chapters 4–5, these papers address the question from Proposition 4.4.1 above; see also Theorem 5.4.1 below. The question and the general theme were central to the paper [JoPe98]. In fact [Str98] came about from Strichartz's suggested alternative approach to the result in [JoPe98]. And other papers followed [JoPe98], for example [ŁaWa02] by Łaba and Wang.

At the conclusion of our work on this book, we received a preprint [Str05] from Strichartz which continues the harmonic analysis theme from [JoPe98] and [Str98], but in a different direction, viz., convergence: The new preprint [Str05] addresses a degree to which fractal Fourier series from [JoPe98] and the papers following it tend to be more localized, and as a result have better convergence properties than do the classical Fourier series. This localization of the Mock Fourier series is interesting as it is analogous to a strong localization property of wavelet bases, and we turn to that in detail in Chapter 7 below.

There is a vast diversity of geometric structures with self-similarity, or with an inherent consistency of scale. It includes wavelets, fractals and classes of models from dynamics. However, within this variety, the fractal structures that are most amenable to mathematical analysis have their self-similarity defined by affine mappings (in ambient Euclidean space). But even this more narrow focus, restricting to affine mappings (or rather affine function systems), encompasses both standard and non-standard wavelets, as well as some of the best-known fractals. Our present viewpoint is to study these geometries in the light of Fourier duality.

But there are lots of other viewpoints: A delightful and student-friendly presentation of the class of fractals we have in mind here is the little book [YaHK97] by Yamaguti, Hata, and Kigami. It is one of the few available books which aims to unify wavelets and fractals, but its aim is potential-theoretic: Laplace operators, resistance inequalities, and so on.

5

Infinite products

Albert Einstein to Oscar Veblen (a math professor):
"The Lord God is subtle, but malicious he is not."
(Raffiniert ist der Herr Gott, aber boshaft ist Er nicht.)
And ten years later:
"I have second thoughts. Maybe God is malicious."
                                                    —Albert Einstein

PREREQUISITES: Riesz; random; Fubini; square-integrable functions.

Prelude

In the first two chapters, we introduced the *random walks* that are used throughout the book. We outlined this in the context of endomorphisms of compact spaces X and combinatorial trees; and we showed in Chapters 3 and 4 how this applies to wavelets and fractals. The combinatorial trees to keep in mind for illustration are sketched in Figures 1.1 (p. 8) and 2.1 (the Farey tree, p. 42). Recall further that the transition probabilities in the random-walk model are assigned via a prescribed function W on X which is assumed to satisfy a certain normalization condition. Within the context of signals, W is the absolute square of some frequency function m, or of a wavelet filter. The various paths within our tree can originate at points x chosen from the set X. As before, X carries a fixed finite-to-one endomorphism σ. If x and y are points in X such that $\sigma(y) = x$, then the number $W(y)$ represents the probability of a transition from x to y. Step-by-step conditional probabilities and finite products are used in assigning probabilities to *finite* paths which originate at x. (The simplest instance of this idea is for the case when X is the circle, i.e., the one-torus $\mathbb{T}$. For each N, we may then consider $\sigma(z) := z^N$. And in the context of wavelet constructions, we introduced the additive formulation of the distinct branches of the inverse of $z \to z^N$ when z is complex and restricted to $\mathbb{T}$.)

Here we are concerned with the case of *infinite* paths. For this we must use infinite products coupled with a fundamental idea of Kolmogorov. These infinite products are the subject of the present chapter. The measure which assigns probabilities to subsets of paths starting at x is called P_x. To understand the measures P_x and their support, convergence issues for infinite products come into play.

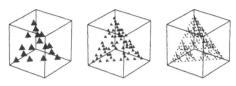

5.1 Riesz products

The study of infinite products has a long history in analysis, see especially [BeBK05] and the references given there; in number theory [Mey79], lacunary trigonometric series [Zyg32]; and in ergodic theory [BrMo75, Kak48, Kat87], as well as in other applications, e.g., [BeBe95, Rit79]. A special case of the infinite products we discuss in the present chapter includes the so-called Riesz products [Rie18], and their many variants. While the treatment in [BeBK05] is centered around certain multi-scale properties of a class of generalized Riesz products, our present discussion is motivated instead by our probabilistic viewpoint, i.e., the use of random walk, iterated function systems (IFS), and probability theory.

5.2 Random products

In this chapter, we consider a general class of infinite products which is connected to the random-walk systems from Chapter 2. A special case of these infinite products arises in the analysis of wavelets, to which we shall turn in the next chapter.

We begin with a lemma.

Lemma 5.2.1. *Let $(X, \mathcal{B})$ be a measure space as described in Chapter 2. Let $\sigma\colon X \to X$ and N be as described, and let $\tau_0, \dots, \tau_{N-1}$ be a choice of branches of σ^{-1}. Let $W\colon X \to [\,0, 1\,]$ be measurable and satisfy (2.4.1), i.e., $\sum_{\sigma(y)=x} W(y) = 1$ for all $x \in X$. Then the infinite product*

$$F(x) := \lim_{n\to\infty} \prod_{k=1}^{n} W\left(\tau_0^k(x)\right), \qquad x \in X, \tag{5.2.1}$$

converges; and the identity

$$F(x) = W(\tau_0(x)) F(\tau_0(x)), \qquad x \in X, \tag{5.2.2}$$

holds if and only if $P_x(\{0\}) > 0$.

Proof. As in Chapter 2, set $\Omega := \{0, 1, \ldots, N-1\}^{\mathbb{N}}$, and let $\mathbf{0} = \{0, 0, 0, \ldots\}$ be the point in Ω which is given by an infinite string of zeroes. Let $A(\underbrace{0, 0, \ldots, 0}_{n \text{ times}})$ be the cylinder sets from (2.3.5), and let P_x, $x \in X$, be the Radon measures constructed in Lemma 2.4.1. By (2.4.2), we have

$$P_x\left(A(\underbrace{0, 0, \ldots, 0}_{n \text{ times}})\right) = \prod_{k=1}^{n} W\left(\tau_0^k(x)\right). \tag{5.2.3}$$

Since

$$\{\mathbf{0}\} = \bigcap_{n=1}^{\infty} A(\underbrace{0, 0, \ldots, 0}_{n \text{ times}})$$

and

$$A(\underbrace{0, 0, \ldots, 0}_{n+1 \text{ times}}) \subset A(\underbrace{0, 0, \ldots, 0}_{n \text{ times}}),$$

we get

$$P_x(\{\mathbf{0}\}) = \lim_{n \to \infty} P_x\left(A(\underbrace{0, 0, \ldots, 0}_{n \text{ times}})\right).$$

In view of (5.2.3), the desired conclusion (5.2.1) follows, and

$$F(x) = P_x(\{\mathbf{0}\}).$$

The second conclusion (5.2.2) is also immediate from the convergence of the products in (5.2.3) as $n \to \infty$. $\qquad\square$

5.3 The general case

We begin with a remark concerning the embedding of natural numbers in Ω.

Remark 5.3.1. Let $(i_1, \ldots, i_n, 0)$ be the point in Ω which is the concatenation of $(i_1, \ldots, i_n)$ with an infinite string of zeroes. For the measure of the singleton $\{(i_1, \ldots, i_n, 0)\}$ we then get

$$\begin{aligned} P_x(\{(i_1, \ldots, i_n, \mathbf{0})\}) \\ = W(\tau_{i_1} x) \cdots W(\tau_{i_n} \cdots \tau_{i_1} x) F(\tau_{i_n} \cdots \tau_{i_1} x), \qquad x \in X. \end{aligned} \tag{5.3.1}$$

By the Euclidean algorithm, the natural numbers $k \in \mathbb{N}_0 = \{0, 1, 2, \ldots\}$ have a unique representation

$$k = i_1 + i_2 N + \cdots + i_n N^{n-1} \tag{5.3.2}$$

with $i_s \in \mathbb{Z}_N = \{0, 1, \ldots, N-1\}$. We recall that $\mathbb{N}_0$ is naturally embedded in Ω. If n is fixed, (5.3.2) is a unique representation of all k, $0 \le k \le N^n - 1$. It is convenient to identify k with the singleton $\{\omega(k)\} = \{(i_1, \ldots, i_n, \mathbf{0})\}$ in Ω. So each $k \in \mathbb{N}_0$ represents a unique singleton in Ω, and the mapping $k \mapsto (i_1, \ldots, i_n, \mathbf{0})$ is 1–1. Hence

$$P_x(\mathbb{N}_0) = \sum_{k=0}^{\infty} P_x(\{k\}), \qquad (5.3.3)$$

or more precisely,

$$P_x(\mathbb{N}_0) = \sum_{n=1}^{\infty} \sum_{(i_1,\ldots,i_n)} P_x(\{(i_1, \ldots, i_n, \mathbf{0})\}). \qquad (5.3.4)$$

Proposition 5.3.2. *Let X, σ, τ_0, $\ldots$, τ_{N-1}, W, and $(P_x)_{x \in X}$ be as specified in Lemma 5.2.1. Then the function*

$$h(x) := P_x(\mathbb{N}_0), \qquad x \in X, \qquad (5.3.5)$$

is harmonic for R_W.

Proof. Since P_x is a Radon probability measure on Ω for each $x \in X$, by Lemma 2.4.1, it follows that the following infinite-sum representation for $h(x)$ is convergent:

$$h(x) = \sum_{n=1}^{\infty} \sum_{(i_1,\ldots,i_n)} W(\tau_{i_1}x) \cdots W(\tau_{i_n} \cdots \tau_{i_1}x) F(\tau_{i_n} \cdots \tau_{i_1}x). \qquad (5.3.6)$$

With the Ruelle operator $R = R_W$, we get

$$(Rh)(x) = \sum_{s=0}^{N-1} W(\tau_s x) h(\tau_s x)$$

$$= \sum_{s} \sum_{n} \sum_{i_1,\ldots,i_n} W(\tau_s x) W(\tau_{i_1} \tau_s x) \cdot$$

$$\cdots W(\tau_{i_n} \cdots \tau_{i_1} \tau_s x) F(\tau_{i_n} \cdots \tau_{i_1} \tau_s x)$$

$$= h(x),$$

which is the desired conclusion. $\qquad\square$

5.4 A uniqueness theorem

In our next result, we give a sufficient condition for the property

$$P_x(\mathbb{N}_0) = 1 \qquad (5.4.1)$$

to hold. In [Gun00], the process $(P_x)_{x \in X}$ is said to be *tight* if (5.4.1) is satisfied.

By now the transfer operator is often called the Ruelle operator because of D. Ruelle's use of it in the 1960s on phase-transition problems in statistical mechanics [Rue69]. The probability aspect of this endeavor was stressed by R. Gundy [Gun00], and others, e.g., [CoRa90]. Our presentation here relies in crucial ways on Gundy's viewpoint, as it seems to unify the different threads in the subject that came before it. Three early elements of the theory may be summarized in three different but closely related aspect of filters (as filter response functions) in the form of: (1) tilings (A. Cohen), (2) the transfer operator (W. Lawton), and (3) cycles (I. Daubechies, among others). For more citations, we refer to the comments at the end of this chapter, and to the references in the papers and books cited above.

Mathematically, a filter is just a sequence, but a very special one, and filters were used originally in operations on discrete time signals. In its simplest form, this operation is merely the Cauchy product of sequences. If the filter sequence is taken as the Fourier coefficients of a periodic function m, then we say that m is the frequency response function. The operation on functions is now just pointwise multiplication. The numbers that occur as filter sequences are closely related to the masking coefficients of computer graphics; see, e.g., [BrJo02b] and [Jor03].

The filters have been used in the form of subband filters, and quadrature-mirror filters, in image/signal processing for half of a century, and it is from signal engineering of processing that the subject of wavelet theory has adopted such engineering terms as low-pass/high-pass filters, down-sampling, up-sampling, and perfect signal (or image) reconstruction.

Since wavelets ideally aim for orthogonal bases, initially in the Hilbert space $L^2(\mathbb{R})$, properties of filters which detect orthogonality of the basis functions were the focus of attention for both the initial work on wavelet filters, and the subsequent more probabilistic approach. The probabilistic approach in fact merges the three initial criteria, i.e., tiling (A. Cohen), the transfer operator (W. Lawton), and cycles (graph theory on trees, discrete paths, and random walk). Each of the three elements alone misses some important features of orthogonality tests for filters, with filter response functions that are singular, for example filter functions that are only measurable, and not continuous. This generalization is not just idle abstraction, but is motivated by uses on wavelet bases with localization in frequency bands; see, e.g., [BaMe99]. If more smoothness in the time domain is imposed, then (by uncertainty) irregularities in the frequency domain tend to pop up.

A further advantage of the new meeting ground for analysis and probability is its impact on other basis issues in harmonic analysis, such as those arising in the joint work of the author with S. Pedersen and D. Dutkay, e.g., [Kat87], [JoPe96], [DuJo06b], and related research by R. Strichartz, Y. Wang and others. See [Jor03], [JoPe98], [DuJo06b], and the papers cited there, for additional discussion and references.

We aim to have the theorems which follow in this chapter combine the diverse ideas and results that came out in the last two decades. While these results originated with diverse mathematical problems or engineering applications in mind, they all seem to share a fundamental mathematical principle, which perhaps now with hindsight finally emerges as a sharper contour. So at this time, the subject seems to have reached a level of maturity, and we hope it is by now ready for the classroom. But the individual results (over the two decades) taken in isolation are likely to miss some of the common threads.

Theorem 5.4.1. *Let* X, σ, τ_0, ..., τ_{N-1}, W, *and* $(P_x)_{x \in X}$ *be as above. Suppose for some* $x \in X$ *there is an* $n_0 \in \mathbb{N}$ *and* $b \in \mathbb{R}_+$ *such that*

$$\prod_{p \geq n_0} W \left(\tau_{i_p} \cdots \tau_{i_1} x \right) \geq b \qquad for\ all\ (i_1, i_2, \dots). \tag{5.4.2}$$

Then it follows that

$$P_x (\mathbb{N}_0) = 1. \tag{5.4.3}$$

Remark 5.4.2. In probabilistic terms, condition (5.4.2) is an assertion about the tail sequences, i.e., the estimate

$$P_x (\underbrace{\mathbb{Z}_N \times \cdots \times \mathbb{Z}_N}_{n_0\ \text{times}} \times \{\omega\}) \geq b \qquad \text{for all } \omega \in \Omega. \tag{5.4.4}$$

Note that each set in (5.4.4) is finite, of cardinality N^{n_0}, but there is an infinite number of sets.

Proof of Theorem 5.4.1. Suppose condition (5.4.2) above holds. Let n_0 and b be chosen as stated. Since $W \leq 1$, we get

$$\prod_{p \geq n} W \left(\tau_{i_p} \cdots \tau_{i_1} x \right) \geq \prod_{p \geq n_0} W \left(\tau_{i_p} \cdots \tau_{i_1} x \right) \geq b \qquad \text{for all } n \geq n_0. \tag{5.4.5}$$

Using the unique representation

$$k = i_1 + i_2 N + \cdots + i_n N^{n-1} \qquad for\ k \in \mathbb{N}_0,$$

we set length $(k) = n$ if i_n is the last non-zero term, and

$$F_x^{(n)} (k) = \begin{cases} \displaystyle\prod_{p=1}^{n} W \left(\tau_{i_p} \cdots \tau_{i_1} x \right) & \text{if length } (k) \leq n, \\ 0 & \text{otherwise.} \end{cases}$$

Then

$$\sum_{k \in \mathbb{N}_0} F_x^{(n)} (k) = 1, \tag{5.4.6}$$

and

$$\lim_{n \to \infty} F_x^{(n)} (k) = P_x (\{k\}). \tag{5.4.7}$$

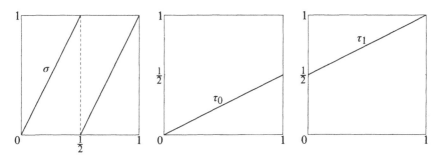

Fig. 5.1. The 2-adic fractions.

For $n \geq n_0$, we get the estimate

$$F_x^{(n)}(k) \leq b^{-1} P_x(\{k\}) \qquad \text{for } k \in \mathbb{N}_0. \qquad (5.4.8)$$

Since

$$\sum_{k \in \mathbb{N}_0} P_x(\{k\}) = P_x(\mathbb{N}_0) \leq 1,$$

the estimate (5.4.8) shows that the convergence (5.4.7) is dominated. Hence we may exchange the limits. Condition (5.4.6) shows that, as claimed,

$$\sum_{k \in \mathbb{N}_0} P_x(\{k\}) = P_x(\mathbb{N}_0) = 1. \qquad \square$$

Example 5.4.3. $W(x) := \cos^2(3\pi x)$, $X = [0, 1]$, $\sigma : x \to 2x \bmod 1$, $\tau_i(x) = (x + i)/2$, $i \in \{0, 1\}$. See Figure 5.1. The condition (5.4.2) is *not* satisfied for any $x \in [0, 1]$, and

$$0 < P_x(\mathbb{Z}) < 1.$$

To see this, recall that if

$$k = i_1 + 2i_2 + \cdots + 2^{n-1} i_n,$$

then

$$W(\tau_{i_n} \cdots \tau_{i_1} x) = \cos^2\left(\frac{3\pi (x + k)}{2^{n+1}}\right).$$

To show that (5.4.2) does not hold, we check that for all $b \in \mathbb{R}_+$, all $n_0 \in \mathbb{N}$, we can find $n > n_0$ and $k \in \mathbb{N}_0$, $k < 2^{n-1}$, such that

$$\cos^2\left(\frac{3\pi (x + k)}{2^n}\right) < b.$$

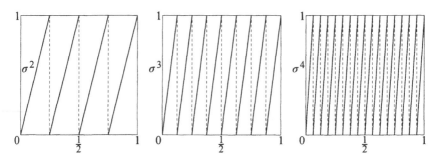

Fig. 5.2. Powers of σ.

Since $\lim_{n\to\infty} (3\pi x/2^n) = 0$, the conclusion follows: just approximate $1/6$ with a sequence of dyadic rationals $k/2^n$, $0 \le k < 2^{n-1}$. Then

$$\lim_{(n,k)} \cos^2 \left(\frac{3\pi\,(x+k)}{2^n} \right) = \lim_{(n,k)} \cos^2 \left(\frac{3\pi k}{2^n} \right)$$
$$= \cos^2 \left(\frac{3\pi}{6} \right) = 0.$$

As an application to the usual N-adic representation of fractions, we now read off the following corollary. First set $X = [0, 1] = $ the unit interval, and let

$$\begin{cases} \sigma\,(x) = Nx \bmod 1, & \text{and} \\ \tau_s\,(x) = \dfrac{x+s}{N}, & x \in [0,1],\ s = 0, 1, \ldots, N-1. \end{cases} \tag{5.4.9}$$

If $N = 2$, these mappings are graphed as in Figure 5.1. Moreover, for this example, we can compute

$$h\,(x) = P_x\,(\mathbb{Z})$$

explicitly. In Section 6.2, we show that

$$P_x\,(\mathbb{Z}) = \left(\frac{\sin 3\pi x}{3 \sin \pi x} \right)^2.$$

Corollary 5.4.4. *Let $X = [0, 1]$, $N \in \mathbb{N}$, $N \ge 2$, be given, and let σ, τ_0, $\ldots$, τ_{N-1} be the N-adic maps of (5.4.9). Let $W: [0, 1] \to [0, 1]$ satisfy (2.4.1), i.e.,*

$$\sum_{s=0}^{N-1} W \left(\frac{x+s}{N} \right) = 1, \qquad x \in [0,1]. \tag{5.4.10}$$

Let $(P_x)_{x\in[0,1]}$ be the transition measures of Lemma 2.4.1. Then

$$h(x) = P_x(\mathbb{N}_0) \tag{5.4.11}$$

$$= \sum_{k=0}^{\infty} \prod_{n=1}^{\infty} W\left(\frac{x+k}{N^n}\right)$$

is convergent and represents an R_W-harmonic function on $[0, 1]$.

Following Remark 1.4.2, we extend the measure P_x on $\mathbb{N}_0$ to $\mathbb{Z}$, making use of two copies of $\Omega = \{0, 1, \ldots, N-1\}^{\mathbb{N}}$. Identifying $k \in \mathbb{N}_0$ with $\omega(k)$, consider the case $-N^n \le k < 0$. Then set

$$P_x(\{k\}) := P_x\left(\left\{\omega\left(N^{n+1} + k\right)\right\}\right). \tag{5.4.12}$$

5.5 Wavelets revisited

> *Then dulcet music swelled*
> *Concordant with the life-strings of the soul;*
> *It throbbed in sweet and languid beatings there,*
> *Catching new life from transitory death;*
> *Like the vague sighings of a wind at even*
> *That wakes the wavelets of the slumbering sea...*
> —Percy Bysshe Shelley

We now use the martingale method of Remark 2.7.2 in the computation of the cocycle V associated with the distinguished harmonic function h from (5.4.11).

Example 5.5.1. It may very well happen that the measure P_x assigns zero mass to singletons in Ω, i.e., that it is non-atomic.

(a) Let $X = [0, 1]$, and let σ be the endomorphism in Figure 5.1, i.e., $\sigma(x) = 2x \bmod 1$. Let W be the constant function, i.e., $W = 1/2$, $x \in [0, 1]$. Then it is immediate that P_x is the product measure on $\Omega = \{0, 1\}^{\mathbb{N}}$ with weights $p_0 = p_1 = 1/2$ for all $x \in [0, 1]$, and therefore $P_x(\{\omega\}) = 0$ for all $\omega \in \Omega$.

(b) Let $\varphi \in L^2(\mathbb{R})$, and suppose φ satisfies the scaling identity (1.3.1) for $N = 2$ and some sequence a_k of masking coefficients with

$$\sum_{k\in\mathbb{Z}} \bar{a}_k a_{k+2l} = \frac{1}{2}\delta_{0,l}.$$

Set

$$W(x) = \left|\sum_k a_k e^{-i2\pi kx}\right|^2.$$

Suppose

$$\int_{\mathbb{R}} |\varphi(x)|^2 \, dx = 1.$$

Then it follows from Corollary 5.4.4 that

$$P_x\left(\{\omega(k)\}\right) = |\hat{\varphi}(x+k)|^2, \qquad k \in \mathbb{Z}, \tag{5.5.1}$$

where $\omega(k) = (\omega_1, \omega_2, \dots)$ is given by Euclid and $k = \omega_1 + \omega_2 2 + \cdots + \omega_n 2^{n-1}$, $0 \le k \le 2^n - 1$.

Proposition 5.5.2. *There is a shift-invariant function $v: \Omega \to [0, 1]$ such that*

$$V(x, \omega) = h(v(\omega)), \qquad \omega \in \Omega, \tag{5.5.2}$$

is the cocycle corresponding to the harmonic function h in (5.4.11). Moreover, if $\omega = (\omega_1, \omega_2, \dots) \in \Omega = \{0, \dots, N-1\}^{\mathbb{N}}$, then

$$v(\omega) = \lim_{n \to \infty} \left(\frac{\omega_1}{N^n} + \frac{\omega_2}{N^{n-1}} + \cdots + \frac{\omega_n}{N} \right). \tag{5.5.3}$$

In particular, v vanishes on the N-adic rational fractions.

Proof. Since there is a 1–1 correspondence between harmonic functions and cocycles, see Theorem 2.7.1, the cocycle corresponding to h in (5.4.11) is unique. If we show that it has the form (5.4.11), it follows from Corollary 5.4.4 that the function v must be shift-invariant, i.e., that

$$v(\omega_1, \omega_2, \dots) = v(\omega_2, \omega_3, \dots). \tag{5.5.4}$$

In view of Remark 2.7.2 (or the martingale convergence theorem), we know that, for P_x a.e. ω, we have

$$V(x, \omega) = \lim_{n \to \infty} h\left(\tau_{\omega_n} \cdots \tau_{\omega_1} x\right), \tag{5.5.5}$$

but

$$\tau_{\omega_n} \cdots \tau_{\omega_1} x = \frac{x}{N^n} + \frac{\omega_1}{N^n} + \frac{\omega_2}{N^{n-1}} + \cdots + \frac{\omega_n}{N}, \tag{5.5.6}$$

and it follows that the limit in (5.5.5) is independent of x. But the sequence of fractions in (5.5.3) or (5.5.6) is non-increasing, i.e.,

$$\frac{\omega_1}{N^n} + \frac{\omega_2}{N^{n-1}} + \cdots + \frac{\omega_n}{N} \ge \frac{\omega_1}{N^{n+1}} + \frac{\omega_2}{N^n} + \cdots + \frac{\omega_{n+1}}{N}.$$

The monotonicity follows from an easy induction argument. The fractions are clearly in the compact interval $[0, 1] \subset \mathbb{R}$.

In order to understand the function $v: \Omega \to [0, 1]$ from (5.5.3), note that

$$v(\,\omega_1, \,\omega_2, \,\dots, \,\omega_n, \,\underbrace{0, \,0, \,0, \,\dots}_{\infty \text{ string of zeroes}}\,) = 0, \tag{5.5.7}$$

i.e., v vanishes on the N-adic rationals. $\qquad\square$

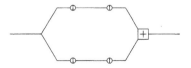

Exercises

5.1. Let
$$m(z) = \sum_{k \in \mathbb{Z}} a_k z^k \in L^\infty(\mathbb{T}),$$
and set
$$(Sf)(z) = \sqrt{2}\, m(z)\, f\left(z^2\right), \qquad f \in L^2(\mathbb{T}).$$

(By $L^2(\mathbb{T})$, we mean the Hilbert space of all L^2-functions on $\mathbb{T}$ where $\mathbb{T}$ is equipped with the unique normalized Haar measure.)

Show that the following three conditions are equivalent.

(i) S defines an isometry of $L^2(\mathbb{T})$.

(ii) $|m(z)|^2 + |m(-z)|^2 = 1$ a.e. $z \in \mathbb{T}$.

(iii) $\displaystyle\sum_{k \in \mathbb{Z}} \bar{a}_k a_{k+2l} = \frac{1}{2}\delta_{0,l}, l \in \mathbb{Z}.$

5.2. Let $N \in \mathbb{N}$, $N \geq 2$, and let
$$m(z) = \sum_{k \in \mathbb{Z}} a_k z^k \in L^\infty(\mathbb{T}).$$

Set
$$(Sf)(z) = \sqrt{N}\, m(z)\, f\left(z^N\right), \qquad f \in L^2(\mathbb{T}).$$

Show that the following three conditions are equivalent.

(i) S defines an isometry of $L^2(\mathbb{T})$.

(ii) $\displaystyle\sum_{k=0}^{N-1} \left| m\left(ze^{i2\pi k/N}\right)\right|^2 = 1$ a.e. $z \in \mathbb{T}$.

(iii) $\displaystyle\sum_{k \in \mathbb{Z}} \bar{a}_k a_{k+Nl} = \frac{1}{N}\delta_{0,l}, l \in \mathbb{Z}.$

5.3. Let $N \in \mathbb{N}$, $N \geq 2$, and let
$$m(z) = \sum_{k \in \mathbb{Z}} a_k z^k \in L^\infty(\mathbb{T}).$$

As in Exercise 5.2, set
$$Sf(z) = \sqrt{N}\, m(z)\, f\left(z^N\right), \qquad f \in L^2(\mathbb{T}).$$

The adjoint operator $F = S^*$ is defined by the identity
$$\langle Ff \mid g \rangle_{L^2} = \langle f \mid Sg \rangle_{L^2}, \qquad f, g \in L^2(\mathbb{T}).$$

(a) Show that

$$(Ff)(z) = \frac{1}{\sqrt{N}} \sum_{\substack{w \in \mathbb{T} \\ w^N = z}} \overline{m(w)} f(w), \qquad f \in L^2(\mathbb{T}), \; z \in \mathbb{T}.$$

(b) Let $M = M_z$ be the multiplication operator $(Mf)(z) = zf(z)$, $f \in L^2(\mathbb{T})$, $z \in \mathbb{T}$. Then show that M commutes with S^*S, i.e., $(S^*S)M = M(S^*S)$.

(c) Does M commute with SS^*?

(d) Does $M^N = M_{z^N}$ commute with SS^*?

5.4. Let N, m, and S be defined as in Exercise 5.3. Then show that S is a partial isometry (i.e., S^*S is a projection operator) if and only if there is a measurable subset $E \subset \mathbb{T}$ such that

$$S^*S = M_{\chi_E}$$

where

$$(M_{\chi_E} f)(z) := \chi_E(z) f(z), \qquad f \in L^2(\mathbb{T}), \; z \in \mathbb{T}.$$

5.5. Let $(X, \mathcal{B})$ be a measure space, and let μ be a probability measure defined on the σ-algebra $\mathcal{B}$. Let $N \in \mathbb{N}$, $N \geq 2$, and let $\sigma: X \to X$ and $\tau_k: X \to X$ be measurable endomorphisms of X such that

$$\sigma \circ \tau_k = \mathrm{id}_X \qquad \text{for } 0 \leq k < N.$$

Consider functions $m \in L^\infty(X, \mathcal{B}) =: L^\infty$. Set

$$QF(\tau) := \left\{ m \in L^\infty \;\middle|\; \sum_{k=0}^{N-1} |m \circ \tau_k|^2 = 1 \; \mu\text{-a.e. on } X \right\}.$$

Set

$$(S_m f)(x) = \sqrt{N}\, m(x) f(\sigma(x)), \qquad f \in L^2(X, \mu), \; x \in X.$$

Show that $S_m: L^2(X, \mu) \to L^2(X, \mu)$ is an isometry for all $m \in QF(\tau)$ if and only if μ satisfies

$$\mu = \frac{1}{N} \sum_{k=0}^{N-1} \mu \circ \tau_k^{-1}. \tag{5E.1}$$

5.6. Let $N \in \mathbb{N}$, $N \geq 2$, be given, and set

$$\begin{cases} \sigma(x) = Nx \mod 1, \\ \tau_k(x) = \dfrac{x+k}{N}, & 0 \leq k < N. \end{cases}$$

(a) Then show that the restriction μ to $[0, 1)$ of Lebesgue measure on $\mathbb{R}$ satisfies

$$\mu = \frac{1}{N} \sum_{k=0}^{N-1} \mu \circ \tau_k^{-1}.$$

(b) With the identification $\mathbb{R}/\mathbb{Z} \cong [0, 1)$, and a function $m \in L^\infty (0, 1)$, set

$$(Sf)(x) = \sqrt{N}\, m(x)\, f(Nx \bmod 1), \tag{5E.2}$$

or

$$Sf = \sqrt{N}\, m\, f \circ \sigma, \qquad f \in L^2(0, 1).$$

Then show that S is an isometry in $L^2(0, 1)$ if and only if

$$\sum_{k=0}^{N-1} \left| m\left(\frac{x+k}{N}\right)\right|^2 = 1 \qquad \text{a.e. on } [0, 1).$$

(c) Let $S = S_m$ be defined as in (5E.2) for some $m \in L^\infty$. Then show that S^*S is a multiplication operator, i.e., that $S^*S = M_F$ for some $F \in L^\infty$.

(d) For F in (c), show that

$$F(x) = \sum_{k=0}^{N-1} \left| m\left(\frac{x+k}{N}\right)\right|^2 \qquad \text{a.e. } x.$$

(e) What can you say about SS^*?

(f) Let $m_j,\ j = 1, 2$, be two 1-periodic functions in L^∞, and let S_j be the corresponding subdivision operators defined as in (5E.2). Then show that $S_1^* S_2$ is a multiplication operator; specifically, $S_1^* S_2$ is multiplication by

$$\sum_{k=0}^{N-1} \overline{m_1\left(\frac{x+k}{N}\right)}\, m_2\left(\frac{x+k}{N}\right).$$

5.7. Let $\Phi \colon \mathbb{R} \to \mathbb{C}$ be a given function such that the sum

$$\mathrm{Av}\,\Phi(x) := \sum_{n\in\mathbb{Z}} \Phi(x+n)$$

is pointwise convergent a.e. $x \in \mathbb{R}$. Let W be a 1-periodic function on $\mathbb{R}$ (i.e., $W(x+1) = W(x),\ x \in \mathbb{R}$), and suppose that for some $N \in \mathbb{N},\ N \geq 2$,

$$W(x)\,\Phi(x) = \Phi(Nx), \qquad x \in \mathbb{R},$$

holds.

Set

$$(R_W f)(x) = \sum_{k=0}^{N-1} W\left(\frac{x+k}{N}\right) f\left(\frac{x+k}{N}\right)$$

for periodic functions f on $\mathbb{R}$. Then show that the function

$$h(x) := \mathrm{Av}\,\Phi(x)$$

satisfies

$$R_W h = h,$$

i.e., that h is a harmonic function for the Ruelle operator R_W.

5.8. Let $W: \mathbb{R} \to \mathbb{C}$ be a measurable function, and suppose (i), (ii), and (iii) below hold.

(i) $W(x) = W(x + 1)$ a.e. $x \in \mathbb{R}$, i.e., W is 1-periodic.
(ii) For some $N \in \mathbb{N}$, $N \geq 2$, the infinite product

$$\Phi(x) := \prod_{k=1}^{\infty} W\left(\frac{x}{N^k}\right) \tag{5E.3}$$

is convergent a.e. $x \in \mathbb{R}$.

(iii) $\displaystyle\sum_{k=0}^{N-1} \left| W\left(\frac{x+k}{N}\right) \right| \leq 1$ a.e. $x \in \mathbb{R}$.

Then prove that the function Φ in (5E.3) is in $L^1(\mathbb{R})$, and that

$$\int_{-\infty}^{\infty} |\Phi(x)| \, dx \leq 1.$$

5.9. Let $W \in L^\infty(\mathbb{R})$, and assume that W is 1-periodic, and further that it satisfies

$$W(x) + W\left(x + \frac{1}{2}\right) = 1 \qquad \text{a.e. } x \in \mathbb{R}. \tag{5E.4}$$

(a) Show that $\int_0^1 W(x) \, dx = \frac{1}{2}$.
(b) Show that for all $k \in \mathbb{N}$, the following identity holds:

$$\int_0^{2^k} W\left(\frac{x}{2}\right) W\left(\frac{x}{2^2}\right) \cdots W\left(\frac{x}{2^k}\right) dx = \int_{-2^{k-1}}^{2^{k-1}} W\left(\frac{x}{2}\right) W\left(\frac{x}{2^2}\right) \cdots W\left(\frac{x}{2^k}\right) dx.$$

(c) Show that for all $k \in \mathbb{N}$, the following identity holds:

$$\int_{-2^{k-1}}^{2^{k-1}} W\left(\frac{x}{2}\right) W\left(\frac{x}{2^2}\right) \cdots W\left(\frac{x}{2^k}\right) dx = 1.$$

(d) Suppose, in addition to the above, that $W \geq 0$ a.e. on $\mathbb{R}$, and further that the infinite product

$$\Phi(x) := \lim_{k \to \infty} \prod_{n=1}^{k} W\left(\frac{x}{2^n}\right)$$

is (pointwise) convergent on $\mathbb{R}$ a.e. x. Then show that

$$\int_{-\infty}^{\infty} \Phi(x) \, dx \leq 1. \tag{5E.5}$$

(e) Under the assumptions on W listed in (d), give examples of when the inequality (5E.5) is strict (i.e., $<$), and when it is "$=$".

Hints to 5.9: (a) Introduce the $\mathbb{R}/\mathbb{Z}$-Fourier coefficients $(c_k)_{k\in\mathbb{Z}}$ for the function W, and note that the identity (5E.4) is equivalent to

$$2c_{2n} = \delta_{0,n}, \qquad n \in \mathbb{Z}.$$

Also recall that $c_0 = \int_0^1 W(x)\,dx$.

(b) Prove this by induction, noting that the case $k = 1$ is equivalent to

$$\int_{-\frac{1}{2}}^{\frac{1}{2}} W\left(x + \frac{1}{2}\right) dx = \int_{-\frac{1}{2}}^{\frac{1}{2}} W(x)\,dx.$$

But both sides of this last equation agree with the Fourier coefficient c_0 $(= \frac{1}{2})$ from (a).

(c) Again this may be proved by induction. While the case $k = 1$ is clear, the next case $k = 2$ is instructive:

$$\int_{-2}^{2} W\left(\frac{x}{2}\right) W\left(\frac{x}{4}\right) dx \underset{\text{by (b)}}{=} \int_0^4 W\left(\frac{x}{2}\right) W\left(\frac{x}{4}\right) dx = 4\int_0^1 W(x) W(2x)\,dx$$

$$\underset{\text{using that } W \text{ is 1-periodic}}{=} 4\int_0^{\frac{1}{2}} \left(W(x) + W\left(x + \frac{1}{2}\right)\right) W(2x)\,dx$$

$$\underset{(5E.4)}{=} 4\int_0^{\frac{1}{2}} W(2x)\,dx = 2\int_0^1 W(x)\,dx \underset{(a)}{=} 1.$$

(d) For each $k \in \mathbb{N}$, we have

$$\int_{-2^{k-1}}^{2^{k-1}} \prod_{n=1}^{k} W\left(\frac{x}{2^n}\right) dx \underset{\text{by (c)}}{=} 1.$$

Letting $k \to \infty$, we get the estimate (5E.5) by an application of Fatou's lemma. Verify that Fatou applies in this case.

References and remarks

Some relevant references (books and papers) covering Riesz products are [Rie18, Mey79], and a list covering related infinite-product constructs includes the following: [Zyg32, May91, Kat87, Kak48, BeBK05].

The idea of using the Ruelle operator and the Kolmogorov extension principle in the construction of wavelets from Perron–Frobenius eigenfunctions was suggested in Jorgensen's Memoir [Jor01a], and in two papers by Dorin Dutkay, [Dut02] and [Dut04a].

One of the advantages of this approach is that we get multiresolution wavelets *in other Hilbert spaces* than the familiar $L^2(\mathbb{R}^d)$: for example, in Hilbert spaces built on fractals by the use of Hausdorff measure; see [DuJo06b]. See also [Dut04b].

In the prelude, we mentioned that random-walk models are realized on infinite discrete sets S such as the standard lattices $\mathbb{Z}^d$, $d = 1, 2, \ldots$, and on various combinatorial trees rooted at points in a given compact space. The first model is widely studied in probability (see, e.g., Revuz [Rev84], Stroock [Stro05], and Spitzer [Spi76]); and we have stressed here uses of the tree models in the study of scale-similarity, as it is used in the analysis of wavelets and of fractals.

In all the models, it makes sense to introduce spaces of paths, and path-space measures, and there is a separate literature on this; see e.g., [Nel73] and [Sim79]. Somewhere between these two structures (lattice and combinatorial tree) there are yet other uses of the idea and related probabilistic models. They are encountered for example in thermodynamics, e.g., in percolation models from mathematical physics [FiEs61]. The infinite sets S we meet there could be Cayley trees, Bethe lattices, or bond graphs; see figures 1 and 4 in [FiEs61]. In these models the standard combinatorial tree is modified. Instead of a distinguished "root" or starting node, these models allow more complicated cactus-like root configurations, and the resulting shapes are called pseudolattices. While this theory does combine analysis and probability, it is however beyond the scope of our book; and we refer the interested reader to [FiEs61] and the papers cited there.

The relation between our tree in Figure 1.1 (p. 8) and the Bethe lattice is like the relation between a lattice of $\mathbb{N}$-points (non-negative integer coordinates) and a lattice of $\mathbb{Z}$-points (integer coordinates of either sign). (In a Bethe lattice there would be a third subtree attached above the point labeled "x.") The "Bethe lattice" is uniform, having no distinguished root, point, origin. The shapes in the figures from [FiEs61] are "cactus-like" in appearance.

The minimal eigenfunction

Anything that, in happening, causes itself to happen again, happens again.
—Douglas Adams

PREREQUISITES: Eigenvalues, eigenvectors; eigenfunctions; a curiosity about wavelets as seen by a petroleum engineer.

Prelude

This brief chapter serves as a bridge between the iterated function systems (IFS) in Chapter 4 and the more detailed wavelet analysis in Chapters 7 and 8. We wish to examine a variation of scale, i.e., examine the effect on the Perron–Frobenius–Ruelle theory induced by a change of scale in a wavelet basis. After stating a general result (Theorem 6.1.1), we take a closer look at a single example: Recall that Haar's wavelet is dyadic, i.e., it is a wavelet basis for $L^2(\mathbb{R})$ which arises from the operations of translation by the integers $\mathbb{Z}$, and by scaling with all powers of two, i.e., scaling by 2^j, as j ranges over $\mathbb{Z}$. But the process begins with the unit box function, say supported in the interval from $x = 0$ to $x = 1$. The scaling by 3, i.e., $f \to f(x/3)$, stretches the support to the interval $[0, 3]$. It is natural to ask what happens to an ONB dyadic wavelet under scaling by 3, i.e., $f \to f(x/3)$. This is related to oversampling: The simplest instance of this is the following scaling of the low-pass filter $m_0(x)$, i.e., $m_0(x) \to m_0(3x)$.

Using Perron–Frobenius–Ruelle theory, it can be shown that the ONB property typically is lost, but still a number of essential wavelet features are preserved. Recall that a consequence of the ONB property is a version of the Parseval identity. Even though the ONB property is lost, it follows from our discussion below that the Parseval property is preserved under stretching, i.e., the stretched wavelet will still be a Parseval frame, also called a normalized tight frame.

We have chosen to restrict our discussion of this to one example, the "stretched Haar wavelet." However, we emphasize that much more is known, but beyond the scope of our book. While there are many ways to extend these developments, we have restricted the discussion here to one example. Still a lot more can be done: We know that if ψ is a frame wavelet ($N = 2$) and if p is a fixed odd integer, then the scaled function $(1/p) \, \psi \, (x/p)$ is also a frame wavelet. And even in higher dimensions, the theory takes a nice form.

From wavelets in one dimension to higher dimensions: Instead of the familiar 1-D translation by $\mathbb{Z}$ and scaling with all powers of two, in higher dimensions d the translation will instead be by a rank-d lattice and we will be scaling by an integral and expansive matrix A, i.e., scaling by A^j, as j ranges over $\mathbb{Z}$.

In the context of the path-space measures P_x and the associated harmonic functions from Chapter 2 a lot is known about change of scale. Specifically, in Chapter 2 we introduced the family of probability measures P_x for the case of wavelets on $\mathbb{R}^d$ (with an expansive matrix A over $\mathbb{Z}$), and we showed that each P_x is atomic. Is the transformed P_x family again atomic? Or in other words, are the transformed (or stretched) P_x measures still concentrated on a rank-d lattice, i.e., on some version of $\mathbb{Z}^d$, just as in the 1-dimensional case. Further it is important to consider the effect on cycles (for the random walk) under "matrix-stretching," and the effect on other structures such as the zeroes of the P_x-harmonic functions. And try the same for self-affine tilings. Or develop a theory for an over-sampling in the general case of higher dimensions and even for fractals.

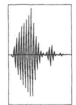

6.1 A general construction of $h_{\min}$

The function $h\,(x) := P_x\,(\mathbb{N}_0)$ is special among the solutions $h \geq 0$ to the eigenvalue problem

$$R_W h = h. \tag{6.1.1}$$

Our next result shows that $x \mapsto P_x\,(\mathbb{N}_0)$ is minimal among the solutions to (6.1.1), and we shall use the notation

$$h_{\min}\,(x) := P_x\,(\mathbb{N}_0)\,, \qquad x \in X. \tag{6.1.2}$$

In an indexed family of wavelet examples, Figure 6.2 (p. 107) contains plots of these functions $h_{\min}$.

Theorem 6.1.1. *Let X, B, N, W be as in Chapter 2, and $\sigma: X \to X$ an endomorphism such that $\#\sigma^{-1}(\{x\}) = N$, $x \in X$, and assume in addition that X is a compact Hausdorff space. Suppose branches of σ^{-1} may be chosen such that, for some measure v_0 on X,*

$$\lim_{n \to \infty} \sum_{(\omega_1, \ldots, \omega_n)} \left(W^{(n)} \cdot g \right) \left(\tau_{\omega_n} \cdots \tau_{\omega_1} x \right) = v_0 (g) = \int_X g \, dv_0 \qquad (6.1.3)$$

for all $g \in C(\Omega)$. The function $W^{(n)}$ is defined by

$$W^{(n)}(y) = W(y) W(\sigma(y)) \cdots W\left(\sigma^{n-1}(y) \right). \qquad (6.1.4)$$

Let $h \in C(\Omega)$ be a solution to (6.1.1) such that $h \geq 0$. Then

$$h_{\min}(x) v_0(h) \leq h(x), \qquad x \in X. \qquad (6.1.5)$$

Remark 6.1.2. With the normalization $v_0(h) = 1$, (6.1.5) reads $h_{\min} \leq h$, and hence the reference to $h_{\min}$ as the minimal eigenfunction. We saw that there are examples where $h_{\min} = 0$.

Proof of Theorem 6.1.1. Let $k \in \mathbb{N}_0$, and consider the N-adic representation $k = i_1 + i_2 N + \cdots + i_n N^{n-1}$. Note that

$$\omega(k) = (i_1, \ldots, i_n, \underbrace{0, 0, 0, \ldots}_{\infty \text{ string of zeroes}}),$$

and that

$$h(x) = R_W^{n+p} h(x) \qquad (6.1.6)$$

$$= \sum_{(\omega_1, \ldots, \omega_{n+p})} W\left(\tau_{\omega_1} x \right) \cdots W\left(\tau_{\omega_n} \cdots \tau_{\omega_1} x \right) \cdots$$

$$\cdots W\left(\tau_{\omega_{n+p}} \cdots \tau_{\omega_1} x \right) h \left(\tau_{\omega_{n+p}} \cdots \tau_{\omega_1} x \right).$$

For n fixed, let $p \to \infty$. Then

$$\lim_{p \to \infty} \sum_{(\omega_{n+1}, \ldots, \omega_{n+p})} W\left(\tau_{\omega_1} x \right) \cdots W\left(\tau_{\omega_n} \cdots \tau_{\omega_1} x \right) \cdots \qquad (6.1.7)$$

$$\cdots W\left(\tau_{\omega_{n+p}} \cdots \tau_{\omega_1} x \right) h \left(\tau_{\omega_{n+p}} \cdots \tau_{\omega_1} x \right) = P_x (\{\omega(k)\}) v_0(h)$$

$$\text{for } k = \omega_1 + \omega_2 N + \cdots + \omega_n N^{n-1}. \qquad (6.1.8)$$

We now exchange limits, and use Fatou's lemma in the form

$$\sum_k \left(\lim_p \cdots \right) \leq \lim_p \sum_k \cdots.$$

Combining (6.1.6) and (6.1.7), we get

$$\sum_{k \in \mathbb{N}_0} P_x \left(\{ \omega (k) \} \right) v_0 (h) \leq h (x) . \tag{6.1.9}$$

But the factor on the left-hand side in (6.1.9) is $P_x (\mathbb{N}_0) = h_{\min} (x)$, so the desired estimate (6.1.5) follows. □

Remark 6.1.3. The wavelet representation is included in the framework of the theorem. Then $X = [0, 1]$, and $v_0 = \delta_0 =$ the Dirac mass at $x = 0$; see [BrJo02a], and [BrJo02b, Proposition 5.4.11].

6.2 A closed expression for $h_{\min}$

Example 6.2.1. Haar wavelets. We now illustrate the minimal eigenfunction for R_W with the following family of Haar wavelets; see also [BrJo02b] for more details. First, note that the simplest version of the scaling identity (1.3.1) from Chapter 1 is

$$\varphi (t) = \varphi (2t) + \varphi (2t - 1) , \qquad t \in \mathbb{R}. \tag{6.2.1}$$

The corresponding wavelet function ψ is given by

$$\psi (t) = \varphi (2t) - \varphi (2t - 1) , \qquad t \in \mathbb{R}. \tag{6.2.2}$$

Even without Fourier transformation (1.3.3), it is immediate by inspection that the equations (6.2.1)–(6.2.2) are solved by the Haar father function,

$$\varphi (t) = \begin{cases} 1, & 0 \leq t < 1, \\ 0 & \text{otherwise,} \end{cases} \tag{6.2.3}$$

and the Haar mother function,

$$\psi (t) = \begin{cases} 1, & 0 \leq t < 1/2 , \\ -1, & 1/2 \leq t < 1 , \\ 0 & \text{otherwise;} \end{cases} \tag{6.2.4}$$

see also Figure 6.1(a). Also consider the functions

$$\varphi_p (t) = \frac{1}{p} \varphi \left(\frac{t}{p} \right) , \qquad t \in \mathbb{R}, \tag{6.2.5}$$

and

$$\psi_p (t) = \frac{1}{p} \psi \left(\frac{t}{p} \right) , \qquad t \in \mathbb{R}, \tag{6.2.6}$$

for $p = 3, 5$, odd numbers. The pair φ_3 and ψ_3 are sketched in Figure 6.1(b).

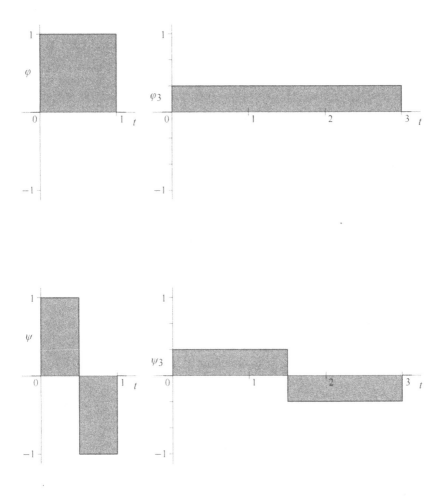

Fig. 6.1. Haar's wavelets (compare Figure 1.2, p. 13): Haar's two functions φ (6.2.3) and ψ (6.2.4) are illustrated in the two columns: The system in the column on the left in the figure illustrates Haar's orthonormal (ONB) wavelet basis, and the scaling identities are visually apparent. The system of functions φ_3 (6.2.5) and ψ_3 (6.2.6), for $p = 3$, in the right-hand column illustrates the two stretched Haar functions. The two scaling identities (6.2.1) and (6.2.2) are visually apparent for both function systems, on the left and on the right. Moreover, for both systems, the ψ function yields a double-indexed Parseval basis (see (1.3.16)), i.e., a function system for which the Parseval identity (6.2.12) holds for every function f in $L^2(\mathbb{R})$. If $p = 1$ (the left-hand-side case), then the inequality in (6.2.11) is an equality, i.e., is an $=$; while for $p = 3$ (the right-hand-side column in the figure), the term on the left in (6.2.11) is strictly smaller than $\|f\|^2_{L^2(\mathbb{R})}$ for non-zero f. The reason for this is the overlap for the $\mathbb{Z}$-translated functions, which is graphically illustrated too.

As suggested from Figure 6.1(b), the wavelet ψ_p, for $p = 3, 5, \ldots$, is called the p-stretched Haar wavelet.

We leave it to the reader to check that the low-pass filter functions m_p for the wavelet pair φ_p, ψ_p are

$$m_p(x) = \frac{1 + e^{-i2\pi px}}{2}, \qquad x \in \mathbb{R},$$

and as a result,

$$W_p(x) = |m_p(x)|^2 = \cos^2(\pi px).$$

It is known, and easy to check, that the orthonormality relations hold for φ, ψ, but not for φ_p, ψ_p, $p = 3, 5, \ldots$.

For φ, ψ, the orthonormality relations are

$$\|\varphi\|_{L^2(\mathbb{R})} = \|\psi\|_{L^2(\mathbb{R})} = 1, \tag{6.2.7}$$

$$\{\varphi(\cdot - k) \mid k \in \mathbb{Z}\} \text{ is orthonormal,} \tag{6.2.8}$$

i.e.,

$$\langle \varphi \mid \varphi(\cdot - k) \rangle_{L^2(\mathbb{R})} = \delta_{0,k}, \qquad k \in \mathbb{Z},$$

and

$$\left\{ 2^{n/2} \psi(2^n t - k) \mid n, k \in \mathbb{Z} \right\} \text{ is an orthonormal basis (ONB) for } L^2(\mathbb{R}). \tag{6.2.9}$$

In contrast, φ_p, ψ_p satisfy

$$\|\varphi_p\|_{L^2(\mathbb{R})} = \|\psi_p\|_{L^2(\mathbb{R})} = \frac{1}{\sqrt{p}}, \tag{6.2.10}$$

$$\sum_{k \in \mathbb{Z}} |\langle \varphi_p(\cdot - k) \mid f \rangle|^2 \leq \|f\|_{L^2(\mathbb{R})}^2 \tag{6.2.11}$$

for all f in the closed subspace V_0 spanned by the translates $\left\{ \varphi_p(\cdot - k) \mid k \in \mathbb{Z} \right\}$, and

$$\sum_{k,n \in \mathbb{Z}} \left|\left\langle 2^{n/2} \psi_p(2^n \cdot - k) \mid f \right\rangle\right|^2 = \|f\|_{L^2(\mathbb{R})}^2 \qquad \text{for all } f \in L^2(\mathbb{R}). \tag{6.2.12}$$

The properties (6.2.11)–(6.2.12) are called *frame* properties. Basis functions satisfying such a generalized PARSEVAL identity are called *Parseval frames*, or *normalized tight frames*. This frame requirement is evidently weaker than the requirements of an ONB; see (6.2.8)–(6.2.9).

The discrepancy between them may be measured by the autocorrelation coefficients from (6.2.8): since (6.2.8) is *not* satisfied for φ_p, $p = 3, 5, \ldots$, the 1-periodic function

$$h_p(x) := \sum_{k \in \mathbb{Z}} \langle \varphi_p \mid \varphi_p(\cdot - k) \rangle_{L^2(\mathbb{R})} \, e^{i2\pi kx} \tag{6.2.13}$$

is not constant. Of course $h_1(x) = 1, x \in \mathbb{R}$.

In many applications, it is too much to require that the wavelet produce a true ONB, i.e., that (6.2.9) be satisfied, and the weaker requirement (Parseval frame) (6.2.12) is typically good enough. For these wavelets, the minimal eigenfunction satisfies

$$0 < P_x(\mathbb{Z}) < 1, \qquad x \in [0, 1],$$

as we shall now illustrate.

From the analysis in Chapter 1 above, we note that there is a wavelet transfer operator $R_p = R_{W_p}$ for each $p = 1, 3, 5, \ldots$. An inspection of (6.2.5)–(6.2.6) shows that

$$W_p(x) = \cos^2(\pi p x). \tag{6.2.14}$$

Now take

$$\nu = \delta_0 = \delta(x - 0). \tag{6.2.15}$$

Then it is clear from (6.2.14) that

$$\nu R_p = \nu, \tag{6.2.16}$$

or equivalently,

$$\int R_p f \, d\nu = \int f \, d\nu, \qquad f \in C([0, 1]).$$

Using now Lemma 1.4.1 and the Fourier transform (1.3.3), we also conclude that

$$h_p(x) = \sum_{k \in \mathbb{Z}} |\hat{\varphi}_p(x - k)|^2 = \sum_{k \in \mathbb{Z}} \left(\frac{\sin \pi p(x - k)}{\pi p(x - k)} \right)^2 = \frac{1}{p^2} \left(\frac{\sin \pi p x}{\sin \pi x} \right)^2, \tag{6.2.17}$$

which is a closed expression for the minimal harmonic function; see also [BrJo02b, page 332, Figure 6.3].

It follows from (6.2.13)–(6.2.17) that

$$\nu(h_p) = \delta_0(h_p) = 1,$$

and that

$$R_{W_p} h_p = h_p, \tag{6.2.18}$$

and we conclude from Theorem 6.1.1 that h_p is the minimal harmonic function. Specifically, if h is any other continuous function satisfying

$$h(0) = 1, \qquad R_{W_p} h = h, \qquad 0 \le h \le 1, \tag{6.2.19}$$

then

$$h_p \le h \le 1 \qquad \text{pointwise.} \tag{6.2.20}$$

See Figure 6.2.

Exercises

6.1. (a) Set $W(x) = \cos^2(3\pi x)$, and show that

$$\prod_{k=1}^{\infty} W\left(\frac{x}{2^k}\right) = \frac{\sin^2(3\pi x)}{(3\pi x)^2}.$$

(b) Verify by a direct argument that

$$\int_{-2^{k-1}}^{2^{k-1}} \prod_{n=1}^{k} \cos^2\left(\frac{3\pi x}{2^n}\right) dx = 1,$$

while

$$\int_{-\infty}^{\infty} \frac{\sin^2(3\pi x)}{(3\pi x)^2} dx = \frac{1}{3}.$$

6.2. Let ψ be the Haar wavelet function from Figure 6.1 (p. 103), and set

$$\psi_{j,k}(t) := 2^{j/2} \psi\left(2^j t - k\right).$$

(a) Show that if $j \in \mathbb{N}_0$, and $k = 0, 1, \ldots, 2^j - 1$, then the functions $\psi_{j,k}$ are supported in the unit interval $I = [0, 1]$.

(b) Show that the functions $\psi_{j,k}$ indexed by $A := \{(j, k) \mid j \in \mathbb{N}_0, \ k = 0, 1, \ldots, 2^j - 1\}$ form an orthonormal basis (ONB) in $L^2(I)$ when I is given the Lebesgue measure, i.e., that $\{\psi_{j,k} \mid (j, k) \in A\}$ is an ONB for $L^2(I)$.

(c) Sketch the basis functions in the cases $j = 0$, $j = 1$, and $j = 2$.

6.3. Can you find other "interesting" functions ψ on $I = [0, 1]$ and subsets $A \subset \mathbb{Z} \times \mathbb{Z}$ such that the family $\{\psi_{j,k} \mid (j, k) \in A\}$ forms an ONB for $L^2(I)$, where $\psi_{j,k}(t) := 2^{j/2} \psi(2^j t - k)$?

6.4. Let ψ_3 be the stretched Haar wavelet function from Figure 6.1 (p. 103), and set

$$\psi_{j,k}^{(3)}(t) := 2^{j/2} \psi_3\left(2^j t - k\right).$$

(a) Show that if $j \in \mathbb{N}_0$, and $k = 0, 1, \ldots, 3(2^j - 1)$, then the functions $\psi_{j,k}^{(3)}$ are supported in the stretched interval $I_3 := [0, 3]$; see Figure 6.1.

(b) Show that the functions $\psi_{j,k}^{(3)}$ indexed by $A_3 := \{(j, k) \mid j \in \mathbb{N}_0, \ k = 0, 1, \ldots, 3(2^j - 1)\}$ form a Parseval frame for $L^2(I_3)$, i.e., $\{\psi_{j,k}^{(3)} \mid (j, k) \in A_3\}$ is a normalized tight frame in $L^2(I_3)$; specifically that

$$\sum_{(j,k) \in A_3} \left|\left\langle \psi_{j,k}^{(3)} \mid f \right\rangle_{L^2(I_3)}\right|^2 = \int_0^3 |f(t)|^2 \, dt$$

holds for all $f \in L^2(I_3)$.

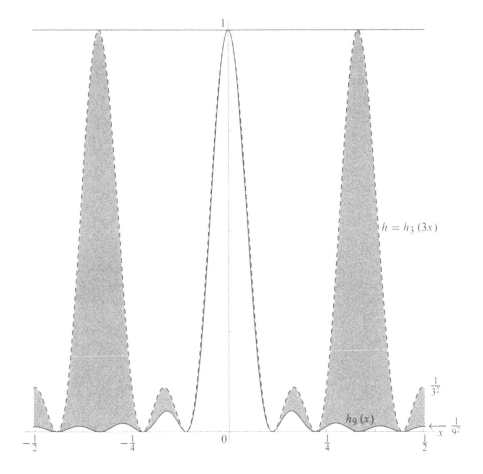

Fig. 6.2. Solutions to the eigenvalue problem (6.2.19).

References and remarks

Some relevant references (books and papers) covering the Ruelle operator and its Perron–Frobenius eigenspace are [Kea72, PaPo90, Bal00, BrJo02b, CoRa90, Jam64, May91, Rue02, Rue69, Rue94].

The wavelet transfer operator is used in a variety of wavelet applications not covered here, or only touched upon tangentially: stability of refinable functions, regularity, approximation order, unitary matrix extension principles, and data mining, to mention only a few. The reader is referred to the following papers for more details on these subjects: [DaHRS03, RoSh03, RST01, JiJS01, RoSh00, RiSh00, JiSh99, She98, RoSh98, LaLS98, RoSh97].

Several of these topics and papers invite the kind of probabilistic tools that we stress in our book, but a more systematic discussion is outside the scope of our book. We only hope to offer an introduction to a variety of more specialized topics.

Generalizations and applications

One cannot expect any serious understanding of what wavelet analysis means without a deep knowledge of the corresponding operator theory.
—Yves Meyer

PREREQUISITES: Having seen a few approximation problems; spectrum; tensor product of matrices; unitary matrices; Hilbert space; a rough idea about recursive algorithms (visual representations); large matrices; a curiosity about some cute ideas from engineering.

Prelude

In our earlier discussion of "wavelet-like" bases in Hilbert space $\mathcal{H}$, we stressed the geometric point of view, which begins with a subspace V_0 and two operations. For standard wavelets in one variable, $\mathcal{H}$ will be the Hilbert space $L^2(\mathbb{R})$, and a suitable "resolution subspace" V_0 will be chosen and assumed invariant under translation by the group of integers $\mathbb{Z}$. In addition, it will be required that V_0 be invariant under some definite scaling operator, for example under "stretching" $f \to f(x/2)$. Thirdly, the traditional multiresolution (MRA) approach to $L^2(\mathbb{R})$-wavelets demands that the chosen subspace V_0 be singly generated, i.e., generated by a single function φ, the father function, i.e., the normalized L^2-function which solves the scaling identity (see (1.3.1) in Chapter 1). As is known, it turns out that these demands for a subspace V_0 are rather stringent.

Hence in this and the next chapter, we shall generalize the familiar MRA picture in two ways. First, we shall allow V_0 to be multiply generated: more than one father function. When V_0 is multiply generated, it is said to give a generalized multiresolution analysis (GMRA). Secondly, we shall extend the MRA idea to other Hilbert spaces than $L^2(\mathbb{R})$ or $L^2(\mathbb{R}^d)$.

We saw in Chapter 4 that the idea of a "multiresolution" applies to fractals. An inherent feature about fractals X is a scaling law. Intuitively a fractal X is a "fernlike" geometric object which looks the same when a natural "scale" is varied, i.e., the same at small scales and at large scales. The notion of scaling can take many forms: it can be arithmetic (e.g., dyadic scaling, N-adic scaling, or matrix scaling), or geometric (e.g., iterated composition of rational functions of one complex variable), or symbolic such as is employed in encoding of discrete automata-dynamics by shifts or by substitution in a finite alphabet.

We will see that the geometric feature of a traditional wavelet "multiresolution" is very adaptable. If we think of a multiresolution as a selection of a distinguished subspace V_0 in a "fractal" or symbolic Hilbert space $\mathcal{H}$, then it turns out that computational algorithms from wavelet theory carry over. But in these more non-traditional variants of "multiresolutions," perhaps the analogue of the familiar group of $\mathbb{Z}$-translations in the Hilbert space $L^2(\mathbb{R})$ is not immediately transparent. Yet it is well known, and recalled in (7.1.4) below, that the group of $\mathbb{Z}$-translations in the Hilbert space $L^2(\mathbb{R})$ is Fourier equivalent to multiplication in $L^2(\mathbb{R})$ by the Fourier frequencies $e^{i2\pi kx}$. (Note that the spectral transform in (7.1.4) below is more general. Specifically, the transform for a generalized multiresolution (GMRA) should be thought of as an extension of the basic Fourier equivalence principle!) And it turns out that all the three non-traditional variants of "multiresolutions" do have abelian algebras of *multiplication* operators which leave invariant suitable resolution subspaces V_0.

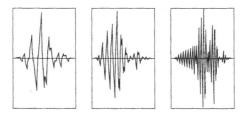

7.1 Translations and the spectral theorem

Special to this chapter is a set of sequential figures and illustrations: Figures 7.1, 7.2, and 7.3 (decision-tree view, pp. 111–113), and Figures 7.4 and 7.5 (graphs of two classes of wavelet packets, pp. 118–121); the sequence from Figure 7.6 to 7.15 (subspace analysis, pp. 123–128, 132–133); and Figure 7.16 (visual exhibit of the sequential cascade algorithm, here applied to the two Daubechies wavelet functions φ and ψ, p. 134.)

Indeed, the central theme in the whole book is captured in the figures here in Chapter 7. We resume specific and detailed citation of these figures by number later in Chapter 7.

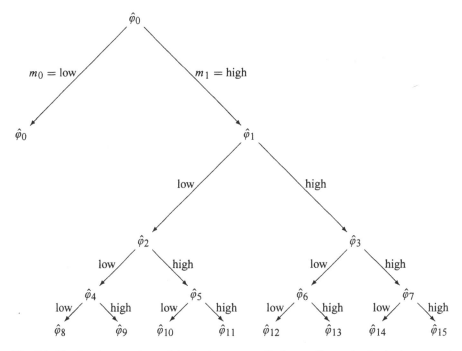

Fig. 7.1. The Fourier transform of the basis sequence (before scaling and selection) generated from the scaling function φ_0, using the full combinatorial tree.

The first block of figures, i.e., Figures 7.1, 7.2, and 7.3, illustrate how the pyramid algorithm from Chapter 1 takes shape as a decision tree. While in our present applications we emphasize the wavelet context for all of this, in fact it is the same underlying idea which is used in our fractal constructions from Chapters 3 and 4. And the same idea may be used even more generally in a variety of data structures which happen to come equipped with some inherent notion of scaling and similarity, such as is known to be the case for digital data clouds, for graphs and for certain manifolds.

For a number of applications, it is convenient to have a matrix variant of the measures P_x constructed in Chapter 2; see especially (2.4.6). For the wavelet applications, this is relevant when the scaling identity, or refinement equation, (1.3.1) does not have solutions that are scalar-valued $L^2(\mathbb{R})$-functions. For multiwavelets this happens when the starting resolution subspace $V_0 \subset L^2(\mathbb{R})$ has multiplicity. By this, we mean that the representation of $\mathbb{Z}$ by translation in V_0 is not cyclic. Equivalently, setting

$$T_k f(x) = f(x-k), \qquad f \in V_0, \ x \in \mathbb{R}, \ k \in \mathbb{Z}, \tag{7.1.1}$$

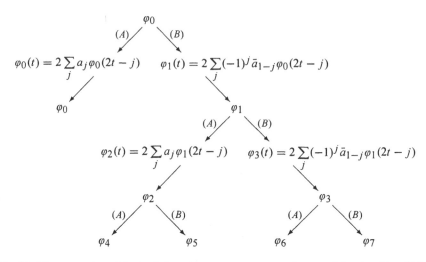

Fig. 7.2. The generation of the basis functions φ_0, φ_1, φ_2, ... by use of the algorithm (7.5.5) initiated with $\varphi_0 = \varphi$ such that $\varphi(t) = 2 \sum_j a_j \varphi(2t - j)$, the functional equation by which, in the first (A) branch, φ_0 "re-generates" itself.

we get a spectral representation in the following form: there is an isometric isomorphism

$$J: V_0 \to L^2(S_1) \oplus L^2(S_2) \oplus \cdots \qquad (7.1.2)$$

such that

$$\cdots S_{j+1} \subset S_j \subset \cdots \subset S_2 \subset S_1 \subset [0, 1] \qquad (7.1.3)$$

and

$$J T_k f = e^{i 2\pi k \cdot} J f, \qquad k \in \mathbb{Z}, \ f \in V_0. \qquad (7.1.4)$$

To see this, note that, by the spectral theorem, there is a projection-valued measure

$$p: [0, 1] \to \text{projections of } L^2(\mathbb{R}) \qquad (7.1.5)$$

such that

$$T_k f = \int_0^1 e^{i 2\pi k \lambda} \, dp(\lambda) \, f, \qquad k \in \mathbb{Z}, \ f \in V_0. \qquad (7.1.6)$$

To get the sets S_j, $j = 1, 2, \ldots$, take

$$S_j := \{ \lambda \in [0, 1] \mid \dim p(\lambda) \geq j \}. \qquad (7.1.7)$$

The reader is referred to [BaMe99], [BaMM99], [BaCM02], and [BaJMP04].

These applications motivate two generalizations of the more traditional wavelet setup, see, e.g., [Dau92]: first, the wavelet filters and the functions W (see Chapter 1 above) are not continuous, and second, they are matrix-valued.

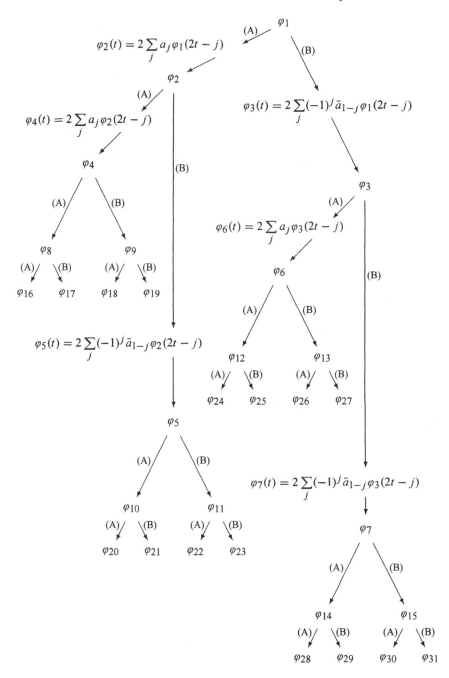

Fig. 7.3. The generation of the basis functions φ_1, φ_2, φ_3, $\ldots$ by use of the algorithm (7.5.5) initiated with $\varphi_1 = \psi$.

7.2 Multiwavelets and generalized multiresolution analysis (GMRA)

We now outline the generalizations of the multiresolutions from Chapter 1 which are entailed by the case of multiply generated resolution subspaces $V_0 \subset L^2(\mathbb{R})$. The multiplicity function μ is identically $\equiv 1$ for the cases covered by (1.3.1). For the general case, we consider $\varphi: \mathbb{R} \to \mathcal{H}$ for some Hilbert space $\mathcal{H}$, and we are interested in solutions $\varphi \in L^2(\mathbb{R})$. In this interpretation, the coefficients a_k from (1.3.1) are operators $a_k: \mathcal{H} \to \mathcal{H}$, and the filter function (1.3.2) is operator-valued. Its Fourier-transformed variant (1.3.4) must also be interpreted in this context: $\hat{\varphi}: \mathbb{R} \to \mathcal{H}$, $m(x): \mathcal{H} \to \mathcal{H}$, and

$$\hat{\varphi}(x) = m\left(\frac{x}{N}\right) \hat{\varphi}\left(\frac{x}{N}\right) \tag{7.2.1}$$

is an identity for vectors in $\mathcal{H}$. Since

$$\int_{\mathbb{R}} \|\varphi(t)\|_{\mathcal{H}}^2 \, dt = \int_{\mathbb{R}} \|\hat{\varphi}(x)\|_{\mathcal{H}}^2 \, dx,$$

we need a product formula for $\|\hat{\varphi}(x)\|_{\mathcal{H}}^2$.

Iteration of (7.2.1) yields

$$\|\hat{\varphi}(x)\|_{\mathcal{H}}^2 = \left\langle \hat{\varphi}\left(\frac{x}{N^n}\right) \,\middle|\, W_n(x)\, \hat{\varphi}\left(\frac{x}{N^n}\right) \right\rangle,$$

where

$$W_n(x) := m\left(\frac{x}{N^n}\right)^* \cdots m\left(\frac{x}{N}\right)^* m\left(\frac{x}{N}\right) \cdots m\left(\frac{x}{N^n}\right). \tag{7.2.2}$$

The function m is assumed to satisfy the normalization condition

$$\sum_{\sigma(y)=x} m(y)\, m(y)^* = \mathbb{1}_{\mathcal{H}}, \qquad x \in X. \tag{7.2.3}$$

To state our result, we first provide the setting for our operator-valued variant of Lemma 2.4.1.

7.3 Operator-coefficients

Definitions 7.3.1. (a) Let $\mathcal{H}$ be a complex Hilbert space. An operator T in $\mathcal{H}$ is said to be positive (alias semidefinite) if $\langle u \mid Tu \rangle \geq 0$ for all $u \in \mathcal{H}$. The inner product in $\mathcal{H}$ is denoted $\langle \cdot \mid \cdot \rangle$, and is assumed linear in the second variable. If $(\Omega, \mathcal{B}_\Omega)$ is a probability space, we say that a function

$$P: \mathcal{B}_\Omega \to \text{Pos}(\mathcal{H})$$

is an operator-valued measure if:

(i) $P(\cdot)$ is σ-additive,

(ii) $0 \le P(A) \le \mathbb{1}_{\mathcal{H}}$, or equivalently

$$0 \le \langle u \mid P(A) u \rangle \le \|u\|^2, \qquad u \in \mathcal{H}, \ A \in \mathcal{B}_\Omega,$$

and

(iii) $P(\Omega) = I_{\mathcal{H}}$.

(b) Let $(X, \mathcal{B})$ be a measure space, and let $W: X \to \mathrm{Pos}(\mathcal{H})$ be a measurable function, i.e., for every $u \in \mathcal{H}$, $x \mapsto \langle u \mid W(x) u \rangle$ is measurable, and

$$0 \le \langle u \mid W(x) u \rangle \le \|u\|^2. \tag{7.3.1}$$

Let $\sigma: X \to X$ be an N-to-1 measurable mapping, with measurable inverse branches $\tau_0, \ldots, \tau_{N-1}$. Suppose

$$\sum_{i=1}^{N-1} W \circ \tau_i = \mathbb{1}_{\mathcal{H}}. \tag{7.3.2}$$

We then define a corresponding transfer operator

$$R_W f(x) = \sum_{y \in X, \, \sigma(y) = x} W(y) f(y) \tag{7.3.3}$$

acting on $L^\infty(X, \mathcal{H})$, i.e., bounded measurable functions $f: X \to \mathcal{H}$.

With these definitions, we now outline how the main results in Chapter 2 carry over. We state them with only sketches of proof, as the modifications in Chapter 2 that are required are mainly technical. The main added issue is the non-commutativity, so when we write products like

$$W\left(\sigma^{n-1} y\right) W\left(\sigma^{n-2} y\right) \cdots W(\sigma y) W(y), \tag{7.3.4}$$

then we mean products of operators acting on $\mathcal{H}$.

7.4 Operator-valued measures

Our next result, Lemma 7.4.1, is an operator-valued variant of the scalar case above, in the form of Lemma 2.4.1. In the operator-valued context, we get again the existence and uniqueness of the measures P_x.

Lemma 7.4.1. *Let* X, σ, N, $\tau_0, \ldots, \tau_{N-1}$, $\mathcal{H}$, *and* W *be as described above.*

(a) *Then, for every* $x \in X$, *there is a unique positive operator-valued Radon probability measure* P_x *on* $\Omega = \{0, 1, \ldots, N-1\}^{\mathbb{N}}$ *such that*

$$P_x(A(i_1, \ldots, i_n)) = W(\tau_{i_1} x) W(\tau_{i_2} \tau_{i_1} x) \cdots W(\tau_{i_n} \cdots \tau_{i_1} x), \tag{7.4.1}$$

where $A(i_1, \ldots, i_n)$ *denotes a cylinder set as defined in (2.3.5).*

(b) *Let the assumptions be as in* (a), *but consider instead the operator function*

$$W_n (i_1, \ldots, i_n; x)$$
$$= m \left(\tau_{i_n} \cdots \tau_{i_1} x \right)^* \cdots m \left(\tau_{i_1} x \right)^* m \left(\tau_{i_1} x \right) \cdots m \left(\tau_{i_n} \cdots \tau_{i_1} x \right),$$

with m satisfying (7.2.3). *Then, for every* $x \in X$, *there is a unique Radon measure* P_x *on* Ω *such that*

$$P_x (A (i_1, \ldots, i_n)) = W_n (i_1, \ldots, i_n; x).$$

Proof sketch. For each $n \in \mathbb{N}$, consider functions $f: \Omega \to \mathcal{H}$ such that $f(\omega) = f(\omega_1, \ldots, \omega_n)$, and define

$$P_x^{(n)} [f] = \sum_{(\omega_1, \ldots, \omega_n) \in \mathbb{Z}_N^n} W \left(\tau_{\omega_1} x \right) \cdots W \left(\tau_{\omega_n} \cdots \tau_{\omega_1} x \right) f (\omega_1, \ldots, \omega_n). \quad (7.4.2)$$

As in Chapter 2, we check that $P_x^{(n+1)} [f] = P_x^{(n)} [f]$. Using this, the conclusion in Lemma 7.4.1 may be obtained as in Chapter 2, *mutatis mutandis.*   □

We now list some of the other conclusions which carry over.

Theorem 7.4.2. *Let the setting be as described in the lemma, and let* $(P_x)_{x \in X}$ *be the corresponding operator-valued process. Then* (i)–(v) *below hold.*

(i) *The infinite product*

$$\prod_{n=1}^{\infty} W \left(\tau_0^n (x) \right) =: F(x) \quad (7.4.3)$$

exists if and only if $P_x (\{0\}) > 0$, *where* $0 = \underset{\infty \text{ string of zeroes}}{(0, 0, 0, \ldots)} \in \Omega$. *The condition is that the operator* $P_x (\{0\})$ *has zero kernel.*

(ii) *The function*

$$h(x) = P_x (\mathbb{N}_0), \qquad x \in X, \quad (7.4.4)$$

solves the eigenvalue problem

$$R_W h = h. \quad (7.4.5)$$

(iii) *As before,* $P_x (\cdot)$ *extends from* $\mathbb{N}_0$ *to* $\mathbb{Z}$, *according to formula* (1.4.5).

(iv) *Returning to the multiwavelet case of* (7.1.1)–(7.1.7), *let* σ, τ_0, $\ldots$, τ_{N-1} *be given as in* (5.4.9). *Choose* φ_1, φ_2, $\ldots$ *in* V_0 *such that*

$$\sum_{k \in \mathbb{Z}} \overline{\hat{\varphi}_i (x+k)} \hat{\varphi}_j (x+k) = \delta_{i,j} \chi_{S_i}. \quad (7.4.6)$$

Then

$$h(x) = P_x(\mathbb{Z}) = \begin{pmatrix} \chi_{S_1} & 0 & \cdots \\ 0 & \chi_{S_2} & \cdots \\ \vdots & \vdots & \ddots \end{pmatrix}$$

solves (7.4.5). In this case the matrix function $x \mapsto W(x)$ is as described in [BaJMP04].

(v) *In the setting of (iv), the multiplicity function μ of (7.1.7) is*

$$\mu(x) = \sum_i \sum_{k \in \mathbb{Z}} |\hat{\varphi}_i(x+k)|^2, \tag{7.4.7}$$

and the projection $Q(x)$ onto the range subspace of

$$JV_0 = \{(\hat{f}(\cdot + k))_{k \in \mathbb{Z}} \mid f \in V_0\} \tag{7.4.8}$$

is

$$Q_{k,l}(x) = \sum_i \overline{\hat{\varphi}_i(x+l)}\,\hat{\varphi}_i(x+k). \tag{7.4.9}$$

Specifically, the range of $Q(x)$ is the subspace

$$\left\{(\hat{f}(x+k))_{k \in \mathbb{Z}} \in \ell^2 \mid f \in V_0\right\},$$

and $\mu(x)$ is the dimension of this subspace.

Our next result is motivated by the theory of wavelet packets of Coifman et al.; see [CoMW95], [CoWi93], [Wic93], and the book [Wic94] by Wickerhauser.

Lemma 7.4.3. *Let X, σ, N, τ_0, ..., τ_{N-1}, $\mathcal{H}$, and $(W_i)_{0 \le i < N}$ be given satisfying the conditions in Definitions 7.3.1, and (7.4.10).*

We continue with the setup from Definitions 7.3.1, but with the following addition: instead of a single operator function

$$W : X \to \mathrm{Pos}(\mathcal{H}),$$

we consider a family

$$W_i : X \to \mathrm{Pos}(\mathcal{H}), \qquad i = 0, 1, \ldots, N-1,$$

each one satisfying (7.3.2), i.e., we assume that

$$\sum_{y \in X,\, \sigma(y)=x} W_i(y) = \mathbb{1}_{\mathcal{H}}, \qquad i = 0, 1, \ldots, N-1, \ x \in X. \tag{7.4.10}$$

Then for every $x \in X$, there is a unique positive operator-valued Radon probability measure P_x on $\mathbb{N}_0 \times \Omega$ such that

$$P_x(\{(\omega, \zeta) \in \mathbb{N}_0 \times \Omega \mid \omega_1 = i_1, \ \ldots, \ \omega_n = i_n; \ \zeta_1 = j_1, \ \ldots, \ \zeta_n = j_n\})$$
$$= W_{i_1}(\tau_{j_1}x)\, W_{i_2}(\tau_{j_2}\tau_{j_1}x) \cdots W_{i_n}(\tau_{j_n}\cdots\tau_{j_1}x). \tag{7.4.11}$$

As usual, we are identifying $\mathbb{N}_0$ with a subset of Ω.

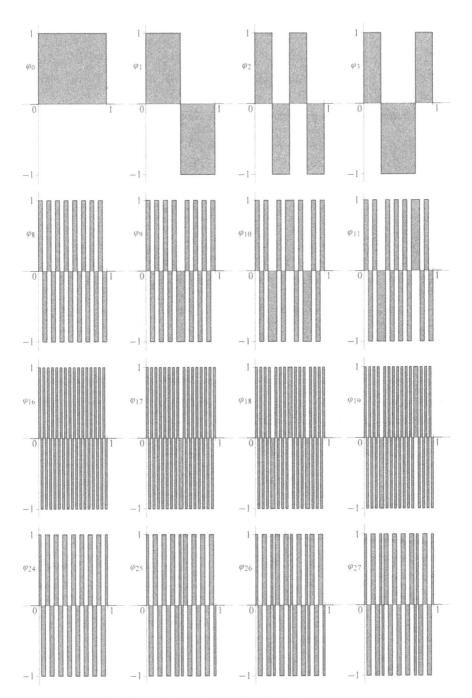

Fig. 7.4. The first thirty-two functions in the sequence φ_n

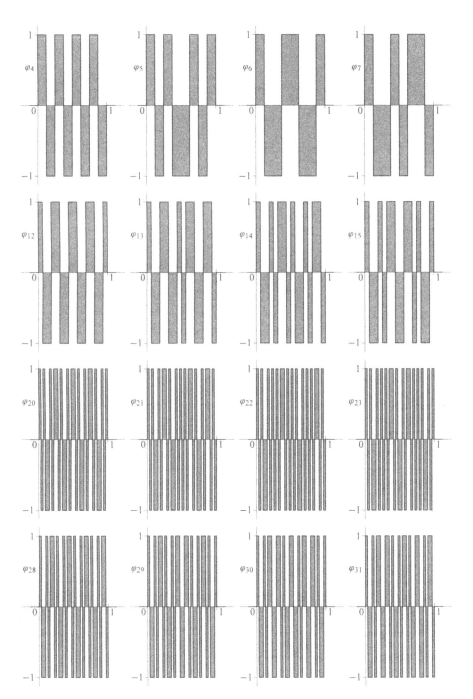

in the case of the Haar wavelet construction.

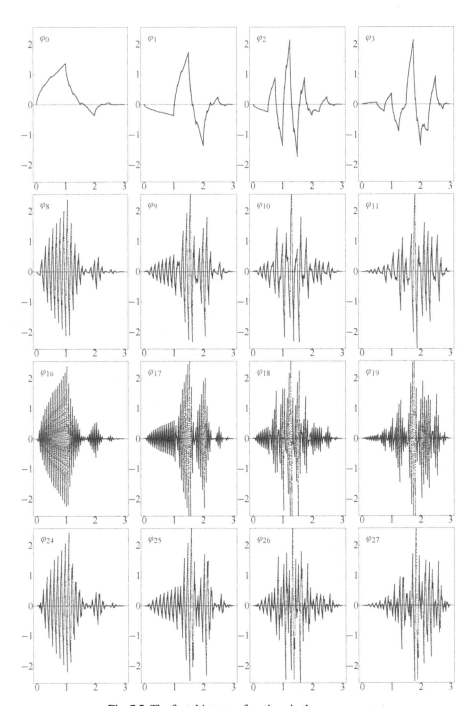

Fig. 7.5. The first thirty-two functions in the sequence φ_n

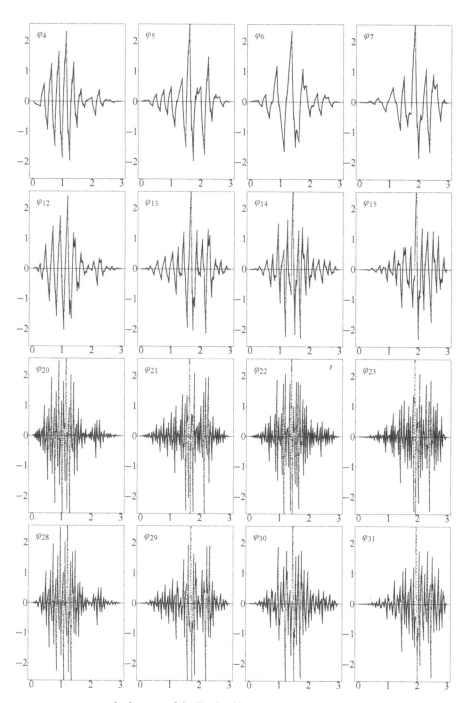

in the case of the Daubechies wavelet construction.

Proof sketch. For each $n \in \mathbb{N}$, consider functions $f : \mathbb{N}_0 \times \Omega \to \mathcal{H}$ such that $f(\omega, \xi) = f(\omega_1, \ldots, \omega_n; \xi_1, \ldots, \xi_n)$. Define

$$P_x^{(n)}[f] = \sum_{(\omega_1, \ldots, \omega_n)} \sum_{(\xi_1, \ldots, \xi_n)} W_{\omega_1}(\tau_{\xi_1} x) W_{\omega_2}(\tau_{\xi_2} \tau_{\xi_1} x) \cdots$$

$$\cdots W_{\omega_n}(\tau_{\xi_n} \cdots \tau_{\xi_1} x) f(\omega_1, \ldots, \omega_n; \xi_1, \ldots, \xi_n), \quad (7.4.12)$$

and check that

$$P_x^{(n+1)}[f] = P_x^{(n)}[f]. \tag{7.4.13}$$

To see this, note that by taking n sufficiently large, we may assume that ω has the form $\omega = \omega(k)$ for some $k \in \mathbb{N}_0$, i.e., that

$$\omega(k) = (\omega_1, \ldots, \omega_n, \underbrace{0, 0, 0, \ldots}_{\infty \text{ string of zeroes}}),$$

where

$$k = \omega_1 + \omega_2 N + \cdots + \omega_n N^{n-1}. \tag{7.4.14}$$

Using (7.4.12), we then get

$$P_x^{(n+1)}[f] = \sum_{(\omega_1, \ldots, \omega_n)} \sum_{(\xi_1, \ldots, \xi_n)} W_{\omega_1}(\tau_{\xi_1} x) W_{\omega_2}(\tau_{\xi_2} \tau_{\xi_1} x) \cdots$$

$$\cdots W_{\omega_n}(\tau_{\xi_n} \cdots \tau_{\xi_1} x) \left[\sum_{\xi_{n+1}} W_0(\tau_{\xi_{n+1}} \tau_{\xi_n} \cdots \tau_{\xi_1} x) \right] f(\omega_1, \ldots, \omega_n; \xi_1, \ldots, \xi_n).$$

But note that $\sum_{\xi_{n+1}} W_0(\tau_{\xi_{n+1}} \cdots) = \mathbb{1}_{\mathcal{H}}$ by (7.4.10), so the desired consistency relation (7.4.13) follows. Now the last step, extending the consistent family $\left(P_x^{(n)} \right)_{n \in \mathbb{N}}$ to a Radon measure on $\mathbb{N}_0 \times \Omega$, follows the reasoning used earlier in Lemmas 7.4.1 and 2.4.1 above. $\square$

Remark 7.4.4. The measures P_x in Lemma 7.4.3 are typically not probability measures. See Proposition 7.5.2 for details.

7.5 Wavelet packets

Remark 7.5.1. In the remaining chapters, we illustrate our presentation of wavelets and wavelet packets with graphics series, both in Chapters 7 and 9. We begin by recalling the wavelet filters and the corresponding pyramid algorithm which is used in the construction of a sequence of wavelet packet functions $\varphi_0, \varphi_1, \varphi_2, \ldots$ Starting with the Daubechies wavelet filter, Figure 7.5 illustrates the first 32 functions in the

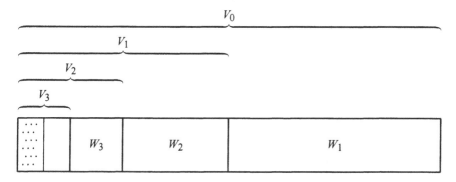

Fig. 7.6. A decreasing family of resolution subspaces $V_0 \supset V_1 \supset V_2 \supset \cdots$, and corresponding detail spaces $W_1, W_2, \ldots$. Dyadic wavelets. $V_n = V_{n+1} + W_{n+1}, n = 0, 1, \ldots$.

sequence. As is expected from the theory, one observes the time-frequency behavior which makes the wavelet packets especially adaptable to a given data set, or a given image (in the case of two variables).

The next seven figures serve to illustrate the multifaceted features of pyramid algorithms, and to stress the distinction between the algorithmic paths of the standard wavelet construction and the choices going into the selection of a function in the library of a wavelet packet construction.

The standard dyadic case begins with formulas (1.3.18) and (1.3.19), while the N-adic case uses (1.3.1) instead of (1.3.18), but then (1.3.19) is replaced by $N - 1$ identities corresponding to the $N - 1$ higher-frequency subbands, and the associated subband-filter functions $m_1, m_2, \ldots, m_{N-1}$, as illustrated in Figures 7.9 and 7.10. The distinction between the dyadic case, i.e., $N = 2$, versus the case of more than two subbands in the encoding of subspaces, is illustrated in Figure 7.10 in the special case of $N = 4$.

Although subband filters were first used in signal processing, see Figure 7.7, they have now been adapted to the wavelet algorithm as outlined in Figures 7.8, 7.9, and 7.10. The coefficients in the two filter functions m_0 and m_1 of (7.5.1) and (7.5.2) are at the same time the masking coefficients for the first two wavelet functions, the father function $\varphi = \varphi_0$ and the mother function $\psi = \varphi_1$. While for the wavelet algorithm, the same dyadic choice is made in each scaling/subdivision step, in contrast the wavelet packet algorithm is encoded by a string of separate dyadic choices, as is illustrated in Figures 7.11 and 7.12, and in the theory part of this section; see especially formulas (7.5.5)(A)–(B), as well as Figure 7.5 (pp. 120–121). The Mathematica program code for the graphics in Figure 7.5 is included in the "References and remarks" section at the end of this chapter.

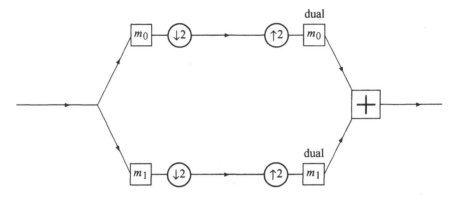

Fig. 7.7. Subband filtering for dyadic wavelets: m_0 = low-pass filter, m_1 = high-pass filter, ⓓ down-sampling, ⓤ up-sampling. The figure refers to input (from left) and output (to the right) of signals from standard signal processing; for example, of speech signals. From the left, we start with (signal) input. The signal is then split into two frequency bands with two filters m_0 and m_1. The first filter, m_0, passes low frequencies, and the second, m_1, passes high. The split into frequency bands is called "analysis." We get two signal strands which are now each followed by signal down-sampling. As we move right, the two bands are then up-sampled. The processed signal bands then pass dual filters, and are finally merged again with + into an output signal. "Perfect reconstruction" means that the output signal to the right is matched up perfectly with the input from the left. From engineering, we know that it *is* possible to find filters m_0 and m_1 that achieve perfect reconstruction; i.e., recovering the input signal by synthesis of the bands. Magically, and by hindsight, these filter systems serve at the same time to give us orthogonal wavelets, subject to a technical condition discussed in Chapter 5. (There can be more than two frequency bands, and we refer to Section 7.6 for the general case.)

The tiling aspect of the fundamental subdivision/wavelet packet issue is perhaps especially clear for Haar's construction as illustrated in the corresponding series of pictures in Figure 7.4 (pp. 118–119). Different geometric and algorithmic formulas are further illustrated in other forms in the pictures and formulas collected in Figure 7.6 (subspaces), Figure 7.7 (the engineering approach to subbands), Figures 7.8–7.9 (subbands and matrix operations), Figures 7.10–7.11 (a particular path in the wavelet-packet tree), and Figure 7.13 which spells out the relation between the subspaces and the associated matrix operations. The same issues are illustrated with the representations from Section 7.6 below. Figure 7.16 (p. 134) outlines the subdivision algorithm which goes into the graphics, creating a step-by-step design of both the father function φ and the mother function ψ for the Daubechies wavelet. The pair of formulas behind Figure 7.16 are special cases of (1.3.1), (d) in Example 1.3.3, (1.3.19) from Chapter 1, as well as (7.5.1)–(7.5.2), and (7.6.6)–(7.6.7) in the present

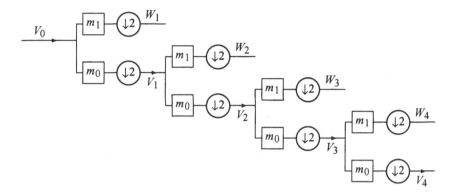

Fig. 7.8. Wavelet algorithm in the dyadic case: $V_n = V_{n+1} + W_{n+1}$, $n = 0, 1, \ldots$.

chapter. The general use of the pyramid is discussed and illustrated further in Figures 8.1 and 8.2 in the next chapter (pp. 159–161).

The corresponding algorithms and figures are created by Brian Treadway in Mathematica. The series of pictures to follow have been created so as to offer visual illustrations of some of the basic wavelet algorithms, both the father function/mother function algorithms, and the related pyramid algorithms used in the creation of wavelet packets. Following the progressions in the picture series, the reader will be able to follow visually the corresponding algorithmic steps, see for example the (A) and (B) parts of equations (7.5.5) and (7.5.6).

Caution: Readers comparing the present figures and definitions with other related ones in the literature, for example in [BrJo02b], will notice some differences in normalization conventions: For example, here we normalize so that the low-pass property reads $|m(\,\cdot\,)|^2 = 1$ at frequency zero. This is to stress the probabilistic meaning of the term $|m(\,\cdot\,)|^2$ for low-pass. The meaning of "low-pass filter" from signal processing: The signals with low frequency will move through the eye of the low-pass filter with high probability, while they will be essentially blocked by the high-pass filters.

Besides the normalization convention, there is another difference between (2.5.25) in [BrJo02b] and our present equation (7.5.5)(B): The index on a (or $\bar{a}$) is $5 - k$ in [BrJo02b], while it is $1 - k$ (actually $1 - j$) here.

This shifts the support interval for the corresponding mother function by an integer. To keep Daubechies' scaling function φ_0, and the wavelet packet series φ_1, φ_2, ... confined to the interval $[\,0, 3\,]$, we need the index to be $3 - k$.

This does not affect the computation, but it changes the tick marks on the horizontal axes of the final figure plots. When comparing the present pictures with others,

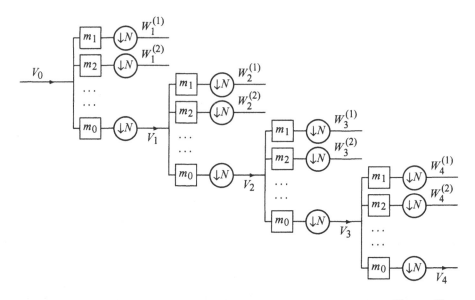

Fig. 7.9. Wavelet algorithm in the N-adic case: $V_{n-1} = V_n + W_n$, $W_n = W_n^{(1)} + W_n^{(2)} + \cdots + W_n^{(N-1)}$, $n = 1, 2, \ldots$. Multiple subbands $m_1, \ldots, m_{N-1}$.

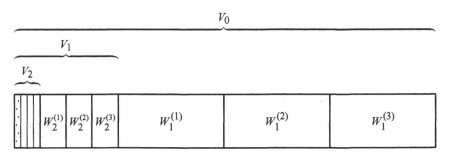

Fig. 7.10. A decreasing family of resolution subspaces $V_0 \supset V_1 \supset V_2 \supset \cdots$, N-adic case, $N = 4$, $V_{n-1} = V_n + W_n$, $W_n = W_n^{(1)} + W_n^{(2)} + W_n^{(3)}$, $n = 1, 2, \ldots$.

the reader should allow for translation on the x-axis by integer amounts for the function φ_1 ($= \psi$); note that there is an integer translation in the frame setup. And for the higher wavelet packets, the offset appears to be by non-integral amounts such as $1/2, 1/4, 1/8$, etc.

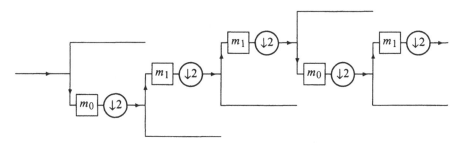

Fig. 7.11. A selection of a dyadic wavelet packet. (An example of a path in a pyramid!)

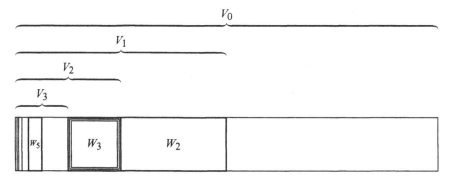

Fig. 7.12. Illustration of a path in the pyramid: $m_0 \to m_1 \to m_1 \to m_0 \to m_1 \to$, or $V_0 \to V_1 \to W_2 \to W_3 \to V_3 \to W_5$.

Similarly, the normalization of m mentioned above will not affect the computation of φ_n provided that a suitable factor appears in (7.5.5): in (7.5.5)(A), for example, φ_0 is given as a convolution of itself with the row of a's, multiplied by the initial factor, so the magnitude of that initial factor is determined by a sum rule.

As we have our "normalization" in (7.5.5), the Haar case, i.e., Example 1.3.3(a), is $a_0 = a_1 = 1/2$, and the other a_i's zero. As noted above, our "normalization" here is a little different from [BrJo02b].

Here we have $\sum a_i = 1$; see (7.6.6).

The a_i numbers for the Daubechies wavelet are given in Example 1.3.3(d), and they are $a_0, \ldots, a_3$ for the non-zero ones, starting with $a_0 = (1 + \sqrt{3})/8$, etc.; see (7.6.6). Remember $\sum a_i = 1$ from our choice (1.3.14).

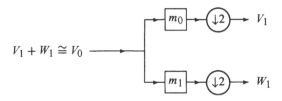

$$V_1 + W_1 \cong V_0$$

Matrix multiplications:

$$\mathbf{v}_k^1 = \sum_j a_{j-2k} \mathbf{v}_j^0 \quad \text{and} \quad \mathbf{w}_k^1 = \sum_j b_{j-2k} \mathbf{v}_j^0$$

$$
\begin{bmatrix}
\mid \\
\mathbf{v}^1 \\
\mid \\
\mid \\
\mathbf{w}^1 \\
\mid
\end{bmatrix}
=
\begin{bmatrix}
a_0 & a_1 & a_2 & a_3 & 0 & 0 & 0 & 0 \\
0 & 0 & a_0 & a_1 & a_2 & a_3 & 0 & 0 \\
0 & 0 & 0 & 0 & a_0 & a_1 & a_2 & a_3 \\
a_2 & a_3 & 0 & 0 & 0 & 0 & a_0 & a_1 \\
b_0 & b_1 & b_2 & b_3 & 0 & 0 & 0 & 0 \\
0 & 0 & b_0 & b_1 & b_2 & b_3 & 0 & 0 \\
0 & 0 & 0 & 0 & b_0 & b_1 & b_2 & b_3 \\
b_2 & b_3 & 0 & 0 & 0 & 0 & b_0 & b_1
\end{bmatrix}
\begin{bmatrix}
\mid \\
\mid \\
\mathbf{v}^0 \\
\mid \\
\mid
\end{bmatrix}
$$

Fig. 7.13. Combined filter/down-sampling in matrix form.

The algorithm in (7.5.5) is simple. Here are the steps. The two first φ_i functions are familiar: $\varphi_0 = \varphi$ (father function), $\varphi_1 = \psi$ (mother function), and we have them in Fig. 1.2(a), the Haar case (p. 13), and Fig. 7.16, the Daubechies case (d) (p. 134).

The general case: List the numbers $a_0, a_1, \ldots,$ up to the last non-zero number. Then do the first step (A) in (7.5.5) to get from φ_1 to φ_2.

The second step (B) in (7.5.5) amounts to running the numbers a_i in reverse, and alternating the signs; see (7.6.7). The second step gets us from φ_1 to φ_3.

Now back to the first step in (7.5.5), and we get from φ_2 to φ_4. Then return back to the second step; this time applied to φ_2, and we get φ_5.

And so on: All the while, walking zig-zag through the algorithm; the first step takes us from φ_k to φ_{2k}, and the second step from φ_k to φ_{2k+1} (see Figures 7.2 and 7.3, pp. 112–113).

After having found the first two, φ_0 and φ_1, in the usual way, one procedure for doing all the steps in succession is simply making a string of zig-zag steps as follows:

(A): $1 \to 2$; (B): $1 \to 3$; (A): $2 \to 4$; (B): $2 \to 5$;

(A): $3 \to 6$; (B): $3 \to 7$; (A): $4 \to 8$; (B): $4 \to 9$; etc.

This zig-zag procedure is done "wholesale" in the Mathematica program: instead of $1 \to 2, 1 \to 3, 2 \to 4, 2 \to 5$, etc., it is expressed (equivalently) in terms of lists:

$$1 \to \{2, 3\} \to \{\{4, 5\}, \{6, 7\}\} \to \{\{\{8, 9\}, \{10, 11\}\}, \{\{12, 13\}, \{14, 15\}\}\},$$

etc., with each arrow representing one instance of the "map" operation. The nested sublists are "flattened" to a single list only in the final step.

In fact, the implementation starting with φ_0 gives the whole series from 0 at each stage because φ_0 regenerates itself in step (A):

$$0 \to \{0, 1\} \to \{\{0, 1\}, \{2, 3\}\} \to \{\{\{0, 1\}, \{2, 3\}\}, \{\{4, 5\}, \{6, 7\}\}\} \to \text{etc.}$$

We now turn to one of the uses of Lemma 7.4.3 in the theory of wavelet packets. To make the ideas more transparent, we state the result only in the special case when $N = 2$, and where the $\mathbb{Z}$-translation-invariant subspace V_0 is generated by a single function $\varphi_0 = \varphi$ in $L^2(\mathbb{R})$ which is known to satisfy (1.3.1), or equivalently (1.3.4). Set

$$m_0(x) = \sum_k a_k e^{-i2\pi kx}, \tag{7.5.1}$$

$$m_1(x) = \sum_k (-1)^k \bar{a}_{1-k} e^{-i2\pi kx}, \tag{7.5.2}$$

and

$$M_i = |m_i|^2, \qquad i = 0, 1. \tag{7.5.3}$$

The orthogonality conditions state that

the matrix $\begin{pmatrix} m_0(x) & m_0\left(x + \frac{1}{2}\right) \\ m_1(x) & m_1\left(x + \frac{1}{2}\right) \end{pmatrix}$ is unitary for $x \in \mathbb{R}$. $\tag{7.5.4}$

The two recursive formulas (7.5.5)(A)–(B) form the basis for the so-called *pyramid algorithm*, i.e., the building basis functions in algorithmic steps following paths in a combinatorial tree, or algorithm. This is illustrated graphically both with the series of figures, Figures 7.1–7.3 (pp. 111–113) and 7.14–7.15 (pp. 132–133), and especially the pair Figures 7.2 and 7.3 (pp. 112–113). It is further illustrated with the figures which follow in the rest of this chapter, as well as the next.

Proposition 7.5.2. *Let the functions $\varphi_0, \varphi_1, \varphi_2, \ldots$ be defined by*

$$\begin{cases} \text{(A)} & \varphi_{2k}(t) = 2\sum_{j \in \mathbb{Z}} a_j \varphi_k(2t - j), \\ \\ \text{(B)} & \varphi_{2k+1}(t) = 2\sum_{j \in \mathbb{Z}} (-1)^j \bar{a}_{1-j} \varphi_k(2t - j), \end{cases} \tag{7.5.5}$$

or equivalently by

$$\begin{cases} \text{(A)} & \hat{\varphi}_{2k}(x) = m_0\left(\frac{x}{2}\right)\hat{\varphi}_k\left(\frac{x}{2}\right), \\ \text{(B)} & \hat{\varphi}_{2k+1}(x) = m_1\left(\frac{x}{2}\right)\hat{\varphi}_k\left(\frac{x}{2}\right). \end{cases} \quad (7.5.6)$$

Suppose $k = i_1 + i_2 2 + \cdots + i_n 2^{n-1}$. *Then*

$$\hat{\varphi}_k(x) = m_{i_1}\left(\frac{x}{2}\right)m_{i_2}\left(\frac{x}{2^2}\right)\cdots m_{i_n}\left(\frac{x}{2^n}\right)\hat{\varphi}_0\left(\frac{x}{2^n}\right) \quad (7.5.7)$$

satisfies

$$\sum_{j\in\mathbb{Z}}\sum_{k=0}^{\infty}|\langle \varphi_k(t-j) \mid f\rangle|^2 = \|f\|^2 = \int_{\mathbb{R}}|f(t)|^2\,dt, \quad f\in L^2(\mathbb{R}). \quad (7.5.8)$$

Let $(P_x)_{x\in[0,1]}$ *be the measure on* $\mathbb{N}_0 \times \Omega$ *from Lemma 7.4.3. Then*

$$P_x(\{\omega(k),\omega(l)\}) = |\hat{\varphi}_k(x+l)|^2, \quad (7.5.9)$$

where the correspondence $\omega(k) \leftrightarrow k$, $\omega(l) \leftrightarrow l$ *is determined as in (7.4.14), i.e.,* $\omega(k) = (\omega_1, \ldots, \omega_n, \mathbf{0})$, *and similarly for* $l \in \mathbb{N}_0$. *Moreover,* $\{\varphi_k(\cdot - l)\}_{k\in\mathbb{N}_0, l\in\mathbb{Z}}$ *is an orthonormal basis for* $L^2(\mathbb{R})$ *if and only if*

$$P_x(\{\omega(k)\}\times\mathbb{Z}) = 1 \quad \text{a.e. } x \in [0,1] \text{ and all } k \in \mathbb{N}_0. \quad (7.5.10)$$

Proof. The detailed steps are quite analogous to those given in Chapter 2, the main difference being that now Lemma 7.4.3 is used in place of Lemma 2.4.1 in the standard wavelet case.   □

Remark 7.5.3. Note that if $k = 0$ in (7.5.5)(A), then we recover the scaling identity (1.3.1) in the special case $N = 2$. Depending on the conditions placed on the coefficients (a_j), we get solutions $\varphi = \varphi_0$ in various function spaces, or in spaces of distributions. If (7.5.5)(A), or (1.3.1), is known to have a solution in $L^1(\mathbb{R})$, then an integration on $\mathbb{R}$ yields $\sum_{j\in\mathbb{Z}}a_j = 1$, and we recover the familiar low-pass property for the wavelet filter

$$m_0(x) = \sum_{j\in\mathbb{Z}}a_j e^{-i2\pi jx}$$

in the form of $m_0(0) = 1$. This is an interesting (perhaps unexpected) link between wavelets and signal processing.

The appearance of the graphs of the progression of functions $\varphi_0, \varphi_1, \varphi_2, \ldots$ in Figure 7.5 (pp. 120–121) offers a visually convincing argument for the name "wavelet packet" for this cascade construction. As we progress in the series of functions from the union of the two figures, we see that each of the functions φ_n, for n sufficiently large, is made up of two separate and distinct visual parts: one is a high-frequency wave, which appears packed or shaped inside a shadow envelope of another form with low frequency (i.e., long wavelength).

The term "wave packet" appears to have been used first by Werner Heisenberg in connection with particle-wave duality in quantum theory in the 1930s. The visual situation in Heisenberg's theory was much the same as the one which comes out from the much later wavelet constructions. In any case, Heisenberg's aim for his construction in the early days of quantum theory was quite different from what came later with wavelets, and Heisenberg most likely did not know about Haar's wavelet from 1910, see [Haa10]. The name "wavelet packet" came much later than both Haar and Heisenberg. But it was probably chosen by analogy to Heisenberg's wave packets by the authors of [CoMW95] and [CoWi93].

Remark 7.5.4. In (A)–(B) in Proposition 7.5.2 and their analogues (1.3.18)–(1.3.19), we considered the crucial recursive identities only in the scalar case. But in fact there are matrix versions. The main modification in the matrix case is that the coefficients are then matrices, and the functions involved are vector-valued. However, both in the scalar case, and in the matrix case, there is a pair of masking coefficients a_k and b_k. The above-mentioned quadrature conditions (see, e.g., Figure 7.7, p. 124) dictate a certain relationship between the two: Both in the scalar and the matrix versions of the pair a_k, b_k, the relationship is

$$b_k = (-1)^k \overline{a_{\text{odd}-k}} . \tag{7.5.11}$$

Depending on the plan of the picture and the number of a_k's, there are different useful choices for the odd number in (7.5.11).

The pair of frequency response functions which correspond to the assignment (7.5.11) made above will then be as follows:

$$\begin{cases} m_0(z) = \sum a_k z^k, \\ m_1(z) = z^{1+2l} \, \overline{m_0(-z)}. \end{cases}$$

7.6 Representations of the Cuntz algebra $\mathcal{O}_2$

The Cuntz algebra $\mathcal{O}_N$, see [Cun77], is a simple C^*-algebra on the relations

$$S_i^* S_j = \delta_{i,j} I, \qquad \sum_{i=0}^{N-1} S_i S_i^* = I. \tag{7.6.1}$$

When $\mathcal{O}_N$ is realized by operators on a Hilbert space $\mathcal{H}$, we take I to be the identity operator on $\mathcal{H}$, i.e., $I: h \mapsto h$, $h \in \mathcal{H}$. These operators are fundamental in signal processing, where they take the form of signal/wavelet diagrams as illustrated in the series of Figures 7.7–7.15 (pp. 124–128, 132–133), and especially in Figures 7.7 and 7.14 from signal processing.

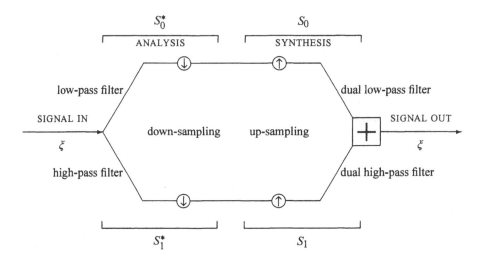

Fig. 7.14. Perfect reconstruction of signals.

The choice of the numbers $(a_j)_{j \in \mathbb{Z}}$ used in m_0, m_1 from (7.5.1)–(7.5.4) guarantees that the corresponding two operators

$$(S_i f)(z) = \sqrt{2}\, m_i (z) f\left(z^2\right), \qquad i = 0, 1, \quad f \in L^2 (\mathbb{T}), \tag{7.6.2}$$

satisfy (7.6.1) for $\mathcal{H} = L^2 (\mathbb{T})$ and $N = 2$.

If we use 1-periodic functions on $\mathbb{R}$ instead of functions on $\mathbb{T}$, then (7.6.2) takes the equivalent form

$$(S_i f)(x) = \sqrt{2}\, m_i (x) f (2x), \qquad i = 0, 1, \quad f \in L^2 (0, 1). \tag{7.6.3}$$

The two functions m_0 and m_1 are called the *low-pass/high-pass filters* respectively, and we have $m_0 (0) = 1$, $m_1 (1/2) = 1$, when the m_i's are viewed as 1-periodic functions.

Lemma 7.6.1. *Let the functions m_0, m_1 satisfy the unitarity condition (7.5.4) and let S_i, $i = 0, 1$, be the corresponding operators. Then the operator relations (7.6.1) of Cuntz are satisfied.*

Proof. We refer to [BrJo02b] for the detailed verification that (7.6.1) is satisfied when the unitarity property (7.5.4) is assumed. The essential step is the following identity:

$$\sum_{i=0}^{1} \left\| S_i^* f \right\|^2 = \| f \|^2, \qquad f \in L^2 (0, 1). \tag{7.6.4}$$

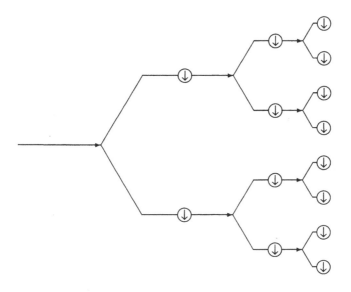

Fig. 7.15. Iteration of the filter/down-sampling operation as it arises in wavelet algorithms.

To verify (7.6.4), first check that

$$\left(S_i^* f\right)(x) = \frac{1}{\sqrt{2}} \sum_{r=0}^{1} \overline{m_i\left(\frac{x+r}{2}\right)} f\left(\frac{x+r}{2}\right), \qquad i = 0, 1. \qquad (7.6.5)$$

And so

$$\sum_{i=0}^{1} \left\| S_i^* f \right\|^2$$

$$= \sum_{i=0}^{1} \frac{1}{2} \int_0^1 \left| \sum_{r=0}^{1} \overline{m_i\left(\frac{x+r}{2}\right)} f\left(\frac{x+r}{2}\right) \right|^2 dx$$

$$= \frac{1}{2} \sum_{i=0}^{1} \sum_{r=0}^{1} \sum_{s=0}^{1} \int_0^1 \overline{m_i\left(\frac{x+r}{2}\right)} m_i\left(\frac{x+s}{2}\right) f\left(\frac{x+r}{2}\right) \overline{f\left(\frac{x+s}{2}\right)} dx$$

$$\underset{\text{(first the } i\text{-summation)}}{=} \frac{1}{2} \sum_{r=0}^{1} \sum_{s=0}^{1} \delta_{r,s} \int_0^1 f\left(\frac{x+r}{2}\right) \overline{f\left(\frac{x+s}{2}\right)} dx$$

$$= \frac{1}{2} \sum_{r=0}^{1} \int_0^1 \left| f\left(\frac{x+r}{2}\right) \right|^2 dx = \int_0^1 |f(x)|^2 \, dx = \|f\|^2,$$

which is the desired identity (7.6.4). $\qquad\qquad\square$

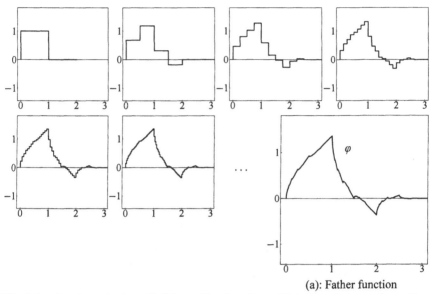

(a): Father function

The father function φ is also called the scaling function and it is the solution to the scaling identity (d) in Example 1.3.3. It is also the first of the sequence $\varphi_0, \varphi_1, \varphi_2, \ldots$ of functions generated by the algorithm (7.5.5), i.e., $\varphi = \varphi_0$.

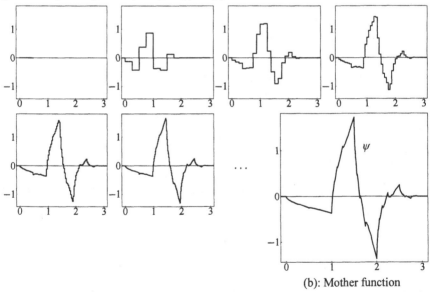

(b): Mother function

The mother function ψ is also called the wavelet function, and it is the second term in the sequence of functions generated by the algorithm (7.5.5), i.e., $\psi = \varphi_1$. So this four-tap Daubechies ψ is the same function as φ_1 in Figure 7.5 (p. 120).

Fig. 7.16. Daubechies wavelet functions and series of cascade approximants.

We note, see [Jor03], that (7.6.4) is known in signal processing as the quadrature-mirror identity for the filter operators defined by the two functions m_i, $i = 0, 1$, or equivalently by the sequence $(a_j)_{j \in \mathbb{Z}}$.

The case of four coefficients a_0, a_1, a_2, a_3 is called "four-tap", and it includes (with our current normalization)

$$a_0 = \frac{1 + \sqrt{3}}{8}, \quad a_1 = \frac{3 + \sqrt{3}}{8}, \quad a_2 = \frac{3 - \sqrt{3}}{8}, \quad \text{and} \quad a_3 = \frac{1 - \sqrt{3}}{8}, \quad (7.6.6)$$

the Daubechies wavelet; see [Dau92, p. 235]. If we take

$$m_1(z) = \frac{1 - \sqrt{3}}{8} - \frac{3 - \sqrt{3}}{8} z + \frac{3 + \sqrt{3}}{8} z^2 - \frac{1 + \sqrt{3}}{8} z^3, \quad (7.6.7)$$

for $z = e^{-i2\pi x}$, then the two functions φ (father function) and ψ (mother function) will be supported in the interval $[0, 3]$, they are differentiable (see [Dau92]), and they graph out as in Figure 7.16.

We now consider the probability space

$$\Omega = \{0, 1\}^{\mathbb{N}},$$

and the finite spaces

$$\Omega(n) = \{0, 1\}^{\{1,2,\dots,n\}}.$$

Specifically, $\Omega(n)$ consists of all functions $\omega: \{1, 2, \dots, n\} \to \{0, 1\}$.

Lemma 7.6.2. *For $n \in \mathbb{N}$ and $\omega \in \Omega(n)$, set*

$$S_\omega := S_{\omega(1)} \cdots S_{\omega(n)}, \quad (7.6.8)$$

and

$$E_\omega := S_\omega S_\omega^* = S_{\omega(1)} \cdots S_{\omega(n)} S_{\omega(n)}^* \cdots S_{\omega(1)}^*. \quad (7.6.9)$$

Then $\{E_\omega\}_{\omega \in \Omega(n)}$ is a commuting family of orthogonal projections satisfying the following matrix-unit identities:

$$E_\omega E_{\omega'} = \delta_{\omega,\omega'} E_\omega, \quad \omega, \omega' \in \Omega(n), \quad (7.6.10)$$

and

$$\sum_{\omega \in \Omega(n)} E_\omega = I. \quad (7.6.11)$$

Proof. This is a direct verification; see also [BrJo02b, Jor05].   □

Theorem 7.6.3. *There is a unique projection-valued measure P defined on the Borel subsets of $[0, 1]$ such that*

$$P\left(\left[\frac{\omega(1)}{2} + \cdots + \frac{\omega(n)}{2^n}, \frac{\omega(1)}{2} + \cdots + \frac{\omega(n)}{2^n} + \frac{1}{2^n}\right]\right) = E_\omega$$

$$\text{for } \omega \in \Omega(n) \text{ and } n \in \mathbb{N}. \quad (7.6.12)$$

Proof. The result follows from Lemmas 2.5.1 (Kolmogorov's construction), 2.6.2, and 7.6.2 above; see also [Jor05, Jor04b].   □

Remark 7.6.4. In view of (7.6.11), the measure P from Theorem 7.6.3 satisfies

$$\int_0^1 P\,(dx) = I, \qquad (7.6.13)$$

where I is the identity operator in the Hilbert space $\mathcal{H}$ which carries the representation of the Cuntz algebra $\mathcal{O}_2$. Specifically, if $f \in \mathcal{H}$, and $\|f\| = 1$, then the measure

$$\mu_f\,(\cdot) = \langle f \mid P\,(\cdot)\,f \rangle = \|P\,(\cdot)\,f\|^2 \qquad (7.6.14)$$

satisfies

$$\int_0^1 d\mu_f\,(x) = \mu_f\,([0, 1]) = 1. \qquad (7.6.15)$$

In the case

$$\mathcal{H} = L^2\,(\mathbb{T}) \cong L^2\,(0, 1) \cong \ell^2\,(\mathbb{Z}),$$

the case $f = \mathbb{1}$ (the constant function 1) was used in [CoMW95] and [CoWi93] in the construction of libraries of orthonormal wavelet packets, and it was conjectured that the measure

$$\mu_{\mathbb{1}}\,(\cdot) = \|P\,(\cdot)\,\mathbb{1}\|^2 \qquad (7.6.16)$$

is absolutely continuous with respect to Lebesgue measure on $[0, 1]$ for all the wavelet filter systems of (7.5.1)–(7.5.4).

We do not solve the conjecture here, but we illustrate the question with the use of the random-walk model from Chapter 2.

We first take a closer look at the measure (7.6.16). Since $e_n\,(z) = z^n$, and $e_0 = \mathbb{1}$, we shall also use the notation μ_0 for the measure $\mu_{\mathbb{1}}$.

Lemma 7.6.5. *For the case $n = 1$ in Theorem 7.6.3, and the measure μ_0 of Remark 7.6.4, we have*

(a) $\mu_0\left(\left[0, \dfrac{1}{2}\right)\right) = 2\sum_{j \in \mathbb{Z}} |a_{2j}|^2$,

(b) $\mu_0\left(\left[\dfrac{1}{2}, 1\right)\right) = 2\sum_{j \in \mathbb{Z}} |a_{2j+1}|^2$,

(c) $\mu_0\,(\{x\}) = 0$ *for all $x \in [0, 1]$.*

Remark 7.6.6. When (a)–(b) are applied to the Daubechies wavelet filters (7.6.6)–(7.6.7), we get

$$\mu_0\left(\left[0, \frac{1}{2}\right)\right) = \frac{4 - \sqrt{3}}{8} \quad \text{and} \quad \mu_0\left(\left[\frac{1}{2}, 1\right)\right) = \frac{4 + \sqrt{3}}{8}.$$

In the case of the dyadic Haar wavelet, it is easy to check that

$$\mu_0\left(\left[\frac{\omega(1)}{2}+\cdots+\frac{\omega(n)}{2^n}, \frac{\omega(1)}{2}+\cdots+\frac{\omega(n)}{2^n}+\frac{1}{2^n}\right)\right) = \frac{1}{2^n}$$

$$\text{for } \omega \in \Omega(n), \ n \in \mathbb{N}.$$

So for the dyadic Haar wavelet, the measure μ_0 is the Lebesgue measure restricted to the unit interval $[0, 1]$.

Proof of Lemma 7.6.5. Part (a):

$$\mu_0\left(\left[0, \frac{1}{2}\right)\right) \underset{\text{by (7.6.12)}}{=} \|S_0^* e_0\|^2 \underset{\text{by (7.6.5)}}{=} 2\int_0^1 \left|\frac{1}{2}\sum_{r=0}^1 m_0\left(\frac{x+r}{2}\right)\right|^2 dx$$

$$\underset{\text{by Parseval}}{=} 2\sum_{j\in\mathbb{Z}} |a_{2j}|^2.$$

Part (b):

$$\mu_0\left(\left[\frac{1}{2}, 1\right)\right) \underset{\text{by (7.6.12)}}{=} \|S_1^* e_0\|^2 \underset{\text{by (7.6.5)}}{=} 2\int_0^1 \left|\frac{1}{2}\sum_{r=0}^1 m_1\left(\frac{x+r}{2}\right)\right|^2 dx$$

$$\underset{\text{by Parseval and (7.5.2)}}{=} 2\sum_{j\in\mathbb{Z}} |a_{1-2j}|^2 = 2\sum_{j\in\mathbb{Z}} |a_{1+2j}|^2.$$

Part (c): Here we refer the reader to [BrJo02b, Theorem 2.2.1, p. 92; Lemma 2.2.3, p. 95]. $\square$

Theorem 7.6.7. *Let* $(a_j)_{j\in\mathbb{Z}}$, m_0, *and* m_1 *be as described above. Let* $n \in \mathbb{N}$, *and* $\omega \in \Omega(n)$. *Then*

$$\mu_0\left(\left[\frac{\omega(1)}{2}+\cdots+\frac{\omega(n)}{2^n}, \frac{\omega(1)}{2}+\cdots+\frac{\omega(n)}{2^n}+\frac{1}{2^n}\right)\right)$$

$$= 2^n \sum_{k\in\mathbb{Z}} \left|\sum_{\zeta_2,\dots,\zeta_n\in\mathbb{Z}} (-1)^{\omega(2)\zeta_2+\cdots+\omega(n)\zeta_n}\right.$$

$$\left. \cdot a_{\omega(1)-k2^n+2\zeta_2+\cdots+2^{n-1}\zeta_n} \cdot a_{\omega(2)-\zeta_2} \cdots a_{\omega(n)-\zeta_n}\right|^2.$$

Proof. For $n \in \mathbb{N}$, $\omega \in \Omega(n)$, set

$$m_\omega^{(n)}(x) = m_{\omega(1)}(x)\, m_{\omega(2)}(2x) \cdots m_{\omega(n)}\left(2^{n-1}x\right). \qquad (7.6.17)$$

Then

$$(S_\omega f)(x) = m_\omega^{(n)}(x)\, f\left(2^n x\right) \qquad (7.6.18)$$

and

$$\left(S_\omega^* f\right)(x) = 2^{-n/2} \sum_{2^n \cdot y \equiv x \bmod 1} \overline{m_\omega^{(n)}(y)} \, f(y) \tag{7.6.19}$$

by the argument from (7.6.5). Note that the summation in (7.6.19) is over the set of all dyadic fractions

$$y \in \left\{ \frac{x+r}{2^n} \; \middle| \; r = 0, 1, 2, \ldots, 2^{n-1} \right\}, \tag{7.6.20}$$

where each r in (7.6.20) has a unique representation

$$r = \xi_1 + \xi_2 2 + \cdots + \xi_n 2^{n-1}, \qquad \xi \in \Omega(n). \tag{7.6.21}$$

Using now Lemma 7.6.5 on $m_\omega^{(n)}$ and (7.6.18), we get

$$\mu_0 \left(\left[\frac{\omega(1)}{2} + \cdots + \frac{\omega(n)}{2^n}, \frac{\omega(1)}{2} + \cdots + \frac{\omega(n)}{2^n} + \frac{1}{2^n} \right) \right)$$

$$= \left\| S_\omega^* e_0 \right\|^2$$

$$= 2^n \int_0^1 \left| \frac{1}{2^n} \sum_{2^n \cdot y \equiv x \bmod 1} m_\omega^{(n)}(y) \right|^2 dx$$

$$= 2^n \sum_{k \in \mathbb{Z}} \left| \sum_{\xi_2,\ldots,\xi_n \in \mathbb{Z}} a_{k \cdot 2^n - 2\xi_2 - \cdots - 2^{n-1}\xi_n}^{(\omega(1))} \cdot a_{\xi_2}^{(\omega(2))} \cdots a_{\xi_n}^{(\omega(n))} \right|^2$$

$$= 2^n \sum_{k \in \mathbb{Z}} \left| \sum_{\xi_2,\ldots,\xi_n \in \mathbb{Z}} (-1)^{\omega(2)\xi_2 + \cdots + \omega(n)\xi_n} \right.$$

$$\left. \cdot a_{\omega(1) - k 2^n + 2\xi_2 + \cdots + 2^{n-1}\xi_n} \cdot a_{\omega(2) - \xi_2} \cdots a_{\omega(n) - \xi_n} \right|^2,$$

which is the desired result.   □

7.7 Representations of the algebra of the canonical anticommutation relations (CARs)

The purpose of the present section is twofold: (1) to illustrate the non-abelian framework for infinite-product constructions; and (2) to point out how a class of measures that are known as determinantal measures (see [LySt03]) arises from a construction from operator algebra theory—Powers–Størmer's construction of the quasi-free states on the C^*-algebra of the canonical anticommutation relations, the CAR-algebra; see [PoSt70].

The construction for both the abelian and the non-abelian setup begins with a fixed operator A in a Hilbert space, such that A is assumed selfadjoint with spectrum in the closed unit interval $[0, 1]$. In the abelian setting, the measure μ_A is defined on cylinder sets $(i_1, \ldots, i_n)$ in Ω, as the determinant of the submatrix obtained from A by using the subset of an orthonormal basis corresponding to the selection $i_1, \ldots, i_n$. As it turns out, μ_A is the restriction of a state ρ_A on the CAR-algebra—a quasi-free state, in the terminology of [PoSt70]—where ρ_A is defined as the Hilbert norm of fermion particles. This is a multistate computed from $i_1, \ldots, i_n$, and computed in a multiple-particle Hilbert space which is constructed directly from A.

In both cases, the abelian and the non-abelian, the extension from the cylinders to the full measure space, or the full C^*-algebra, is performed with a variant of the Kolmogorov extension principle from Section 2.5 above.

We begin with some terminology and definitions.

Definitions 7.7.1. Let M_2 denote the algebra of all 2×2 complex matrices, and set

$$\mathfrak{A}_n = \underbrace{M_2 \otimes \cdots \otimes M_2}_{n \text{ times}} \cong M_{2^n}. \tag{7.7.1}$$

Since $\mathfrak{A}_{n+1} \cong M_2(\mathfrak{A}_n)$, the mapping $T \mapsto \begin{pmatrix} T & 0 \\ 0 & T \end{pmatrix}$ defines a natural embedding of $\mathfrak{A}_n$ into $\mathfrak{A}_{n+1}$, and we get

$$I \in \mathfrak{A}_1 \subseteq \mathfrak{A}_2 \subseteq \cdots \subseteq \mathfrak{A}_n \subseteq \mathfrak{A}_{n+1} \subseteq \cdots \tag{7.7.2}$$

as a non-commutative analogue of (2.4.5) above.

Let $i, j \in \{0, 1\}$, let $e_{i,j}$ be the 2×2 matrix $e_{i,j}(k, l) = \delta_{i,k}\delta_{j,l}$, and set

$$e^{(n)}_{i_1,\ldots,i_n; j_1,\ldots,j_n} = e_{i_1,j_1} \otimes e_{i_2,j_2} \otimes \cdots \otimes e_{i_n,j_n}. \tag{7.7.3}$$

For $\omega, \xi \in \Omega(n)$ set

$$E^{(n)}_{\omega,\xi} = S_\omega S_\xi^*, \tag{7.7.4}$$

where S_ω is defined from a representation of $\mathcal{O}_2$ as in (7.6.8). As noted in [BrJo02b], the assignment

$$E^{(n)}_{\omega,\xi} \mapsto e^{(n)}_{\omega,\xi} \tag{7.7.5}$$

identifies a subalgebra (up to C^*-algebraic isomorphism) of $\mathcal{O}_2$ with the infinite tensor product

$$\mathfrak{A} = \bigotimes_1^\infty M_2 = \operatorname{ind} \lim_{n \to \infty} \mathfrak{A}_n. \tag{7.7.6}$$

The C^*-algebra $\mathfrak{A}$ in (7.7.6) is the inductive limit of the system (7.7.2) of matrix algebras, and $\mathfrak{A}$ is also called the C^*-algebra of the canonical anticommutation relations (CARs) for reasons which are spelled out in [PoSt70].

The purpose of this section is to demonstrate that a family of measures which were studied independently in [PoSt70] and in [LySt03] for very different reasons may be viewed under the heading of this book, i.e., measures defined from functions $\Omega \to$ (matrices), or inductive limits of systems $\Omega(n) \to$ (matrices), for $n \in \mathbb{N}$.

Let $\mathcal{H} = \ell^2(\mathbb{N})$ be the familiar Hilbert space of ℓ^2-sequences, and let $(\varepsilon_j)_{j \in \mathbb{N}}$ be the standard ONB in $\mathcal{H}$, i.e., defined by $\varepsilon_j(k) := \delta_{j,k}$, $j, k \in \mathbb{N}$. Let $A \colon \mathcal{H} \to \mathcal{H}$ be a linear operator such that

$$0 \le \langle h \mid Ah \rangle \le \|h\|^2, \qquad h \in \mathcal{H}. \tag{7.7.7}$$

The matrix representation for A will be defined relative to the ONB (ε_j), i.e., by

$$A(i, j) := \langle \varepsilon_i \mid A\varepsilon_j \rangle, \qquad i, j \in \mathbb{N}. \tag{7.7.8}$$

Let $\Omega = \{0, 1\}^{\mathbb{N}}$, and define the matrix function W on Ω by

$$W(\omega)(i, j) := \left(\omega(i)\, \delta_{i,j} + (-1)^{\omega(i)} \left(\delta_{i,j} - A(i, j) \right) \right). \tag{7.7.9}$$

For the C^*-algebra $\mathfrak{A}$ we shall need the following representation from [PoSt70]: there is an antilinear mapping $a \colon \mathcal{H} \to \mathcal{H}$ such that

$$\begin{cases} a(h)^*\, a(k) + a(k)\, a(h)^* = \langle h \mid k \rangle\, I, \\ a(h)\, a(k) + a(k)\, a(h) = 0 \qquad \text{for all } h, k \in \mathcal{H}. \end{cases} \tag{7.7.10}$$

A *state* ρ on $\mathfrak{A}$ is a linear functional $\rho \colon \mathfrak{A} \to \mathbb{C}$ such that $\rho(I) = 1$, and $\rho(T^*T) \ge 0$ for all $T \in \mathfrak{A}$.

Let A be a fixed operator as specified in (7.7.7). It is known [PoSt70] that there is then a unique state $\rho = \rho_A$ on $\mathfrak{A}$ such that

$$\rho_A \left(a(\varepsilon_{i_n})^* \cdots a(\varepsilon_{i_1})^*\, a(\varepsilon_{j_1}) \cdots a(\varepsilon_{j_m}) \right)$$
$$= \delta_{n,m} \det(A(i_r, j_s))_{1 \le r, s \le n}. \tag{7.7.11}$$

When the CARs (7.7.10) are used, we get the formulas (7.7.3) which are used in the embeddings (7.7.2). As a result, we get the following formulas for the matrix elements in the algebras in (7.7.2), with the superscript referring to the n'th tensor slot (see [PoSt70]):

$$\begin{cases} e_{0,0}^{(n)} = a(\varepsilon_n)\, a(\varepsilon_n)^*, & e_{0,1}^{(n)} = a(\varepsilon_n)\, V_{n-1}, \\ e_{1,0}^{(n)} = a(\varepsilon_n)^*\, V_{n-1}, & e_{1,1}^{(n)} = a(\varepsilon_n)^*\, a(\varepsilon_n), \end{cases} \tag{7.7.12}$$

where $V_0 = I$ and

$$V_n := \prod_{k=1}^{n} \left(I - 2a(\varepsilon_k)^*\, a(\varepsilon_k) \right).$$

Using the diagonal matrices from (7.7.12), it is now clear that $C(\Omega)$ is naturally embedded in $\mathfrak{A}$, and therefore in $\mathcal{O}_2$ as well; see (7.7.3)–(7.7.5).

Theorem 7.7.2. *Let A be a given operator satisfying (7.7.7), and let $W = W_A$ be the corresponding matrix function (7.7.9) defined on Ω. If $n \in \mathbb{N}$, and $\omega \in \Omega(n)$, then $W(\omega)$ is an $n \times n$ complex matrix, and we set*

$$P^{(n)}(\omega) = \det W(\omega). \tag{7.7.13}$$

Then the family $\left(P^{(n)}\right)_{n \in \mathbb{N}}$ is Kolmogorov consistent, see Lemma 2.5.1, and therefore extends to a Borel measure P_A on Ω. This measure is uniquely determined by (7.7.13), and is the restriction to $C(\Omega)$ of the C^*-state ρ_A of (7.7.11). Moreover the state is given uniquely by the two formulas

$$\rho_A\left(a\left(\varepsilon_{i_1}\right) a\left(\varepsilon_{i_1}\right)^* \cdots a\left(\varepsilon_{i_r}\right) a\left(\varepsilon_{i_r}\right)^*\right) = \det\left(I_n - P_{E_0} A P_{E_0}\right) \tag{7.7.14}$$

and

$$\rho_A\left(a\left(\varepsilon_{j_1}\right)^* a\left(\varepsilon_{j_1}\right) \cdots a\left(\varepsilon_{j_s}\right)^* a\left(\varepsilon_{j_s}\right)\right)$$
$$= \det\left(I_n - P_{E_1}(I - A) P_{E_1}\right). \tag{7.7.15}$$

Proof. We know that the state ρ_A on $\mathfrak{A}$ is well defined, and determined uniquely by (7.7.11). Let $C(\Omega)$ be embedded in $\mathfrak{A}$ as described, and let $\rho_A|_{C(\Omega)}$ be the restriction. Clearly the restriction is positive, and so determines a Borel measure on Ω by Riesz's theorem.

We claim that this measure is the same as the one coming from the family $\left(P^{(n)}\right)_{n \in \mathbb{N}}$ in (7.7.13); see also (7.7.9).

Let $n \in \mathbb{N}$, and $\omega \in \Omega(n)$. Set $E_0 = \omega^{-1}(0)$ and $E_1 = \omega^{-1}(1)$. Then $E_0 \cup E_1 = \{1, \ldots, n\}$.

An application of (7.7.11) and (7.7.10) yields the following: Let

$$E_0 = \{i_1, \ldots, i_r\}, \qquad E_1 = \{j_1, \ldots, j_s\},$$

and let P_{E_0}, resp. P_{E_1}, denote the corresponding orthogonal projections. Then the two formulas (7.7.14)–(7.7.15) hold. Moreover, an inspection shows that (7.7.14)–(7.7.15) determine the state uniquely. In view of the identification of Ω as the matrix diagonals in (7.7.12), the two formulas (7.7.14) and (7.7.15), taken together, prove that the restriction of ρ_A satisfies the desired conclusion (7.7.13).   □

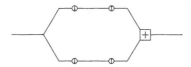

Exercises

Organization. This chapter is longer than the preceding one, and it has more exercises. They are organized as follows: The first seven exercises serve to link the operator theory from inside the text with matrix algorithms. As already stressed in Chapter 1, wavelet bases exist abstractly in an ambient Hilbert space $\mathcal{H}$ (which could be $L^2(\mathbb{R}^d)$), but for computations, Hilbert spaces as such are not very useful: we need to make a connection from these function spaces to some concrete sequence spaces, i.e., ℓ^2-spaces $\mathcal{V}$, and to efficient matrix representations of the objects and transformations in those spaces. The basic idea of a multiresolution wavelet basis is nothing more nor less than an efficient way to make that connection.

A wavelet transform is an operator which relates the sequence space $\mathcal{V}$ to a subspace $\mathcal{V}_0$ of the ambient Hilbert space $\mathcal{H}$. With such a choice the subdivision operators of wavelet geometry are turned into slanted matrices, which we saw are (computationally) fast.

Exercises 7.4–7.7 are a guided tour of the matrix computations connecting the discrete wavelet transform with "real" wavelet computations; see the material in Section 7.6 and Chapters 5 and 8. In a simple case we see that the distribution of expansion coefficients for a given wavelet packet is determined by the measures from (7.6.12) and Theorem 7.6.7. Recall that our starting point is a discrete wavelet transform (7.6.1). As outlined in Lemma 7.6.1, it takes the form of a system of operators S_i in the Hilbert space $L^2(\mathbb{T})$, or equivalently in ℓ^2, while in contrast a wavelet basis refers to functions in $L^2(\mathbb{R})$. In computations, not all Hilbert spaces are equal.

The second block of exercises deals primarily with tensor products of Hilbert space, and the associated geometry for operators and for matrices. One of these, Exercise 7.8, about image processing, serves to link two ideas, slanted matrices and tensor products: For images, i.e., 2D, or other problems in higher dimensions, a popular approach is to build the models simply by taking tensor products of well chosen 1D wavelet algorithms.

The last one, Exercise 7.12, is about representations of the C^*-algebra $\mathcal{O}_N$ for N fixed. It stresses that in the present context the representations of $\mathcal{O}_N$ are more important than $\mathcal{O}_N$ itself.

Notational conventions for slanted matrices. The slanted matrices used in this chapter, and later, are infinite-by-infinite, in fact doubly infinite, i.e., with rows and columns infinity in both positive and negative directions. Specifically, both rows and columns are indexed by the integers $\mathbb{Z}$. That is, the counting of rows and columns starts in the negative segment of $\mathbb{Z}$, going up to 0 in the middle, and then continuing the counting with $1, 2, \ldots$, with three dots indicating recursion. Rows are counted from top to bottom, and columns from left to right: So, in each case, the row index increases as we move from top to bottom in a matrix display; and the column index increases from left to right, consistent with the counting of columns. The matrices have uses in computation, where their slanted feature is significant. The slanting of these matrices reflects the subdivision (from scaling) built into the algorithm.

In computations, we rely on matrix multiplication but choose our index convention to be consistent with the associated operator formalism, i.e., with multiplication of the corresponding operators in Hilbert space. An operator and an orthonormal basis (ONB) will always be specified; typically the ONB is chosen to be the standard canonical basis in $\ell^2(\mathbb{Z})$. But we will have occasion to use more general bases.

Our index convention means that the row/column position $(0, 0)$, i.e., zero row and zero column, is in the center position of each of the slanted matrix displays. We have used shading to illustrate this point: The matrix entries in the center cross, with crossing at $(0, 0)$ is highlighted, meaning that the entries in both row 0 and column 0 are highlighted with a light shading. This is to help the reader see how matrix multiplication is implemented; and it further serves to call attention to the slant in each of the slanted matrices, and to visualize how slanting changes as matrices are multiplied, or as the scaling number changes from one matrix to another.

7.1. Let $\mathcal{H}$ be a complex Hilbert space with inner product $\langle \cdot \mid \cdot \rangle$, and let A be an index set. Two systems of vectors in $\mathcal{H}$, $(e_n)_{n \in A}$ and $(\tilde{e}_n)_{n \in A}$, are said to form a *dual basis system*, also called a *bi-orthogonal basis* in $\mathcal{H}$, if the following three conditions are satisfied:

(i) $\langle e_n \mid \tilde{e}_m \rangle = \delta_{n,m}$ for all $n, m \in A$,
(ii) $\langle e_n \mid f \rangle = 0 \, \forall n \in A \Rightarrow f = 0$ in $\mathcal{H}$,
(iii) $\langle f \mid \tilde{e}_n \rangle = 0 \, \forall n \in A \Rightarrow f = 0$ in $\mathcal{H}$.

(a) Prove the following assertion: If $((e_n), (\tilde{e}_m))$ is a dual basis system, then every vector $f \in \mathcal{H}$ has two representations,

$$f = \sum_{n \in A} \langle \tilde{e}_n \mid f \rangle e_n = \sum_{n \in A} \langle e_n \mid f \rangle \tilde{e}_n.$$

(b) Make precise the notion of convergence used in (a), and supply a detailed epsilon-delta argument.

(c) Prove that if $(e_n)_{n \in A}$ is a system of vectors in $\mathcal{H}$, then $(e_n)_{n \in A}$ is an orthonormal basis (ONB) in $\mathcal{H}$ if and only if the pair $((e_n)_{n \in A}, (e_n)_{n \in A})$ is a dual basis system, i.e., if and only if we get a dual basis system by taking $\tilde{e}_n = e_n$ for all $n \in A$.

Definition. Let $(e_n)_{n \in A}$ be a system of vectors in $\mathcal{H}$. If there are two constants c_1, c_2, $0 < c_1 \le c_2 < \infty$, such that

$$c_1 \|f\|^2 \le \sum_{n \in A} |\langle e_n \mid f \rangle|^2 \le c_2 \|f\|^2 \qquad \text{for all } f \in \mathcal{H},$$

then we say that $(e_n)_{n \in A}$ is a *frame basis* (or just a *frame*) for the Hilbert space, and c_1 and c_2 are called *frame bounds*.

(d) Suppose $(e_n)_{n \in A}$ is a frame. Then show that there is a system $(\tilde{e}_n)_{n \in A}$ such that $((e_n)_{n \in A}, (\tilde{e}_n)_{n \in A})$ is a dual basis system.

(e) If $(e_n)_{n \in A}$ is a frame for $\mathcal{H}$, show that the operator $T : \mathcal{H} \to \ell^2(A)$ defined by $Tf = (\langle e_n \mid f \rangle)_{n \in A}$ for $f \in \mathcal{H}$ is bounded.

(f) Show that the adjoint operator $T^*: \ell^2(A) \to \mathcal{H}$ is given by the formula

$$T^*\left((x_n)_{n\in A}\right) = \sum_{n\in A} x_n e_n.$$

(g) Show that $T^*T: \mathcal{H} \to \mathcal{H}$ is invertible, and that

$$T^*Tf = \sum_{n\in A} \langle e_n \mid f \rangle e_n \qquad \text{for all } f \in \mathcal{H}.$$

(h) Setting $\tilde{e}_n := (T^*T)^{-1} e_n$ for $n \in A$, verify that the two reproduction formulas

$$f = \sum_{n\in A} \langle \tilde{e}_n \mid f \rangle e_n = \sum_{n\in A} \langle e_n \mid f \rangle \tilde{e}_n$$

hold for all $f \in \mathcal{H}$.

7.2. Let $\mathcal{H}$ and $\mathcal{K}$ be two complex Hilbert spaces, and let $T: \mathcal{H} \to \mathcal{K}$ be a bounded linear operator. Let $(e_n)_{n\in A}$ and $(f_m)_{m\in B}$ be ONBs for the respective Hilbert spaces $\mathcal{H}$ and $\mathcal{K}$. Hence we have the two representations

$$h = \sum_{n\in A} x_n e_n \qquad \text{with } x_n = \langle e_n \mid h \rangle \text{ for } h \in \mathcal{H},$$

and

$$Th = \sum_{m\in B} y_m f_m \qquad \text{with } y_m = \langle f_m \mid Th \rangle.$$

A matrix $(T(n,k))_{n\in B,\, k\in A}$ is said to *represent the operator* T in the two bases if

$$y_n = \sum_{k\in A} T(n,k) x_k \qquad \text{for } n \in B.$$

Show that when the two ONBs are given, then the matrix representation is unique, and

$$T(n,k) = \langle f_n \mid Te_k \rangle.$$

7.3. Generalize the result in Exercise 7.2 for $T: \mathcal{H} \to \mathcal{K}$ where $((e_n),(\tilde{e}_n))$ is a dual basis system in $\mathcal{H}$, and $((f_m),(\tilde{f}_m))$ is a dual basis system in $\mathcal{K}$. Specifically, show that then the formula $T(n,k) := \langle \tilde{f}_n \mid Te_k \rangle$ provides a matrix representation for T relative to the two basis systems.

7.4. Consider the Hilbert space $\mathcal{H} = L^2(\mathbb{T}) \; (\cong \ell^2(\mathbb{Z}))$, and let $e_k(z) = z^k$, $k \in \mathbb{Z}$, be the usual Fourier basis.

Show that $(e_k)_{k\in\mathbb{Z}}$ is an ONB for $\mathcal{H}$.

7.5. Let $m \in L^\infty(\mathbb{T})$ and consider the operator

$$(Sf)(z) = \sqrt{2}\, m(z)\, f\left(z^2\right), \qquad f \in \mathcal{H},\ z \in \mathbb{T},$$

and its adjoint operator

$$\left(S^* f\right)(z) = \frac{1}{\sqrt{2}} \left(\bar{m}\left(\sqrt{z}\right) f\left(\sqrt{z}\right) + \bar{m}\left(-\sqrt{z}\right) f\left(-\sqrt{z}\right)\right), \qquad f \in \mathcal{H}, \, z \in \mathbb{T}.$$

Let $m(z) = \sum_{k \in \mathbb{Z}} a_k e_k(z)$ be the Fourier series for m.

(a) Now show that the matrix representations for the two operators S and S^* relative to $(e_k)_{k \in \mathbb{Z}}$ are as follows:

$$S(n, k) = \sqrt{2}\, a_{n-2k} \quad \text{and} \quad S^*(n, k) = \sqrt{2}\, \bar{a}_{k-2n} \qquad \text{for } n, k \in \mathbb{Z}.$$

(b) Show that the two matrices in (a) have the following "slanted form":

$$(7E.1)$$

and

$$(7E.2)$$

7.6. In the case of only two non-zero terms, say a_0 and a_1, the matrix F from (7E.2) takes the form

$$
\begin{array}{c}
\\[2pt]
n=0
\end{array}
\underset{}{
\left(
\begin{array}{cc|cc|cc|cc|cc|cc|cc|cc|cc}
* & * & 0 & 0 & 0 & 0 & 0 & 0 & 0 & 0 & 0 & 0 & 0 & 0 & 0 & 0 & 0 & 0\\
0 & 0 & * & * & 0 & 0 & 0 & 0 & 0 & 0 & 0 & 0 & 0 & 0 & 0 & 0 & 0 & 0\\
0 & 0 & 0 & 0 & * & * & 0 & 0 & 0 & 0 & 0 & 0 & 0 & 0 & 0 & 0 & 0 & 0\\
0 & 0 & 0 & 0 & 0 & 0 & * & * & 0 & 0 & 0 & 0 & 0 & 0 & 0 & 0 & 0 & 0\\
0 & 0 & 0 & 0 & 0 & 0 & 0 & 0 & * & * & 0 & 0 & 0 & 0 & 0 & 0 & 0 & 0\\
0 & 0 & 0 & 0 & 0 & 0 & 0 & 0 & 0 & 0 & * & * & 0 & 0 & 0 & 0 & 0 & 0\\
0 & 0 & 0 & 0 & 0 & 0 & 0 & 0 & 0 & 0 & 0 & 0 & * & * & 0 & 0 & 0 & 0\\
0 & 0 & 0 & 0 & 0 & 0 & 0 & 0 & 0 & 0 & 0 & 0 & 0 & 0 & * & * & 0 & 0\\
0 & 0 & 0 & 0 & 0 & 0 & 0 & 0 & 0 & 0 & 0 & 0 & 0 & 0 & 0 & 0 & * & *
\end{array}
\right)}
;
$$

(with $k=0$ marking the column group)

and hence the term "slanted Toeplitz" matrix.

(a) Identifying the $\infty \times \infty$ matrix with the corresponding transformation in $\ell^2\,(\mathbb{Z})$ relative to the standard basis in $\ell^2\,(\mathbb{Z})$, find the structure of the invariant subspaces for F. Make an infinite list of finite-dimensional subspaces which are invariant under F.

(b) Answer the same questions as those listed in part (a), but now in the case of only four non-zero terms (the four-tap case); say $a_0, a_1, a_2,$ and a_3 non-zero, but $a_k = 0$ if $k \in \mathbb{Z} \setminus \{0, 1, 2, 3\}$.

(c) In the four-tap case from part (b), find some finite-dimensional subspaces in $\ell^2\,(\mathbb{Z})$ which are F-invariant *and* minimally F-invariant.

7.7. Suppose the matrix F has the form from (7E.3) in Exercise 7.6 corresponding to the two-tap case. Then show that F^2 has the following shape:

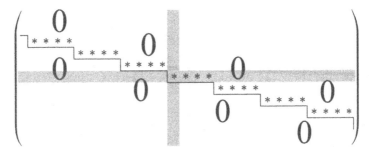

Hint and discussion: From the theory inside the chapter, the reader will notice that there are two numbers which determine the shape of the pair of matrices S and F which occur in Exercises 7.5 to 7.7: First there is the number of taps T (two-tap, four-tap, six-tap, etc.), and secondly there is the scaling number. The scaling number is denoted N, and for the dyadic wavelets, $N = 2$. Each operator, alias matrix, S and F has two lives: first it is represented as an operator in a function space, and secondly we have outlined how it is represented as a matrix, albeit an infinite-by-infinite matrix. If S is represented as an operator acting on functions (see Exercise 7.5, $N = 2$), it is composition with z^N followed by multiplication with a function of z. In each incarnation, we may talk about an adjoint $F = S^*$: In the operator world, the adjoint refers to the inner product of the Hilbert space of functions on the circle $\mathbb{T}$, and in the matrix picture, the adjoint is the usual matrix adjoint, i.e., there the adjoint matrix arises simply as transposed and complex conjugate. We use the same notation in either case, namely $F = S^*$, with the $*$ denoting adjoint. The amount of slanting (i.e., shifting of the terms from one column in S to the next) is equal to the number N. But the matrix transposed explains why the direction of the slanting changes from formula (7E.1) for S to (7E.2) for F in Exercise 7.5. The direction of the slanting is significant for computation, as it turns out. As already noted, the number of taps T is even, 2, 4, 6, etc., and it is simply the length of a minimal band in a column of S, or equivalently a row in F. All the terms outside a band are zero, and minimal means "the shortest" such band. In the present discussion, we will arrange the bands so the index runs from 0 to $T - 1$, so four-tap corresponds to a minimal band $\{a_0, a_1, a_2, a_3\}$. Using the function representation, it is easy to see that if S had tap number T and scale number N, then S^2 has tap number $T + N(T - 1)$, and scale number N^2. For the present discussion (Exercise 7.7), $N = T = 2$. Hence, in this case, both the tap number and the scale number for S^2 are 4.

Images. The next multipart exercise is about images. It involves two features: First, it is a recursive matrix algorithm, and secondly it is a tensor-product construction. The environment of images is 2D, and the tensor product of two separate 1D algorithms thus serves to create a new 2D algorithm. In fact this simple tensor-product construction is the easiest way of producing the type of 2D wavelet algorithms needed for images.

7.8. (a) Search the internet for your favorite visual sequence created with a digital camera, and illustrating image processing for a digital portrait-photo; for example of Lena [WWW5]. Look closely at subdivisions of pictures, and compare the cascading successions. Identify how the pictures change from one subdivision step to the next in the cascade.

(b) Having understood the pictures on the web, then compare with the algorithmic resolution steps in Figures 7.9 and 7.10 in this chapter (pp. 126–126).

A portrait (such as Lena's) consists of numbers arranged into matrix forms: only one matrix is needed for recording of grayscales, but several matrices are used for digitizing color images. An exposure with a digital camera imprints numbers for each pixel. Pixels form checkerboard arrangements which in turn correspond to a chosen resolution. However a digital camera creates both scales of *resolution* and *intermediate differences*; and everything is digitized.

So a picture L which is chosen and fixed at the outset will be represented by a vector in the subspace V_0 from Figure 7.10. Since subdivision in the planar picture is made with horizontal and vertical lines, the first algorithmic analysis step applied to L (in vector form) will split it up into four pieces, i.e., $N = 4$.

(c) In the image of Lena (L) on the Web, identify the corresponding four subpictures. They are usually arranged inside a square, with the NW scaled "quarter-box" showing the same image L but in a slightly more blurred resolution. Identify how the blurring corresponds to "local averages." The other three scaled pictures represent differences in grayscale (for black/white) in three directions, horizontal, vertical, and diagonal.

In the Hilbert-space representation, each of the four subsquares of a picture is a component in the corresponding four subspaces V_1 (the coarser *resolution*), and the three intermediate spaces $W_1^{(1)}$, $W_1^{(2)}$, and $W_1^{(3)}$ from Figure 7.10.

(d) Work out that the three W-subspaces are registers for *intermediate differences* in grayscales.

(e) Finally, from the pictures on the web, identify how this is the start of a cascading process. Show how the process continues on the part of L in the space V_1. As you follow the pictures on the web, note that the process is repeated, and at each step the part of L in the NW subsquare is further subdivided. Check that this algorithm corresponds to the pyramid which is illustrated with Figure 7.9, for $N = 4$.

Note: The following citations throw light on the use of wavelet algorithms/filters in 2D image processing: [Song05] and [StHS+99]. Dr. Myung-Sin Song has created a sample of images which are decomposed this way using the wavelet system of Haar, plus the analogous image decompositions using Coiflets and Symlets. The processing is posted at [Song05a] and the images themselves at [Song05b].

Tensor products. The next three exercises, 7.9, 7.10, and 7.11, highlight tensor products of Hilbert space, both finite and infinite tensor products. Each is composed in a multipart format, so that it is easier for the student to work through the concepts step by step. The exercises reinforce fundamental concepts already used in Chapter 7 above; and at the same time, they motivate and introduce some essential facts (such as Schmidt's decomposition in its infinite-dimensional variant) for tensor products that we will need in the remaining chapters. The tensor-product idea for Hilbert space is central in our present basis constructions and in our analysis in general in that it lets us use Hilbert-space geometry to reduce or to factor "complicated" data into its simpler forms or factors. The reader is encouraged to compare Schmidt's decomposition (Exercise 7.11(e)) with the closely related formulas from Exercises 2.7 and 9.8 for the Karhunen–Loève decomposition.

7.9. Let $\mathcal{H}_i$, $i = 1, 2$, be Hilbert spaces, and consider tensors $f_1 \otimes f_2$, $f_i \in \mathcal{H}_i$. Set

$$\langle f_1 \otimes f_2 \mid g_1 \otimes g_2 \rangle := \langle f_1 \mid g_1 \rangle \langle f_2 \mid g_2 \rangle .$$

(a) Show that this formula extends by sesquilinearity to define an inner product, also denoted $\langle \cdot \mid \cdot \rangle$, on the space of all finite sums

$$\sum_k c_k f_1^{(k)} \otimes f_2^{(k)}, \qquad c_k \in \mathbb{C}, \; f_i^{(k)} \in \mathcal{H}_i.$$

(b) Spell out the completion step which turns the tensor product $\mathcal{H}_1 \otimes \mathcal{H}_2$ into a Hilbert space.

(c) Let A and B be index sets, and consider two indexed families of vectors $f_\alpha \in \mathcal{H}_1, g_\beta \in \mathcal{H}_2, \alpha \in A, \beta \in B$, such that $(f_\alpha)_{\alpha \in A}$ is an ONB in $\mathcal{H}_1$ and $(g_\beta)_{\beta \in B}$ is an ONB in $\mathcal{H}_2$. Then show that $(f_\alpha \otimes g_\beta)_{(\alpha,\beta) \in A \times B}$ is an ONB in $\mathcal{H}_1 \otimes \mathcal{H}_2$.

(d) Conclude from (c) that the tensor-product formula

$$\ell^2 (A) \otimes \ell^2 (B) = \ell^2 (A \times B)$$

holds for the respective ℓ^2-sequence Hilbert spaces.

(e) Let $(X_i, \mathcal{B}_i, \mu_i)$, $i = 1, 2$, be two measure spaces, and let $\mathcal{B}$ be the σ-algebra generated by all sets in $X_1 \times X_2$ of the form $E_1 \times E_2$ where $E_i \in \mathcal{B}_i$. Verify that the *product measure* $\mu := \mu_1 \times \mu_2$ is determined uniquely on $\mathcal{B}$ by completion and the *ansatz*

$$\mu (E_1 \times E_2) = \mu_1 (E_1) \mu_2 (E_2).$$

(f) Let $(X_i, \mathcal{B}_i, \mu_i)$, $i = 1, 2$, and μ be as in (e). Then prove that there is a "natural" Hilbert-space (isometric) isomorphism

$$L^2 (X_1, \mu_1) \otimes L^2 (X_2, \mu_2) \cong L^2 (X_1 \times X_2, \mu).$$

(g) For $i \in \mathbb{N}$, consider compact spaces X_i with Borel probability measures μ_i. Using Kolmogorov's construction (Lemma 2.5.1), carry out the determination of the infinite-product measure

$$\mu := \prod_{i \in \mathbb{N}} \mu_i \qquad \text{on } X := \prod_{i \in \mathbb{N}} X_i.$$

Hint: $\mu \left(\prod_{i=1}^{n} E_i \times \prod_{k=n+1}^{\infty} X_k \right) = \prod_{i=1}^{n} \mu_i (E_i), \qquad E_i \in \mathcal{B}_i.$

(h) Extend the tensor-product formula from (f) above to infinite tensor products.

7.10. Infinite tensor products

Let $\mathcal{H}$ be a Hilbert space, and let $(h_n)_{n \in \mathbb{N}}$ be an infinite sequence of vectors such that $\|h_n\| = 1$, and

- $\lim_{n \to \infty} \|h_n - h\| = 0$ for some $h \in \mathcal{H}$,

- $\sum_{n=1}^{\infty} \|h_n - h_{n+1}\| < \infty,$

and

- $\displaystyle\sum_{n=1}^{\infty}\{\arccos |\langle h_n \mid h \rangle|\}^2 = \infty.$

Consider infinite tensors $\bigotimes_1^{\infty} f_k = f_1 \otimes f_2 \otimes \cdots$ where all but finitely many of the factors f_k agree with the unit vectors h_k, i.e., from a finite step onwards, $f_k = h_k$ holds. On such tensors, define the inner product

$$\left\langle \bigotimes_1^{\infty} f_k \mid \bigotimes_1^{\infty} g_k \right\rangle = \prod_{k=1}^{\infty} \langle f_k \mid g_k \rangle .$$

(a) Use a completion argument to show that this *ansatz* yields a Hilbert space which depends on the chosen system (h_k).

(b) Give a formula for comparing two Hilbert spaces $\mathcal{H}^{\otimes}_{\infty}(h_k)$ and $\mathcal{H}^{\otimes}_{\infty}(h'_k)$ constructed this way from sequences (h_k) and (h'_k) of unit vectors, both satisfying the three conditions stated before (a).

7.11. Let $\mathcal{H}_i$, $i = 1, 2$, be Hilbert spaces, and let C be a conjugation in $\mathcal{H}_1$, i.e., C is conjugate linear and satisfies $C^2 = I$. Let $\psi \in \mathcal{H}_1 \otimes \mathcal{H}_2$, $\|\psi\| = 1$, be given.

(a) Show that there is a unique bounded linear operator $K := K_\psi : \mathcal{H}_2 \to \mathcal{H}_1$ such that

$$\langle \psi \mid Cf_1 \otimes f_2 \rangle_{\mathcal{H}_1 \otimes \mathcal{H}_2} = \langle f_1 \mid Kf_2 \rangle_{\mathcal{H}_1} , \qquad \text{for all } f_i \in \mathcal{H}_i, \ i = 1, 2.$$

(b) Show that the operator $T := K^* K : \mathcal{H}_2 \to \mathcal{H}_2$ is of trace class with trace one, i.e., that for every ONB $(b_a)_{a \in A}$ in $\mathcal{H}_2$, we have

$$\sum_{a \in A} \langle b_a \mid Tb_a \rangle = \sum_{a \in A} \|Kb_a\|^2 = 1.$$

In particular, justify this convergence.

(c) Use the spectral theorem to show that there is an ONB $(b_a)_{a \in A}$ in $\mathcal{H}_2$ and numbers $\lambda_a \geq 0$ such that

$$K^* K = \sum_{a \in A} \lambda_a |b_a\rangle \langle b_a| .$$

(d) Let $K = W (K^* K)^{1/2}$ be the polar decomposition of the operator K with W denoting the partial-isometry factor. Then prove that

$$Kb_a = \sqrt{\lambda_a}\, Wb_a \qquad \text{for all } a \in A.$$

(e) **Schmidt's decomposition** (also called Schmidt's theorem or Schmidt's factorization). Let ψ be given, $\psi \in \mathcal{H}_1 \otimes \mathcal{H}_2$ as in (a), and let C, W, λ_a, and b_a be as specified in (c)–(d). Then prove that

$$\psi = \sum_{a \in A} \sqrt{\lambda_a}\, CWb_a \otimes b_a.$$

This last exercise shows that Kolmogorov's extension principle from Lemma 2.5.1 generalizes naturally to the non-commutative setting that we encountered in our use of the C^*-algebra $\mathcal{O}_N$. The relations which define $\mathcal{O}_N$ are essential for wavelet algorithms, and for our representation of corresponding processes from subband filtering. The formulation below is adapted from [BrJKW00].

7.12. First some notation: Let $N \in \{2, 3, \dots\}$ and let $\mathbb{Z}_N$ be a set of N elements. Let Ω_{fin} be the set of finite sequences $(i_1, \dots, i_m)$ where $i_k \in \mathbb{Z}_N$ and $m \in \{1, 2, \dots\}$. We also include the empty sequence $\varnothing$ in Ω_{fin}, and denote elements in Ω_{fin} by $I, J, \dots$. If $I = (i_1, \dots, i_m) \in \Omega_{\text{fin}}$ and $i \in \mathbb{Z}_N$, we let Ii denote the element $(i_1, \dots, i_m, i)$ in Ω_{fin}, and $s_I = s_{i_1} s_{i_2} \cdots s_{i_m} \in \mathcal{O}_N$ and $s_I^* = s_{i_m}^* s_{i_{m-1}}^* \cdots s_{i_1}^* \in \mathcal{O}_N$. In particular $s_\varnothing = \mathbb{1} = s_\varnothing^*$.

Let $N \in \{2, 3, \dots\}$. Show that there is a canonical one-to-one correspondence between the following objects.

(a) States P on $\mathcal{O}_N$.
(b) Functions $C : \Omega_{\text{fin}} \times \Omega_{\text{fin}} \to \mathbb{C}$ with the following properties:
   (i) $C(\varnothing, \varnothing) = 1$,
   (ii) for any function $\xi : \Omega_{\text{fin}} \to \mathbb{C}$ with finite support we have
$$\sum_{I, J \in \Omega_{\text{fin}}} \overline{\xi(I)} C(I, J) \xi(J) \geq 0,$$
   (iii) $\sum_{i \in \mathbb{Z}_N} C(Ii, Ji) = C(I, J)$ for all $I, J \in \Omega_{\text{fin}}$.
(c) Unitary equivalence classes of objects $(\mathcal{K}, v_0, V_1, \dots, V_N)$ where
   (i) $\mathcal{K}$ is a Hilbert space,
   (ii) v_0 is a unit vector in $\mathcal{K}$,
   (iii) $V_1, \dots, V_N \in \mathcal{B}(\mathcal{K})$,
   (iv) the linear span of vectors of the form $V_I^* v_0$, where $I \in \Omega_{\text{fin}}$, is dense in $\mathcal{K}$,
   (v) $\sum_{i \in \mathbb{Z}_N} V_i V_i^* = \mathbb{1}_\mathcal{K}$.

The correspondence is given by

(d) $P(s_I s_J^*) = C(I, J) = \langle V_I^* v_0 \mid V_J^* v_0 \rangle$.

References and remarks

Images and higher dimension

The early 1990s brought rapid advances on two fronts: wavelets in mathematics and image processing in engineering. The engineering applications include both the projects going into compressing and converting fingerprints into digital files [Bri95], and also the creation of processes used in chips in digital cameras.

On the mathematical side, we note in [Dau92] the use of tensor products in transferring 1D wavelet algorithms into higher-dimensional analogues. This was suggested in Daubechies' classic book [Dau92]. In fact our discussion of this in the general context of Hilbert space (see Figure 7.10, p. 126, and Exercise 7.8 above) is close to the ideas in [Dau92, Chapter 10].

Daubechies suggests the use of wavelets for image processing on page 313 in [Dau92]. She first uses the tensor-product construction in passing from problems in 1D to 2D, and then gives a geometric interpretation of the recursive splitting of resolution subspaces of $L^2(\mathbb{R}^2)$ as an iterated subdivision of squares. With this construction, elements of subsquares simultaneously play two separate roles: On the one hand, (1) vectors in cascades of subspaces of an ambient Hilbert space, as well as (2) the digital components of an image represented in grayscale and processed by a 2D wavelet algorithm. She then reproduces a visual rendition in [Dau92, Fig. 10.3, page 316], and she credits this image-cascade to M. Barlaud.

Other pioneering mathematical presentations involving 2D wavelet algorithms include [GrMa92] and [LaRe91]. Several results from [LaRe91] were later extended and appeared in the next generation of papers such as [LaLS96] and [LaLS98]. (We thank W.M. Lawton for explaining this to us.)

Representations of the Cuntz algebras

The idea of using the representations of the Cuntz algebras $\mathcal{O}_n$ in the study of iterated function systems (IFS) and more general fractals may originate with the paper [JoPe96] by Steen Pedersen and the author.

The figures in this chapter (and elsewhere) were created by Brian Treadway with Mathematica, and the Mathematica program used for Figure 7.5 (pp. 120–121) has been included below.

```
pa0[\[Theta]_] \rcolon= (1/4) - (1/4) (Cos[\[Theta]])
    - (1/4) Sin[\[Theta]]
pa1[\[Theta]_] \rcolon= -(1/4) (-1 + Sin[\[Theta]])
    + (1/4) Cos[\[Theta]]
pa2[\[Theta]_] \rcolon= (1/2) + (1/2) Sin[\[Theta]]
pa3[\[Theta]_] := -(1/2) Cos[\[Theta]]
pa4[\[Theta]_] := (1/4) + (1/4) (Cos[\[Theta]])
    - (1/4) Sin[\[Theta]]
pa5[\[Theta]_] := (1/4) (-1 + Sin[\[Theta]])
    + (1/4) Cos[\[Theta]]
a0[\[Theta]_] := pa0[\[Theta] + (\[Pi]/2)]
    - pa5[\[Theta] + (\[Pi]/2)]
a1[\[Theta]_] := pa1[\[Theta] + (\[Pi]/2)]
    + pa4[\[Theta] + (\[Pi]/2)]
a2[\[Theta]_] := pa2[\[Theta] + (\[Pi]/2)]
    - pa3[\[Theta] + (\[Pi]/2)]
a3[\[Theta]_] := pa3[\[Theta] + (\[Pi]/2)]
    + pa2[\[Theta] + (\[Pi]/2)]
a4[\[Theta]_] := pa4[\[Theta] + (\[Pi]/2)]
```

```
    - pa1[\[Theta] + (\[Pi]/2)]
a5[\[Theta]_] := pa5[\[Theta] + (\[Pi]/2)]
    + pa0[\[Theta] + (\[Pi]/2)]
loctwont[\[Theta]_] := N[Transpose[{{a2[\[Theta]],
    a0[\[Theta]]}, {a3[\[Theta]], a1[\[Theta]]}}]]
cascadestep[phitable_, \[Theta]_] := Flatten[Partition[
    Flatten[{0, phitable, 0}], 2, 1] . loctwont[\[Theta]]]
correlatewavelet[phistart_, itercount_, \[Theta]_] :=
    Flatten[Transpose[Partition[PadRight[
    Nest[cascadestep[#, \[Theta]] &, phistart,
    itercount], 6 (2^itercount)], (2^itercount)]]]
avec[\[Theta]_] := {a0[\[Theta]],
    a1[\[Theta]], a2[\[Theta]], a3[\[Theta]]}
signavec[\[Theta]_] := {-a0[\[Theta]],
    a1[\[Theta]], -a2[\[Theta]], a3[\[Theta]]}
ABstep[wltsc_,\[Theta]_] := {ListConvolve[avec[\[Theta]],
    wltsc, 1, 0], ListCorrelate[signavec[\[Theta]],
    wltsc, -1, 0]}
unscramble[wltsc_] := Flatten[Transpose[Partition[
    wltsc, 6]]]
rescramble[wltsc_] := Flatten[Transpose[Partition[
    Partition[Partition[PadRight[wltsc, 2 Length[wltsc]],
    2], 3], Length[wltsc] / 6], {3, 2, 4, 1}]]
startit = 7
philevelcount = 5
currenttheta = -5 \[Pi]/6
firstphilevel[phistart_, itercount_, \[Theta]_] :=
    Map[ABstep[#, \[Theta]] &, correlatewavelet[
    phistart, itercount, \[Theta]], {-2}]
nextphilevel[wlttree_, \[Theta]_] := Map[ABstep[#,
    \[Theta]] &, Map[rescramble, wlttree, {-2}], {-2}]
Table[Show[Graphics[Map[Point, Transpose[{Table[i (2^(
    -(startit + philevelcount))), {i, 1, 3 (2^(startit
    + philevelcount))}], Flatten[Map[unscramble, Nest[
    nextphilevel[#, currenttheta] &, firstphilevel[{1},
    startit, currenttheta], philevelcount - 1], {-2}],
    philevelcount - 1][[f]]}]}], {AspectRatio \[Rule]
    Automatic, Axes \[Rule] {True, False}, Ticks \[Rule]
    None, Frame \[Rule] True, ImageSize \[Rule] 74,
    FrameTicks \[Rule] {{0, 1, 2, 3}, {-2, -1, 0, 1, 2},
    None, None}, PlotRange \[Rule] {{-0.125, 3.125},
    {-2.5625 , 2.5625}}}]], {f, 1, 32}];
```

We offer the following minimal list of relevant references (books and papers): covering multiresolutions, [Jor03, BaCM02, BaMM99, BrJo02b]; multiwavelets, [BaMe99]; and wavelet packets, [CoWi93, Wic93, Wic94]. In our discussion of families of filters, high-pass and low-pass, in Remark 7.4.4 above, we rely on an operator-theoretic formulation which is only implicit in the formulation we offer here. The operator-theoretic approach uses certain representations of C^*-algebras, the Cuntz algebras $\mathcal{O}_N$, $N = 2, 3, \ldots$; see [Cun77]. However, this representation-theoretic viewpoint is stressed more, and made explicit, in our research papers [BrJo02a, BrJo02b, Jor03, Jor05, Jor04b].

Combining formulas (7.7.9) with (7.7.14)–(7.7.15), we see that the measures from Theorem 7.7.2 are simply restrictions of certain quantum-mechanical states to the canonical maximal abelian subalgebra $\mathcal{D}$ in the CAR-algebra $\mathfrak{A}$, i.e., the C^*-algebra $\mathfrak{A}$ on the canonical anticommutation relations, also called the fermion algebra. The subalgebra $\mathcal{D}$ in $\mathfrak{A}$ is simply the C^*-subalgebra in the CAR-algebra which is generated by the diagonal matrix elements from the list (7.7.12), i.e., by the matrix elements $e_{i,i}^{(n)}$ when n runs over $\mathbb{N}_0$ and $i = 0, 1$.

While the formulas (7.7.14)–(7.7.15) appear to define ρ_A only on $\mathcal{D}$, i.e., appear to only define a measure, the paper [PoSt70] makes it clear that the measure is a restriction of a unique state ρ_A on the CAR-algebra $\mathfrak{A}$, the so-called quasi-free states. These states on the CAR-algebra are called quasi-free states in [PoSt70]. In fact [PoSt70] initiated an important study (in operator-algebra theory) of a notion of equivalence (called quasi-equivalence) of these states (generalizing the more familiar notion of equivalence of measures—two measures are said to be equivalent if they are relatively absolutely continous). The results of Powers–Størmer [PoSt70] are motivated in turn by seminal work of Kakutani [Kak48] on equivalence of infinite-product measures.

The definition of the C^*-algebra $\mathfrak{A}$ on the CARs simply dictates the known relations that arise in models of infinite systems of quantum particles called fermions. In fact, the CARs axiomatize Pauli's exclusion principle for the fermion particles, or fermion gases. At the same time, the CAR-algebra $\mathfrak{A}$ models infinite lattice systems in quantum statistical mechanics; see [Rue69]. The framework applies independently of the lattice dimension, and it allows the development of a mathematical formulation of equilibrium states that does not rely on a chosen way of taking limits of finite subsystems.

More generally, the quasi-free states on the CAR-algebra are important in physics. They are widely used in the study of Fermi gases, and they have played a role in statistical mechanics and in axiomatic quantum field theory over the years; see, e.g., [Hal83] and [Rue69].

Independent of the long history of the study of states on the CAR-algebra, the measures from the conclusion of Theorem 7.7.2 have emerged in statistics and combinatorial probability theory under the name "determinantal measures;" see, e.g., the paper [LySt03] by Lyons and Steif, and the papers cited there. Lyons et al. and Diaconis et al. [DiFr99] used the determinantal measures in giving a new independent proof of Szego's limit theorem, and in further extending the scope of Szego's theorem to cover applications to infinite particle models in physics.

The determinantal measures have especially attractive ergodicity and monotonicity properties; see [LySt03]. In fact, they have been used in other research, e.g., in new proofs of rigorous results on Fredholm determinants in the theory of orthogonal functions, and in the representation theory of infinite-dimensional unitary groups; see the references in [DiFr99].

We saw in this chapter that there are specific non-abelian operator algebras whose representations are of significance for wavelets, fractals, and for the kind of subband filters which are used in both signal processing and in the study of wavelets. Specifically, we studied for each N the Cuntz algebra $\mathcal{O}_N$ and two of its distinguished subalgebras. In the special case of $N = 2$, one of the important subalgebras of $\mathcal{O}_2$ is known as the CAR-algebra. Here we are more interested in particular classes of representations of these C^*-algebras than in the C^*-algebras themselves. The names for the various C^*-algebras are current lingo in the theory of operator algebras and in physics. It turns out that the C^*-algebras we encountered in this chapter have been used for a long time in mathematical physics (especially in statistical mechanics [Rue69, Rue89]), where their representations play a role in the study of infinite particle systems. Ruelle's paper [Rue89] was the one which introduced the transfer operator, the operator which now goes under the name of the Perron–Frobenius–Ruelle operator. As for the C^*-algebras themselves, see, e.g., [Dav96] for a friendly and current treatment.

Unfortunately technical jargon differs from one field to the other. To reduce this linguistic confusion, we have collected a "translation guide," i.e., a separate glossary (pp. xvii–xxv above). Readers not already familiar with operator algebras might find Davidson's little book [Dav96] to be an agreeable introduction.

However, we wish to stress that the representations of the Cuntz algebras $\mathcal{O}_N$ play a role in a rich variety of applications, most of which are outside the scope of this book. Even within electrical engineering itself, signal processing is not the only place where the Cuntz relations show up. They play a crucial role in systems theory as well. Indeed, it has been shown by Joe Ball and his coauthors (see, e.g., [BaCV05] and [BaVi05]) that multidimensional linear input/output systems and their scattering theory may be couched elegantly in terms of representations of the Cuntz algebras $\mathcal{O}_N$.

The central idea in this chapter may be encapsulated in Figure 7.7 (p. 124). While this diagram is from engineering (signal processing), we have stressed that various equivalent forms of it have come up quite independently in mathematics, and for entirely different reasons. We believe that the interdisciplinary connections stressed here have great potential, but apparently that in the mathematics community they have been largely overlooked so far.

For mathematics students looking for a friendly survey of *filter banks*, i.e., the subdivision method for frequency subband filtering (in an engineering treatment), we recommend Vaidyanathan's book [Vai93] (a classic!); and for an excellent review of optimal subband and transform coders, see [VaAk01]. Many uses of filter banks and the associated algorithms in wavelets (pure and applied) are covered in [Mal98], [VeKo95], and [StNg96].

The next chapter continues the same theme, but from a more geometric viewpoint than is traditional.

8

Pyramids and operators

*Mathematics is an experimental science, and definitions do not come first,
but later on.*   —Oliver Heaviside

PREREQUISITES: Operators and their adjoints; Hilbert space; product measure;
set-theoretic partitions; multiindices; a curiosity about some applications outside of
mathematics.

Prelude

In Chapters 4 and 7, we stressed that the crucial feature of *localization* is shared by
a number of basis constructions, most notably by those of wavelets and of certain
classes of fractals. This includes basis constructions in Hilbert spaces built recursively on fractals and on state spaces in dynamics. The recursive approach to the
more general basis constructions is a special case of a refined tool from probability
which is based on *martingales*. (It should be contrasted to classical Fourier expansions, which are notoriously poorly localized.)

The localization can be further refined with the use of pyramid algorithms (see,
e.g., the multipart images in Figures 7.4 and 7.5, pp. 118–121), and we will follow
up on this in the present chapter. What should emerge is that our constructions based
on scale-similarity have an intrinsic recursive nature which immediately suggests
numerical implementations of efficient and iterative matrix algorithms.

We further saw that the use of iteration and scale similarity for bases in function
spaces is intrinsic and closely tied to localization. This in turn is part of active and
current research, and has been made precise in a number of brand new research
papers which go far beyond the scope of our book. Suffice it to call attention to
work by Stephane Jaffard (e.g., [Jaf05]) on oscillation spaces, including the so-called
Besov spaces (also beyond the scope of our book).

In connection with localization, we mention at the conclusion of Chapter 5 that there are further implications for *approximation* of functions. In particular we cited papers by Terence Tao (for wavelets) and R.S. Strichartz (for Hilbert spaces on fractals) which show that localized basis expansions in function spaces yield much better pointwise approximations than is possible for traditional Fourier bases; so contrasting again to classical Fourier expansions. In addition, Chapter 7 above emphasizes that localization is crucial for computation!

In this chapter we shall take up an additional and separate issue related to localization, that of *separation of variables*. Our approach to this will be geometric, and as far as possible, it will be based on the notion of tensor products in Hilbert space, including infinite tensor products. Readers not familiar with Hilbert-space concepts are encouraged to first do the block of multipart exercises in Chapter 7 (starting with Exercise 7.9) which are entirely devoted to the kind of tensor products that are needed.

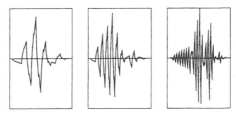

8.1 Why pyramids

In this chapter, we follow up on and generalize the ideas which form the basis for the pyramid algorithm (7.5.5) of dyadic wavelet packets. To see how this ties into more general models, based on branching, we begin with a closer examination of the unitary operator $U_2: L^2(\mathbb{R}) \to L^2(\mathbb{R})$ given by

$$U_2 f(t) := \sqrt{2} f(2t), \qquad f \in L^2(\mathbb{R}), \ t \in \mathbb{R}. \tag{8.1.1}$$

In particular, we show that there are two representations, (P_i) and (S_i), of the Cuntz algebra $\mathcal{O}_2$, see (7.6.1), such that

$$U_2 = \sum_{i=0}^{1} P_i \otimes S_i^*. \tag{8.1.2}$$

We will also study more general pairs of representations (P_i) and (S_i) of the Cuntz algebra $\mathcal{O}_N$ such that the factorization

$$U = \sum_{i=0}^{N-1} P_i \otimes S_i^* \tag{8.1.3}$$

has attractive spectral properties.

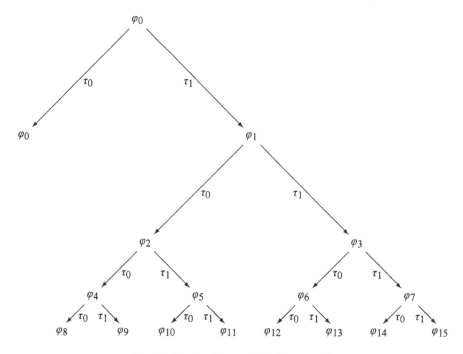

Fig. 8.1. The fundamental dyadic pyramid.

8.2 Dyadic wavelet packets

The simplest instance of the framework in Section 2.1, especially (2.1.2), is the following: Let $X = \mathbb{N}_0 = \{0, 1, 2, \ldots\}$, and set

$$\tau_0(n) = 2n, \qquad \tau_1(n) = 2n + 1, \qquad n \in \mathbb{N}_0. \qquad (8.2.1)$$

Defining

$$\sigma(2n + i) := n, \qquad i = 0, 1, \ n \in \mathbb{N}_0, \qquad (8.2.2)$$

we see that (2.1.2) is satisfied. Moreover the sequence $\varphi_0, \varphi_1, \varphi_2, \ldots$ of wavelet packet functions from (7.5.5) in Proposition 7.5.2 is generated by the pyramid in Fig. 8.1 below.

We say that the pyramid in Fig. 8.1 is singly generated.

Definition 8.2.1. Let $X, \sigma, \tau_i, i = 0, \ldots, N-1$, be a branching system as defined in (2.1.2). We say that the system *has d generators* if there is a subset $E \subset X$ satisfying

$$\# E = d \qquad (8.2.3)$$

and

$$\bigcup_{n \in \mathbb{N}_0} \sigma^{-n} (E) = X, \tag{8.2.4}$$

where

$$\sigma^{-n} (E) = \{ x \in X \mid \sigma^n (x) \in E \}. \tag{8.2.5}$$

We now introduce the following modification in Example 2.2.1 from Chapter 2. We set

$$\begin{cases} \tau_0 (n) = 2n, & \tau_1 (n) = 2n + 3, & n \in \mathbb{N}_0, \\ \sigma (2n + 3i) = n, & & n \in \mathbb{N}_0, \ i = 0, 1. \end{cases} \tag{8.2.6}$$

Setting $X = \mathbb{Z}$, we see that condition (2.1.2) is satisfied, so the system $(\mathbb{Z}, \sigma, \tau_i)$ is a dyadic branching system. Moreover the following diagram in Fig. 8.2 and an induction show that the subset

$$E := \{-3, -2, -1, 0\} \tag{8.2.7}$$

satisfies the condition in Definition 8.2.1. In contrast, (8.2.2) is singly generated.

Another feature which separates the system (8.2.6), with step size 3, is that it contains a non-trivial two-cycle, i.e., $C = \{-2, -1\}$. Note that $\sigma (-2) = -1$, and $\sigma (-1) = -2$. In addition, it has two distinct one-cycles, i.e., $\sigma (-3) = -3$, and $\sigma (0) = 0$.

Lemma 8.2.2. *Let $N \in \mathbb{N}$, $N \geq 2$, and let $\sigma: X \to X$ be an N-to-1 mapping which is onto X. Pick branches of the inverse,*

$$\tau_i: X \to X, \qquad i = 0, 1, \ldots, N - 1, \tag{8.2.8}$$

such that (2.1.2) holds.

On $\ell^2 (X)$, let $|x\rangle$, for $x \in X$, be the canonical basis vector, and set

$$P_i |x\rangle := |\tau_i (x)\rangle, \qquad i = 0, 1, \ldots, N - 1. \tag{8.2.9}$$

The adjoint operator P_i^* is

$$P_i^* |x\rangle = \chi_{\tau_i(X)} (x) |\sigma (x)\rangle, \qquad i = 0, 1, \ldots, N - 1. \tag{8.2.10}$$

Then this system of operators satisfies the Cuntz relations

$$\begin{cases} P_i^* P_j = \delta_{i,j} \mathbb{1}_{\ell^2(X)}, \\ \sum_{i=0}^{N-1} P_i P_i^* = \mathbb{1}_{\ell^2(X)}. \end{cases} \tag{8.2.11}$$

Proof. The formulas (8.2.11) follow directly by an application of the expressions (8.2.9) and (8.2.10) for the operators P_i and their adjoints P_i^*. The computation of the adjoint operator to P_i in (8.2.9) is straightforward. □

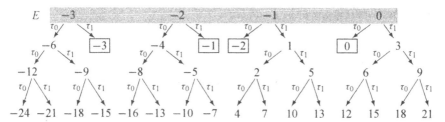

Fig. 8.2. Branching with step size 3.

Lemma 8.2.3. (a) *Let* $(S_i)_{i=0}^{N-1}$ *be a representation of the Cuntz algebra* $\mathcal{O}_N$ *on the Hilbert space* $\mathcal{K}$, *and set*

$$U := \sum_{i=0}^{N-1} P_i \otimes S_i^*. \tag{8.2.12}$$

Then $U : \ell^2(X) \otimes \mathcal{K} \to \ell^2(X) \otimes \mathcal{K}$ *is a unitary operator.*

(b) *Conversely, if* (S_i) *is a system of operators in* $\mathcal{K}$ *such that* U *in* (8.2.12) *is unitary, then the operators* S_i *satisfy the Cuntz relations*

$$\begin{cases} S_i^* S_j = \delta_{i,j} \mathbb{1}_{\mathcal{K}}, \\ \sum_{i=0}^{N-1} S_i S_i^* = \mathbb{1}_{\mathcal{K}}. \end{cases} \tag{8.2.13}$$

Proof. We will prove (a), but leave (b) to the reader.

First,

$$UU^* = \sum_i \sum_j P_i P_j^* \otimes S_i^* S_j$$

$$\underset{\text{by (8.2.13)}}{=} \sum_i \sum_j P_i P_i^* \otimes \delta_{i,j} \mathbb{1}_{\mathcal{K}}$$

$$\underset{\text{by (8.2.11)}}{=} \mathbb{1}_{\ell^2(X) \otimes \mathcal{K}};$$

and secondly,

$$U^* U = \sum_i \sum_j P_i^* P_j \otimes S_i S_j^*$$

$$\underset{\text{by (8.2.11)}}{=} \sum_i \sum_j \delta_{i,j} \mathbb{1}_{\ell^2(X)} \otimes S_i S_i^*$$

$$\underset{\text{by (8.2.13)}}{=} \mathbb{1}_{\ell^2(X) \otimes \mathcal{K}}. \qquad \square$$

Lemma 8.2.4. *Let $(\varphi_n)_{n \in \mathbb{N}_0}$ be the sequence in $L^2(\mathbb{R})$ from Proposition 7.5.2, and let $\mathcal{K}$ be the Hilbert space $L^2(\mathbb{T})$ with basis*

$$e_j(z) := z^j, \qquad z \in \mathbb{T}, \ j \in \mathbb{Z}. \tag{8.2.14}$$

Setting

$$W(|n\rangle \otimes e_j) := \varphi_n(t - j), \tag{8.2.15}$$

this assignment extends to define a co-isometry of $\ell^2(\mathbb{N}_0) \otimes \mathcal{K}$ into $L^2(\mathbb{R})$ with range equal to a dense subspace in $L^2(\mathbb{R})$. This co-isometry will also be denoted W.

Proof. The conclusion (7.5.8) from Proposition 7.5.2 is the assertion that the double-indexed family

$$\{\varphi_n(\cdot - j) \mid n \in \mathbb{N}_0, \ j \in \mathbb{Z}\} \tag{8.2.16}$$

forms a tight frame (also called a PARSEVAL frame) for the Hilbert space $L^2(\mathbb{R})$. It follows from this that W in (8.2.15) maps onto a dense subspace in $L^2(\mathbb{R})$; and we need only check that it is co-isometric.

For $f \in L^2(\mathbb{R})$, we have the following computation:

$$\begin{aligned}
\|W^* f\|^2 &\underset{\text{Parseval}}{=} \sum_{n,j} |\langle n \otimes e_j \mid W^* f \rangle|^2 \\
&= \sum_{n,j} |\langle W(|n\rangle \otimes e_j) \mid f \rangle|^2 \\
&\underset{(8.2.15)}{=} \sum_{n,j} |\langle \varphi_n(\cdot - j) \mid f \rangle|^2 \\
&\underset{\text{by } (7.5.8)}{=} \|f\|_{L^2(\mathbb{R})}^2 .
\end{aligned}$$ $\qquad \square$

Remark 8.2.5. Let W be the operator from (8.2.15) in the lemma. Then W is a unitary isomorphism of $\ell^2(\mathbb{N}_0) \otimes L^2(\mathbb{T})$ onto $L^2(\mathbb{R})$ if and only if the family $\varphi_n(\cdot - j)$ in (8.2.16) forms an orthonormal basis in $L^2(\mathbb{R})$.

In our next result, we show that the familiar dyadic scaling operator U_2 of (8.1.1) has a tensor representation with respect to the two representations of the Cuntz algebra $\mathcal{O}_2$ from above.

Theorem 8.2.6. *Let P_i, $i = 0, 1$, be the representation of $\mathcal{O}_2$ which is described in Lemma 8.2.2 and (8.2.1)–(8.2.2), and let S_i, $i = 0, 1$, be one of the representations of $\mathcal{O}_2$ described in Lemma 7.6.1. Let*

$$W: \ell^2(\mathbb{N}_0) \otimes L^2(\mathbb{T}) \to L^2(\mathbb{R}) \tag{8.2.17}$$

be the co-isometry of Lemma 8.2.4.

Then

$$W \sum_{i=0}^{1} P_i \otimes S_i^* = U_2 W, \tag{8.2.18}$$

where U_2 is the dyadic scaling operator (8.1.1) in $L^2(\mathbb{R})$.

Proof. First

$$W \sum_{i=0}^{1} P_i \otimes S_i^* \left(|n\rangle \otimes e_j \right) = W \left(\sum_{i=0}^{1} |2n+i\rangle \otimes S_i^* e_j \right) \qquad (8.2.19)$$

$$= \sum_{i=0}^{1} \sum_{k \in \mathbb{Z}} \langle e_k \mid S_i^* e_j \rangle \varphi_{2n+i} (t-k)$$

$$= \sum_{i=0}^{1} \sum_{k \in \mathbb{Z}} \sqrt{2} \, \overline{a_{j-2k}^{(i)}} \, \varphi_{2n+i} (t-k),$$

where

$$a_k^{(0)} = a_k \quad \text{and} \quad a_k^{(1)} = (-1)^k \, \bar{a}_{1-k} \qquad \text{for } k \in \mathbb{Z}; \qquad (8.2.20)$$

see also (7.5.1)–(7.5.2). Substituting this back into (8.2.19), we get

$$W \left(\sum_{i=0}^{1} P_i \otimes S_i^* \left(|n\rangle \otimes e_j \right) \right) = \sqrt{2} \, \varphi_n \left(2t - j \right), \qquad (8.2.21)$$

which is the desired conclusion (8.2.18). $\qquad \square$

Corollary 8.2.7. *Let the two representations of $\mathcal{O}_2$ be as described in the theorem, and assume in addition that the functions in (8.2.16) form an orthonormal basis (ONB) in $L^2(\mathbb{R})$.*

Then the unitary scaling operator U_2 in $L^2(\mathbb{R})$ is unitarily equivalent with $\sum_{i=0}^{1} P_i \otimes S_i^*$.

Proof. Immediate from the theorem, and Remark 8.2.5. $\qquad \square$

Proposition 8.2.8. (a) *Let the two representations of $\mathcal{O}_2$ be as described in Theorem 8.2.6, and assume the functions in (8.2.16) are orthonormal.*

Then

$$\langle \varphi_m (\cdot - k) \mid U_2 \varphi_n (\cdot - j) \rangle = \sum_{i=0}^{1} \delta_{m,2n+i} \left\langle S_i e_k \mid e_j \right\rangle \qquad \text{for all } m, n \in \mathbb{N}_0. \quad (8.2.22)$$

(b) *Let $a \in L^\infty(\mathbb{T})$ with Fourier series*

$$a(z) = \sum_{k \in \mathbb{Z}} a_k z^k, \qquad z \in \mathbb{T}, \qquad (8.2.23)$$

and set

$$a * \varphi_n = \sum_{k \in \mathbb{Z}} a_k \varphi_n (\cdot - k). \qquad (8.2.24)$$

Then

$$\langle a * \varphi_m \mid U_2 b * \varphi_n \rangle = \sum_{i=0}^{1} \delta_{m,2n+i} \langle S_i a \mid b \rangle. \qquad (8.2.25)$$

Proof. It follows from sesquilinearity that the second conclusion is implied by the first. To verify (8.2.22), we carry out a computation and use the results in Section 7.5.

Before starting the computation of the left-hand side in (8.2.22), write $m \in \mathbb{N}_0$ in the form $m = p + 2l$, $p \in \{0, 1\}$, and $l \in \mathbb{N}_0$. (This is the familiar Euclidean algorithm in its simplest form!) We now calculate the term for $m = p + 2l$; but since p runs over $\{0, 1\}$, the result must be stated as a sum, as in (8.2.22).

We have

$$\langle \varphi_m (\cdot - k) \mid U_2 \varphi_n (\cdot - j) \rangle$$

$$= \int_{\mathbb{R}} \overline{\varphi_m (t - k)} \sqrt{2} \, \varphi_n (2t - j) \, dt$$

$$\underset{\text{(by Plancherel)}}{=} \int_{\mathbb{R}} \overline{e_k (x) \, \hat{\varphi}_m (x)} \frac{1}{\sqrt{2}} \varphi_n \left(\frac{x}{2}\right) e_j \left(\frac{x}{2}\right) dx$$

$$= \sqrt{2} \int_{\mathbb{R}} \overline{e_k (2x) \, \hat{\varphi}_m (2x)} \, \hat{\varphi}_n (x) \, e_j (x) \, dx$$

$$\underset{\text{by (7.5.8)}}{=} \sqrt{2} \int_{\mathbb{R}} \overline{e_k (2x) \, m_p (x) \, \hat{\varphi}_l (x)} \, \hat{\varphi}_n (x) \, e_j (x) \, dx$$

$$= \sqrt{2} \int_0^1 \overline{e_k (2x) \, m_p (x)} \sum_{r \in \mathbb{Z}} \overline{\hat{\varphi}_l (x + r)} \, \hat{\varphi}_n (x + r) \, e_j (x) \, dx$$

$$\underset{\text{(by orthonormality)}}{=} \sqrt{2} \int_0^1 \overline{e_k (2x) \, m_p (x)} \, \delta_{l,n} e_j (x) \, dx$$

$$\underset{\text{by (7.6.5)}}{=} \delta_{l,n} \sqrt{2} \int_0^1 \overline{e_k (x)} \frac{1}{2} \sum_{2y \equiv x \bmod 1} \overline{m_p (y)} \, e_j (y) \, dx$$

$$= \delta_{l,n} \left\langle e_k \mid S_p^* e_j \right\rangle$$

$$= \delta_{l,n} \left\langle S_p e_k \mid e_j \right\rangle = \sum_{i=0}^1 \delta_{m,2n+i} \left\langle S_i e_k \mid e_j \right\rangle,$$

which is the desired result. Recall that

$$\delta_{l,n} = \sum_{i=0}^1 \delta_{m,2n+i}, \qquad (8.2.26)$$

and only one term on the right-hand side in (8.2.26) is non-zero. $\square$

Corollary 8.2.9. ([CoWi93], [Wic93]) *Let the two representations of $\mathcal{O}_2$ be as described in Theorem 8.2.6, and let $\varphi_0, \varphi_1, \ldots$ be the functions generated by the algorithm (7.5.7). Consider a subset*

$$\mathcal{A} \subset \mathbb{N}_0 \times \mathbb{N}_0. \qquad (8.2.27)$$

Then the following two conditions are equivalent:

(i) *the segments*

$$[2^p n, 2^p (n+1)) \subset \mathbb{N}_0, \qquad (p, n) \in \mathcal{A}, \qquad (8.2.28)$$

form a non-overlapping partition (or tiling) of $\mathbb{N}_0$;

and

(ii)

$$\left\{ U_2^p \varphi_n (\cdot - j) \mid (p, n) \in \mathcal{A}, \ j \in \mathbb{Z} \right\} \qquad (8.2.29)$$

is an ONB in $L^2(\mathbb{R})$.

Proof. We give a proof which relies on Theorem 8.2.6 above. Having the representation

$$U_2 = \sum_{i=0}^{1} P_i \otimes S_i^* \qquad (8.2.30)$$

makes it clear that

$$U_2^p = \sum_I P_I \otimes S_I^* \qquad (8.2.31)$$

(where the summation is over all multiindices I of length p).

Using elementary properties of tensor product in Hilbert space, we similarly get

$$\left(U_2^p\right)^* = U_2^{*p} = \sum_I P_I^* \otimes S_I. \qquad (8.2.32)$$

Recall, the formula for P_I^* is given in (8.2.10). With the multiindex notation

$$I = (i_1, i_2, \ldots, i_p), \qquad i_j \in \{0, 1\}, \ 1 \le j \le p,$$

it is then easy to verify the formula (8.2.32) for $\left(U_2^p\right)^*$. The reader only has to insert the expressions for the multiindexed operator monomials. Specifically, we have

$$\begin{cases} P_I = P_{i_1} \cdots P_{i_p}, \\ S_I = S_{i_1} \cdots S_{i_p}, \\ S_I^* = S_{i_p}^* \cdots S_{i_2}^* S_{i_1}^*. \end{cases} \qquad (8.2.33)$$

We further refer to the formulas (7.6.18)–(7.6.19) for the explicit computation of the multioperators S_I, and adjoints S_I^*.

With this, it is clear from Proposition 8.2.8 that

$$\left\langle \varphi_m (\cdot - k) \mid U_2^p \varphi_n (\cdot - j) \right\rangle = \int_{\mathbb{R}} \overline{\varphi_m (t - k)} \, 2^{p/2} \varphi_n \left(2^p t - j\right) dt$$

$$= \sum_I \delta_{m, 2^p n + i_1 + \cdots + i_p 2^{p-1}} \left\langle S_I e_k \mid e_j \right\rangle.$$

The two transformation rules follow immediately from this. We have

$$U_2^P \varphi_n \left(\cdot - j \right) = \sum_{\substack{(i_1,...,i_p),\, m, \\ 2^P n + i_1 + \cdots + i_p 2^{p-1} = m}} \left\langle S_I e_k \mid e_j \right\rangle \varphi_m \left(\cdot - k \right). \qquad (8.2.34)$$

Moreover, when $\mathcal{A}$ is chosen, we get the converse basis transformation:

$$\varphi_m \left(\cdot - k \right) = \sum_{\substack{(i_1,...,i_p),\, n, \\ 2^P n + i_1 + \cdots + i_p 2^{p-1} = m}} \left\langle e_j \mid S_I e_k \right\rangle U_2^P \varphi_n \left(\cdot - j \right). \qquad (8.2.35)$$

The equivalence of (i) and (ii) is immediate from this.   □

The next section gives more details on the choice of the sets $\mathcal{A}$ which make the segments $[2^P n, 2^P (n + 1))$ tile $\mathbb{N}_0$. We will show that the measures from Section 7.6 allow us to make "good" selections of sets $\mathcal{A} \subset \mathbb{N}_0 \times \mathbb{N}_0$ and therefore "good" ONBs.

8.3 Measures and decompositions

In this section we revisit the measures from Section 7.6. Indeed these measures were introduced in [CoWi93] and [CoMW95] for the purpose of choosing between the families of orthonormal bases (ONBs) which are listed in (8.2.28) from Corollary 8.2.9. The measures help in the use of entropy methods in the selection of the "best" ONBs.

In (8.2.28) from Corollary 8.2.9, we consider segments in $\mathbb{N}_0$, and when two segments $[2^P n, 2^P (n + 1))$ and $\left[2^{P'} n', 2^{P'} (n' + 1)\right)$ are disjoint then the corresponding basis functions $U_2^P \varphi_n (\cdot - j)$ and $U_2^{P'} \varphi_{n'} (\cdot - j')$ are orthogonal, and vice versa. This follows from the two transformation rules (8.2.34)–(8.2.35) which make it clear that a segment $[2^P n, 2^P (n + 1))$ consists precisely of the numbers $m \in \mathbb{N}_0$ which admit a dyadic representation

$$m = 2^P n + i_1 + \cdots + i_p 2^{p-1} = 2^P n + x. \qquad (8.3.1)$$

Working in $\mathbb{R}/\mathbb{Z} \cong [0, 1)$, we see from (8.3.1) that the partitions from (i) in Corollary 8.2.9 correspond to dyadic partitions of the unit interval. The correspondence between (a) the "p-subintervals," or segments of the integers $\mathbb{N}_0$, and (b) the dyadic fractional intervals in $[0, 1)$ is

$$[2^P n, 2^P (n + 1)) \rightarrow \left[\frac{i_1}{2^p} + \cdots + \frac{i_p}{2}, \frac{i_1}{2^p} + \cdots + \frac{i_p}{2} + \frac{1}{2^p} \right), \qquad (8.3.2)$$

where the integer x in (8.3.1) is specified by the multiindex I, and the Euclidean algorithm, i.e.,

$$x = i_1 + i_2 2 + \cdots + i_p 2^{p-1}, \quad \text{with } i_j \in \{0, 1\}. \qquad (8.3.3)$$

In the sequel, we will use this 1–1 correspondence m (natural number) $\leftrightarrow I$ $(i_1, \dots)$. If m is given, and i_p is the last non-zero term in (8.3.3), we say that p is the length of m, or of I.

Comparing with (8.3.1), the length is the smallest p for which there is a representation (8.3.1) with $n = 0$. The number p in (8.3.2) is this length, i.e., $p := \text{length}\,(I)$. As a result, p is determined by m in (8.3.2), and 2^{-p} is then the length of the corresponding dyadic subinterval in $[0, 1)$ on the right-hand side in (8.3.2).

If m is as in (8.3.1), then $2^{-p}m = n + i_1 2^{-p} + \cdots + i_p 2^{-1} = i_1 2^{-p} + \cdots + i_p 2^{-1}$ modulo $\mathbb{Z}$; and indeed $i_1 2^{-p} + \cdots + i_p 2^{-1}$ is the left endpoint in the subinterval on the right-hand side in the formula (8.3.2).

Left endpoints to left endpoints, and the same for rights! So $2^p n$ should correspond to $i_1 2^{-p} + \cdots + i_p 2^{-1}$, and $2^p (n+1)$ to $i_1 2^{-p} + \cdots + i_p 2^{-1} + 2^{-p}$. Now

$$2^p \left(i_1 2^{-p} + \cdots + i_p 2^{-1} \right) = i_1 + \cdots + i_p 2^{p-1} = x,$$

and

$$2^p \left(i_1 2^{-p} + \cdots + i_p 2^{-1} + 2^{-p} \right) = x + 1.$$

So when I varies over the p-tuples $(i_1, \dots, i_p)$, then x covers $[0, 2^p)$; and when n is chosen as in (8.3.1), then the integers $m = 2^p n + x$ cover $[2^p n, 2^p (n+1))$.

Hence, a specific multiindex $I = (i_1, \dots, i_p)$ "selects" a unique subinterval in $[0, 1)$ of length 2^{-p}, and with endpoints which are dyadic rationals.

Definition 8.3.1. If $(S_i)_{i=0}^1$ is a representation of $\mathcal{O}_2$ in $L^2\,(\mathbb{T})$, and

$$S_I := S_{i_1} \cdots S_{i_p},$$

then

$$P\,(I) := S_I S_I^*$$

is the orthogonal projection of $L^2\,(\mathbb{T})$ onto the subspace $S_I L^2\,(\mathbb{T})$.

We saw in Section 7.6 (Chapter 7 above) that the correspondence

$$I \mapsto P\,(I) \tag{8.3.4}$$

extends naturally to a projection-valued measure defined on the Borel subsets $\mathcal{B}$ of $[0, 1)$; see also [Jor05] and [Jor04b] for additional details.

Specifically, this measure extension (also denoted $P\,(\cdot)$) will be σ-additive, and it is *orthogonal*. This means that the identity

$$P\,(B_1 \cap B_2) = P\,(B_1)\,P\,(B_2) \tag{8.3.5}$$

holds for all $B_1, B_2 \in \mathcal{B}$.

As a result, every $h \in L^2\,(\mathbb{T})$, $\|h\|^2 = 1$, induces a probability measure μ_h according to the formula

$$\mu_h\,(B) := \|P\,(B)\,h\|^2, \qquad \text{for } B \in \mathcal{B}. \tag{8.3.6}$$

Proposition 8.3.2. *Let* $(S_i)_{i=0}^{1}$ *be some representation of* $\mathcal{O}_2$ *on* $L^2(\mathbb{T})$ *which corresponds to a quadrature-mirror filter* (m_0, m_1) *as described in Lemma 7.6.1. Let* $p, n \in \mathbb{N}_0$, *and* $j \in \mathbb{Z}$.

Then the measure $\mu_{e_j}(\cdot)$ *on* $[0, 1)$ *prescribes the distribution of the wavepacket coefficients of the function*

$$\left(U_2^p \varphi_n \right)(t - j) = 2^{p/2} \varphi_n \left(2^p t - j \right) \tag{8.3.7}$$

relative to the ONB

$$\{ \varphi_m (\cdot - k) \mid m \in \mathbb{N}_0, \ k \in \mathbb{Z} \}. \tag{8.3.8}$$

Proof. The result follows from (8.2.34) in Corollary 8.2.9 above. This is the formula which gives the expansion of $U_2^p \varphi_n (\cdot - j)$ in the ONB (8.3.8).

Hence, to prove the proposition, we only need to compute the ℓ^2-norm of the expansion coefficients from (8.2.34). The computation is just a simple application of Parseval's formula to the standard Fourier basis

$$e_k(z) := z^k \qquad \text{for } k \in \mathbb{Z}, \text{ and } z \in \mathbb{T}.$$

Indeed, summing the expansion coefficients over k, we get

$$\sum_{k \in \mathbb{Z}} |\langle S_I e_k \mid e_j \rangle|^2 \quad = \quad \sum_{k \in \mathbb{Z}} |\langle e_k \mid S_I^* e_j \rangle|^2$$

$$\underset{\text{(by Parseval)}}{=} \quad \| S_I^* e_j \|^2$$

$$= \quad \langle e_j \mid S_I S_I^* e_j \rangle$$

$$= \quad \langle e_j \mid P(I) e_j \rangle$$

$$\underset{\text{(see (8.3.4))}}{=} \quad \| P(I) e_j \|^2$$

$$= \quad \mu_{e_j} \text{ (the dyadic interval labeled by } I),$$

which is the desired conclusion.   □

8.4 Multiresolutions and tensor products

In this section we show that the tensor factorization of the unitary scaling operator U from Section 8.2 gives rise to a general class of multiresolutions. Multiresolutions were introduced into wavelet theory by Mallat [Mal89], and they are based on ideas of Kolmogorov [Kol77] from dynamics, and on the notion of a martingale from probability theory [Wil91], as we noticed in Chapters 2 and 3 above.

In the present context, we shall take "multiresolution" to be defined as follows.

Definition 8.4.1. Let U be a unitary operator in a Hilbert space $\mathcal{H}$, and let $\mathcal{H}_0$ be a closed subspace in $\mathcal{H}$. We say that $\mathcal{H}_0$ generates a *multiresolution* for U if the following two conditions (i)–(ii) hold (if all three conditions (i)–(iii) hold, we say that the multiresolution is *pure*):

(i) $\mathcal{H}_0 \subset U\mathcal{H}_0$,

(ii) $\bigvee\limits_{n\in\mathbb{Z}} U^n\mathcal{H}_0 = \mathcal{H}$,

(iii) $\bigwedge\limits_{n\in\mathbb{Z}} U^n\mathcal{H}_0 = \{0\}$,

where the symbols $\bigvee$ and $\bigwedge$ denote the *lattice operations* from Hilbert space, i.e., $\bigvee$ applied to a family of closed subspaces in $\mathcal{H}$ means "the closed linear span", and $\bigwedge$ means "intersection".

Remark 8.4.2. Let a system $(U, \mathcal{H}, \mathcal{H}_0)$ be given as in Definition 8.4.1, but suppose only (i)–(ii) are satisfied. Then U and $\mathcal{H}$ may be modified such that the resulting reduced system $(U', \mathcal{H}', \mathcal{H}_0')$ satisfies all three conditions (i)–(iii). This follows from a simple application of the Wold decomposition; see [BrJo02b].

We now sketch the details of proof: Suppose only (i)–(ii) hold. Then set

$$K := \bigwedge\limits_{n\in\mathbb{Z}} U^n\mathcal{H}_0, \tag{8.4.1}$$

$$\mathcal{H}' := \mathcal{H} \ominus K = \{ f \in \mathcal{H} \mid \langle f \mid k \rangle = 0 \text{ for all } k \in K \}, \tag{8.4.2}$$

and

$$\mathcal{H}_0' = \mathcal{H}_0 \ominus K.$$

We leave to the reader the verification of the assertions; i.e., that the reduced system $\mathcal{H}_0 \to \mathcal{H}_0'$, $\mathcal{H} \to \mathcal{H}'$, and $U \to U'$, $U' := U|_{\mathcal{H}'}$, satisfies all three conditions (i)–(iii). $\qquad\qquad\square$

The significance of Definition 8.4.1 is reflected in the following general result on unitary equivalence.

Theorem 8.4.3. *Let $(U, \mathcal{H}, \mathcal{H}_0)$ and $(U', \mathcal{H}', \mathcal{H}_0')$ be two given systems as stated in Definition 8.4.1, and assume that all three conditions (i)–(iii) hold for both systems, i.e., that the two multiresolutions are pure.*

Then there is a unitary isomorphism

$$W: \mathcal{H} \to \mathcal{H}' \tag{8.4.3}$$

which satisfies the following two conditions:

$$W\mathcal{H}_0 = \mathcal{H}_0' \tag{8.4.4}$$

and

$$WU = U'W \quad \text{(intertwining).} \tag{8.4.5}$$

(We say that the systems are unitarily equivalent.*)*

Proof. This is a standard result in operator theory, and we refer the reader to [BrJo02b, Chapter 2]. We further add that the underlying ideas date back to Kolmogorov [Kol77] in the 1930s.   □

We now show that the tensor factorization $U = \sum_i P_i \otimes S_i^*$ from Section 8.2 above gives rise to multiresolutions.

Theorem 8.4.4. *Let $N \in \mathbb{N}$, $N \geq 2$, and let (X, σ, τ_i) satisfy the conditions in Lemma 8.2.2. Let $(P_i)_{i=0}^{N-1}$ be the corresponding representation of $\mathcal{O}_N$ in $\ell^2(X)$. Let $(S_i)_{i=0}^{N-1}$ be a representation of $\mathcal{O}_N$ in a Hilbert space $\mathcal{K}$, and set*

$$\mathcal{H} := \ell^2(X) \otimes \mathcal{K}, \tag{8.4.6}$$

$$U := \sum_{i=0}^{N-1} P_i \otimes S_i^*. \tag{8.4.7}$$

Let a subset $E \subset X$ satisfy (a) *and* (b) *below,*

(a) $\sigma(E) = E$

and

(b) $\bigcup_{n \in \mathbb{N}_0} \sigma^{-n}(E) = X,$

and set

$$\mathcal{H}_n := \ell^2\left(\sigma^{-n}(E)\right) \otimes \mathcal{K}. \tag{8.4.8}$$

Then

$$U^n \mathcal{H}_0 = \mathcal{H}_n \tag{8.4.9}$$

and

$$(U, \mathcal{H}, \mathcal{H}_0) \text{ is a multiresolution system,} \tag{8.4.10}$$

i.e.,

$$\mathcal{H}_0 := \ell^2(E) \otimes \mathcal{K}$$

generates a multiresolution for U.

Proof. To prove that (i) in Definition 8.4.1 is satisfied note that for every subset $E \subset X$, we have

$$E \subset \sigma^{-1}(\sigma(E)). \tag{8.4.11}$$

Substituting (a) from the theorem, we get

$$E \subset \sigma^{-1}(E) = \bigcup_{i=0}^{N-1} \tau_i(E). \tag{8.4.12}$$

But if $e \in E$ and $k \in \mathcal{K}$, then

$$|e\rangle \otimes k = UU^* |e\rangle \otimes k \qquad (8.4.13)$$

$$= U \left(\sum_i P_i^* |e\rangle \otimes S_i k \right)$$

$$= U \left(\sum_i \chi_{\tau_i(X)} (e) |\sigma(e)\rangle \otimes S_i k \right).$$

The desired conclusion $\mathcal{H}_0 \subset U\mathcal{H}_0$ follows.

If $n \in \mathbb{N}_0$, then

$$U^n (|e\rangle \otimes k) = \sum_{i_1, \ldots, i_p} |\tau_{i_1} \tau_{i_2} \cdots \tau_{i_p} e\rangle \otimes S_{i_p}^* \cdots S_{i_1}^* k. \qquad (8.4.14)$$

Now, combining (8.4.14) and (8.4.12), we conclude that

$$U^n \mathcal{H}_0 \subset \mathcal{H}_n.$$

However, the argument from (8.4.13) shows that this inclusion is in fact an identity.

The remaining property (ii) from Definition 8.4.1 clearly follows from this, and (b) in the theorem. □

Remark 8.4.5. In applications of Theorem 8.4.4, it is useful to reduce general multiresolutions to a system of minimal ones. If N and (X, σ, τ_i) are as stated in Theorem 8.4.4, it is helpful to make a careful choice of the sets E to be used in (a) and (b) of the theorem.

If $E \subset X$ satisfies $\sigma(E) = E$, we say that E is *minimal* if the following holds:

$$\left. \begin{array}{c} \varnothing \neq A \subset E, \\ \sigma(A) = A \end{array} \right\} \Rightarrow A = E. \qquad (8.4.15)$$

In our example (8.2.6) above, we had $E = \{-3, -2, -1, 0\}$ satisfy $\sigma(E) = E$, but each of the sets

$$E_1 = \{0\},$$
$$E_2 = \{-2, -1\},$$

and

$$E_3 = \{-3\}$$

satisfies $\sigma(E_i) = E_i$, and each E_i is minimal.

Remark 8.4.6. The next result shows that such minimal sets E_i may be chosen in general. However, it is only for rather special branching systems (X, σ, τ_i) that the choices are natural.

Lemma 8.4.7. *Let $N \in \mathbb{N}$, $N \geq 2$, and let (X, σ, τ_i) satisfy the conditions in Lemma 8.2.2. Suppose some subset $E \subset X$ satisfies conditions* (a) *and* (b) *in Theorem 8.4.4. Then there are subsets $E_i \subset E$ such that*

$$\sigma(E_i) = E_i, \tag{8.4.16}$$

$$E_i \cap E_j = \emptyset \quad for\ i \neq j, \tag{8.4.17}$$

$$\bigcup_i E_i = E, \tag{8.4.18}$$

and

$$each\ E_i\ is\ a\ minimal\ solution\ to\ (8.4.16). \tag{8.4.19}$$

Proof. Zorn's lemma. □

Definition 8.4.8. If A is a subset of X, we set

$$\bar{A} := \bigcup_{n \in \mathbb{N}_0} \sigma^{-n}(A). \tag{8.4.20}$$

Proposition 8.4.9. *Let $N \in \mathbb{N}$, $N \geq 2$, and let (X, σ, τ_i) satisfy the conditions in Lemma 8.2.2. Let $\left(E, (E_i)_{i \in I}\right)$ be a system of subsets in X which satisfies the conditions in Lemma 8.4.7, where I is a chosen index set.*
  Then

$$\bar{E}_i \cap \bar{E}_j = \emptyset \quad for\ i \neq j \tag{8.4.21}$$

and

$$\bigcup_{i \in I} \bar{E}_i = X. \tag{8.4.22}$$

Proof. We leave the easy details to the reader. □

Remark 8.4.10. The significance of conditions (8.4.21)–(8.4.22) in Proposition 8.4.9 is that they generate mutually orthogonal multiresolutions in the Hilbert space $\ell^2(X) \otimes \mathcal{K}$. Specifically, we get an orthogonal decomposition

$$\ell^2(X) \otimes \mathcal{K} = \sum_{i \in I}^{\oplus} \ell^2(\bar{E}_i) \otimes \mathcal{K} \tag{8.4.23}$$

which reduces the operators, and the representations on $\ell^2(X) \otimes \mathcal{K}$ considered above.
  Returning to the three sets E_1, E_2, and E_3 from Remark 8.4.5 (and Figure 8.2, p. 161, from (8.2.6)), we get $\mathbb{Z}$ written as a disjoint union of the associated three sets $\bar{E}_1$, $\bar{E}_2$, and $\bar{E}_3$. The sets are equivalence classes for an equivalence relation studied in [BrJo99a]:

$$\bar{E}_1 = \{0, 3, 6, 9, 12, 15, 18, 21, 24, 27, 30, 33, 36, 39, 42, 45, \dots\},$$
$$\bar{E}_2 = \{-2, -1, -4, 1, -8, -5, 2, 5, -16, -13, -10, -7, 4, 7, 10, 13, \dots\},$$

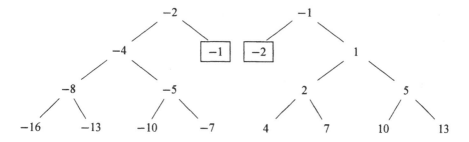

Fig. 8.3. The pyramid on $E_2 = \{-2, -1\}$ (may be seen as a subdiagram of Figure 8.2, p. 161).

and

$$\bar{E}_3 = \{-3, -6, -12, -9, -24, -21, -18, -15, \ldots\}.$$

The two sets $\bar{E}_1$ and $\bar{E}_3$ are singly generated. The middle one can be understood from the pyramid shown in Figure 8.3.

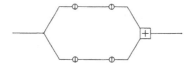

Exercises

8.1. Let $\mathcal{H}$ be a complex Hilbert space. By a *projection*, say P, we mean a linear operator $P: \mathcal{H} \rightarrow \mathcal{H}$ which satisfies $P = P^2 = P^*$. An operator $S: \mathcal{H} \rightarrow \mathcal{H}$ is called a *partial isometry* if $S^* S$ is a projection. Recall that the *norm* of a bounded linear operator $T: \mathcal{H} \rightarrow \mathcal{K}$ is defined as

$$\|T\| = \sup\{\|Th\| \mid h \in \mathcal{H}, \ \|h\| = 1\}.$$

(a) Suppose that an operator P satisfies $P = P^2$. Show that P is a projection if and only if $\|P\| = 1$.

(b) Let S be an operator such that $S^* S$ is a projection. Then show that SS^* is also a projection. The two projections are called the *initial*, resp., the *final projection* if S is given to be a partial isometry.

(c) Show that if S is a non-zero partial isometry, then $\|S\| = 1$.

8.2. Let $\mathcal{H}$ be a Hilbert space, and let $N \in \mathbb{N}$. A set $S_0, \ldots, S_{N-1}$ of N operators is said to satisfy the *Cuntz relations* if (i) and (ii) hold:

(i) $S_i^* S_j = \delta_{i,j} I$ (where I denotes the identity operator), and

(ii) $\displaystyle\sum_{i=0}^{N-1} S_i S_i^* = I$.

(a) Suppose it is given that the individual operators S_i are isometries, and that (ii) holds. Then show that (i) is automatic.

(b) Suppose that for some N, the Cuntz relations have a representation in $\mathcal{H}$. Then show that $\mathcal{H}$ must be infinite-dimensional.

8.3. Let $\mathcal{H} = \ell^2(\mathbb{Z})$, and let $N \in \mathbb{N}$ be fixed. Let E be a subset of $\mathbb{Z}$ such that there is a bijection between E and the cyclic group $\mathbb{Z}_N = \mathbb{Z}/N\mathbb{Z}$. Define

$$S_r e_k := e_{r+Nk}, \qquad r \in E, \ k \in \mathbb{Z}.$$

Then show that

$$\begin{cases} S_r^* S_{r'} = \delta_{r,r'} I & \text{for all } r, r' \in E, \\ \displaystyle\sum_{r \in E} S_r S_r^* = I. \end{cases}$$

8.4. Let $\mathcal{H} = L^2(\mathbb{T})$, and let $N \in \mathbb{N}$ be given. Let $m_0, m_1, \ldots, m_{N-1} \in L^\infty(\mathbb{T})$, where we give $\mathbb{T}$ the representation $\mathbb{R}/\mathbb{Z}$. Set

$$S_j f(x) = \sqrt{N}\, m_j(x)\, f(Nx) \qquad \text{for } f \in L^2(\mathbb{T}), \text{ and } 0 \le j < N.$$

(We identify functions on $\mathbb{T}$ with 1-periodic functions on $\mathbb{R}$.)

(a) Show that the operators $(S_j)_{j=0}^{N-1}$ yield a representation of the Cuntz relations if and only if the matrix

$$\begin{pmatrix} m_0(x) & m_0\left(x + \frac{1}{N}\right) & \cdots & m_0\left(x + \frac{N-1}{N}\right) \\ m_1(x) & m_1\left(x + \frac{1}{N}\right) & \cdots & m_1\left(x + \frac{N-1}{N}\right) \\ \vdots & \vdots & \ddots & \vdots \\ m_{N-1}(x) & m_{N-1}\left(x + \frac{1}{N}\right) & \cdots & m_{N-1}\left(x + \frac{N-1}{N}\right) \end{pmatrix}$$

is unitary for a.e. $x \in \mathbb{R}$.

(b) Show that the following three conditions are equivalent:

(i) the functions $(m_j)_{j=0}^{N-1}$ satisfy the unitarity condition in (a),

(ii) $\displaystyle\sum_{j=0}^{N-1} \overline{m_j\left(x + \frac{k}{n}\right)}\, m_j\left(x + \frac{l}{n}\right) = \delta_{k,l}$, and

(iii) $\sum_{j=0}^{N-1} \overline{m_k\left(x + \dfrac{j}{n}\right)} m_l\left(x + \dfrac{j}{n}\right) = \delta_{k,l}.$

8.5. Examples

For convenience, make the identification $\mathbb{T} \cong [0, 1)$, $\mathcal{H} = L^2\,(\mathbb{T}) \cong L^2\,(0, 1)$, so that Haar measure on $\mathbb{T}$ corresponds to the restricted Lebesgue measure on the unit interval. Functions on $[0, 1)$ will be identified with 1-periodic functions on $\mathbb{R}$ via the obvious extension. Set $e_n\,(x) := e^{i2\pi nx}$, $n \in \mathbb{Z}$, $x \in \mathbb{R}$.

(a) For $N = 2$, check that the following pairs of functions satisfy the unitarity conditions which are listed in (a) (and (b)) from Exercise 8.4.

Example 1: $m_0\,(x) = \chi_{[0,1/2)}\,(x)$, $m_1\,(x) = \chi_{[1/2,1)}\,(x)$.

Example 2: $m_0\,(x) \equiv \dfrac{1}{\sqrt{2}}$, $m_1\,(x) = \dfrac{e_1\,(x)}{\sqrt{2}}$.

Example 3: $m_0\,(x) \equiv \dfrac{1}{\sqrt{2}}$, $m_1\,(x) = \dfrac{e_3\,(x)}{\sqrt{2}}$.

Example 4: $m_0\,(x) = \cos\,(\pi x)$, $m_1\,(x) = \sin\,(\pi x)$.

Example 5: $m_0\,(x) = \dfrac{1 + e_1\,(x)}{2}$, $m_1\,(x) = \dfrac{1 - e_1\,(x)}{2}$.

Example 6: $m_0\,(x) = \dfrac{1 + e_3\,(x)}{2}$, $m_1\,(x) = \dfrac{1 - e_3\,(x)}{2}$.

(b) For $N = 3$, check that the following systems of three functions satisfy the unitarity conditions which are listed in (a) (and (b)) in Exercise 8.4.

Example 7: $m_0\,(x) = \chi_{[0,1/3)}\,(x)$, $m_1\,(x) = \chi_{[1/3,2/3)}\,(x)$, $m_2\,(x) = \chi_{[2/3,1)}\,(x)$.

Example 8: $m_0\,(x) \equiv \dfrac{1}{\sqrt{3}}$, $m_1\,(x) = \dfrac{e_1\,(x)}{\sqrt{3}}$, $m_2\,(x) = \dfrac{e_2\,(x)}{\sqrt{3}}$.

Example 9: Set $\zeta_3 := e^{i\frac{2\pi}{3}} = -\dfrac{1}{2} + i\dfrac{\sqrt{3}}{2}$, and

$$m_0\,(x) = \frac{1}{3}\,(1 + e_1\,(x) + e_2\,(x)),$$

$$m_1\,(x) = \frac{1}{3}\,(1 + \zeta_3 e_1\,(x) + \bar{\zeta}_3 e_2\,(x)),$$

$$m_2\,(x) = \frac{1}{3}\,(1 + \bar{\zeta}_3 e_1\,(x) + \zeta_3 e_2\,(x)).$$

Example 10: $m_0\,(x) = \dfrac{1 + e_2\,(x)}{\sqrt{6}}$, $m_1\,(x) = \dfrac{1 - e_2\,(x)}{\sqrt{6}}$, $m_2\,(x) = \dfrac{e_1\,(x)}{\sqrt{3}}$.

8.6. For the function m_0 in the examples in Exercise 8.5, consider the corresponding isometric operators in $\mathcal{H} = L^2(0, 1)$ given by

$$S_0 f(x) = \sqrt{2}\, m_0(x)\, f(2x) \qquad \text{if } N = 2,$$

and

$$S_0 f(x) = \sqrt{3}\, m_0(x)\, f(3x) \qquad \text{if } N = 3.$$

Show that the condition

$$\lim_{n \to \infty} S_0^{*\,n} f = 0, \qquad f \in \mathcal{H}, \tag{8E.1}$$

is satisfied in Examples 1, 4, 5, 6, 7, 9, and 10, but *not* in Example 2, 3, or 8.

8.7. (a) For the representations of $\mathcal{O}_2$ in Examples 1, 4, 5, and 6, verify irreducibility, i.e., that there is no Hilbert space $\mathcal{K}$, $0 \subsetneqq \mathcal{K} \subsetneqq \mathcal{H}$, which reduces the action of $\mathcal{O}_2$ on $\mathcal{H}$.

(b) For the representations of $\mathcal{O}_3$ in Examples 7, 9, and 10, verify irreducibility on the Hilbert space $\mathcal{H} = L^2(0, 1)$.

(c) For the representations in Examples 2, 3, and 8, directly verify reducibility.

8.8. Show that the respective representations of $\mathcal{O}_2$ and $\mathcal{O}_3$ lift to wavelet bases (or normalized tight frames) for $L^2(\mathbb{R})$ in the cases of Examples 1, 4, 5, and 6 (the dyadic case), and for examples 7 and 9 (the triadic case).

8.9. Show that the respective representations of $\mathcal{O}_2$ and $\mathcal{O}_3$ do *not* lift to wavelet bases (or frames) in the Hilbert space $L^2(\mathbb{R})$ in the cases of Examples 2, 3, 8, or 10.

8.10. Discuss the relevance of the representation of $\mathcal{O}_3$ from Example 10 (in Exercise 8.5) for the middle-third Cantor set X_3, and its Hausdorff measure h_s of Hausdorff dimension $s = \log_3 2 = \dfrac{\ln 2}{\ln 3}$.

References and remarks

We were [initially] entirely in Heisenberg's footsteps. He had the idea that one should take matrices, although he did not know that his dynamical quantities were matrices. . . . And when one had such a programme of formulating everything in matrix language, it takes some effort to get rid of matrices. Though it seemed quite natural for me to represent perturbation theory in the algebraic way, this was not a particularly new way.   —Max Born

Wavelet packets were pioneered by Coifman, Meyer, and Wickerhauser; see especially the seminal papers [CoMW95], [CoWi93], and [Wic93]. The idea and the motivation come from the equivalence of the two properties (i) and (ii) in Corollary

8.2.9. By a careful choice of the set $\mathcal{A}$, one is able to adjust the orthonormal basis (8.2.29) in such a way that the frequency bands are adapted to the space (or time) localization. Since the functions in (8.2.29) have the form

$$2^{p/2}\varphi_n\left(2^p t - j\right),$$

it is clear that large choices of p yield narrow frequency bands and vice versa.

Other helpful references on the subject may be found in Wickerhauser's book [Wic94]; see also [CoMW95], [BeBe95], [Jor05], and [Jor04b].

We have outlined in this chapter a particular interplay between on the one hand, certain selection, or optimal choice problems, in wavelet theory, and on the other, the wider field which often goes under the label of "non-commutative probability theory." While we are only scratching the surface of this very active research area, we want to mention two more directions of non-commutative probability which are not covered here: (1) Free probability, and (2) dilations of finite or infinite sets of non-commuting operators in Hilbert space. Readers who wish to learn more about (1) might wish to consult the monograph [VoDN92], [JoSW95], or [KoSp04]; and for (2) we recommend [Pop89], and [DaKS01].

Pairs of representations of the Cuntz algebras $\mathcal{O}_n$, and their application to multiresolutions

If one finds a difficulty in a calculation which is otherwise quite convincing, one should not push the difficulty away; one should rather try to make it the centre of the whole thing. —Werner Heisenberg

PREREQUISITES: Permutations; trace; tensor products of matrices; Cantor.

Prelude

This chapter will resume our study of the geometric approach via Hilbert space to separation of variables/tensor product stressed in the last two chapters; and we will note a number of applications of this idea. The approach further serves to clarify a number of themes involving combinatorics of the recursive bases studied throughout the book. The separate themes are as follows.

(1) The tensor-product idea yields an explicit representation of the unitary operator U which we use to model scale-similarity in our constructions both for standard wavelets and for fractals; see especially Lemma 9.3.2.

(2) Using tensor products we show that there are *two* representations of the Cuntz relations involved in modeling basis constructions on scale-similarity (such as was pioneered first for the standard wavelet bases in $L^2\left(\mathbb{R}^d\right)$). As already noted, our use of multiresolutions naturally entails representation of the Cuntz relations; representations which come directly from subband filters. But in addition, we find a second family of representations, one which reveals symmetry under certain permutations; see Section 9.3. The resulting second class of representations of the Cuntz relations has in fact already been studied earlier (for different purposes) under the name "permutative representations."

(3) The tensor-product idea further shows that the representation-theoretic approach is as useful for new basis constructions in function spaces on *fractals* as it is

for the standard wavelet bases in $L^2(\mathbb{R}^d)$. In Chapter 4 we introduced natural Hilbert spaces on affine fractals, and in Theorems 9.6.1 and 9.6.2 below we show how these spaces admit bases of generalized wavelets (i.e., "fractal wavelets") and of wavelet packets.

(4) Our use of tensor products helps organize the possibilities for the wavelet packets introduced in Chapter 7. In Theorem 9.4.3 we show that when a system of (admissible) digital filters is given, then the feasible choices of wavelet packets are in one-to-one correspondence with certain discrete pavings, or tilings.

(5) Finally, in Section 9.5 we outline how our use of tensor products clarifies the *discrete wavelet transform*. Recall that a choice of a multiresolution (in the generalized sense outlined in Chapter 7) automatically entails a discrete wavelet transform. When a resolution subspace is selected, this allows us to process data which is organized in an associated sequence space (i.e., in an ℓ^2-space); and it is precisely in these ℓ^2-sequence spaces where our Cuntz relations are realized.

9.1 Factorization of unitary operators in Hilbert space

In this chapter we show that the examples from Sections 8.2 to 8.4 in the previous chapter may be formulated and understood within an operator-theoretic framework. This abstract formulation helps to unify the examples, and to bring to light an underlying representation-theoretic flavor to the subject. At the same time, this general formulation may be of independent interest in operator theory. The examples from Chapter 8, i.e., wavelet packets and permutative representations, have appeared in various research papers in pure and applied mathematics; and it may now be an opportune time to try to give them a general and more axiomatic formulation.

This concluding chapter begins with a study of unitary operators U in Hilbert space. Motivated by the examples from Sections 8.2, 8.3, and 8.4, we consider the following general question: If U is a unitary operator in a Hilbert space $\mathcal{H}$, when does it admit factorizations

$$U = \sum_i S_i \otimes V_i^*, \tag{9.1.1}$$

where (S_i) and (V_i) are representations of the Cuntz algebras $\mathcal{O}_n$? We outline a number of results and applications regarding these factorizations.

We show that fractals and wavelet constructions have attractive computational features. What the different examples have in common is a kind of scaling-similarity. The scaling will be represented by the unitary operator U. As we move up and down a scale of powers of U, there will be intermediate bands corresponding to subdivisions. One representation (S_i) of $\mathcal{O}_n$ serves to encode these bands, and a second representation is then used in recovering U from (S_i). This leads to a representation (9.1.1) for the operator U.

9.2 Generalized multiresolutions

The relations known in operator theory as the Cuntz relations, i.e., $S_i^* S_j = \delta_{i,j} \mathbb{1}$ and $\sum_i S_i S_i^* = \mathbb{1}$, and which define the Cuntz algebras $\mathcal{O}_n$, $n = 2, 3, \ldots$, also play a big role in signal processing and wavelet analysis. A common feature in these applications is a detailed spectral analysis of some unitary operator $U: \mathcal{H} \to \mathcal{H}$ which plays the role of scaling. This could be scaling between different resolutions in a sequence of closed subspaces of the underlying Hilbert space $\mathcal{H}$, or the scaling could refer to a system of frequency bands.

Two structures are present: scaling from one band to the next, and operations within each band. In this chapter, we show that these applications may be subsumed in a certain tensor factorization of $\mathcal{H}$.

In the simplest case, $\mathcal{H} = L^2(\mathbb{R})$ and U is the dyadic scaling operator

$$Uf(t) = \sqrt{2}\, f(2t) \qquad \text{for } f \in L^2(\mathbb{R}) \text{ and } t \in \mathbb{R}. \tag{9.2.1}$$

In the case of a multiresolution analysis (MRA), there is a subspace $\mathcal{V}_0 \subset \mathcal{H} = L^2(\mathbb{R})$ such that

$$\mathcal{V}_0 \subset U \mathcal{V}_0, \tag{9.2.2}$$

$$\bigwedge_{n \in \mathbb{Z}} U^n \mathcal{V}_0 = \{0\}, \tag{9.2.3}$$

and

$$\bigvee_{n \in \mathbb{Z}} U^n \mathcal{V}_0 = \mathcal{H}, \tag{9.2.4}$$

where $\bigwedge$ and $\bigvee$ refer to the usual lattice operation on closed subspaces of $\mathcal{H}$.

In the MRA case for wavelets, see [Dau92], there is a function $\varphi_0 \in \mathcal{V}_0$ such that $\mathcal{V}_0$ is the closed span of the translates

$$\{\varphi_0(\cdot - k) \mid k \in \mathbb{Z}\}. \tag{9.2.5}$$

It is then possible (in favorable cases) to arrange that the translates in (9.2.5) are mutually orthogonal vectors of unit norm, i.e., that

$$\int_{\mathbb{R}} \overline{\varphi_0(t)}\, \varphi_0(t - k)\, dt = \delta_{0,k}. \tag{9.2.6}$$

There is a pyramid algorithm (defined below) for generating a sequence $\varphi_0, \varphi_1, \ldots$ with

$$\varphi_n \in U^n V_0 \tag{9.2.7}$$

and such that

$$\left\{ \varphi_n \left(\cdot - k \right) \mid n \in \mathbb{N}_0, \ k \in \mathbb{Z} \right\} \tag{9.2.8}$$

is an orthonormal basis (ONB) for $L^2(\mathbb{R})$, i.e., such that

$$\left\langle \varphi_n \left(\cdot - k \right) \mid \varphi_{n'} \left(\cdot - k' \right) \right\rangle = \delta_{n,n'} \delta_{k,k'}.$$

We show that this structure arises from two representations of the Cuntz algebra $\mathcal{O}_2$, see [Cun77], (S_i) and (V_i), such that the unitary operator U of (9.2.1) has the form

$$U = \sum_i S_i \otimes V_i^*. \tag{9.2.9}$$

The two representations are defined naturally from the wavelet data: the isometries S_i act in $\ell^2(\mathbb{N}_0)$ and the V_i's in $L^2(\mathbb{T})$. In the simplest case, we have

$$S_i \left| n \right\rangle = \left| 2n + i \right\rangle \qquad \text{for } n \in \mathbb{N}_0 \text{ and } i = 0, 1, \tag{9.2.10}$$

where we used Dirac's terminology for the natural basis $\left| n \right\rangle$ in $\ell^2(\mathbb{N}_0)$. The isometries V_i, $i = 0, 1$, are defined by two functions m_i on $\mathbb{T} = \mathbb{R}/\mathbb{Z}$ by

$$(V_i f)(x) = \sqrt{2} \, m_i(x) \, f(2x) \qquad \text{for } f \in L^2(\mathbb{T}), \ x \in \mathbb{R}, \ i = 0, 1. \tag{9.2.11}$$

The Cuntz relations for (9.2.11) are equivalent to the requirement that the matrix

$$\begin{pmatrix} m_0(x) & m_0\left(x + \frac{1}{2}\right) \\ m_1(x) & m_1\left(x + \frac{1}{2}\right) \end{pmatrix} \tag{9.2.12}$$

is unitary a.e. $x \in \mathbb{T}$.

It turns out that there are much more general systems of representations of the Cuntz algebras $\mathcal{O}_n$ which nonetheless involve the same geometry. The applications include the theory of iterated function systems (IFS), symbolic dynamics, tilings, harmonic analysis, and fractals.

9.3 Permutation of bases in Hilbert space

Definition 9.3.1. Let $\mathcal{H}$ be a complex Hilbert space. We say that a finite set of isometries $S_i: \mathcal{H} \to \mathcal{H}$, $i = 1, \ldots, n$, forms a representation of the Cuntz algebra $\mathcal{O}_n$ if the following system of identities holds:

$$\text{(a)} \quad S_i^* S_j = \delta_{i,j} \mathbb{1} \quad \text{and} \quad \text{(b)} \quad \sum_{i=1}^{n} S_i S_i^* = \mathbb{1}, \tag{9.3.1}$$

where $\mathbb{1}$ denotes the identity operator.

It is well known, see, e.g., [Cun77] and [BrJP96], that there is a one-to-one correspondence between representations of the C^*-algebra $\mathcal{O}_n$, defined by the relations (9.3.1), and the set of all systems of isometries (S_i) subject to (9.3.1). Moreover, Cuntz [Cun77] showed that the C^*-algebra $\mathcal{O}_n$ is *simple*.

As a result, we will identify the set of all representations of $\mathcal{O}_n$ on some Hilbert space $\mathcal{H}$ with the systems (9.3.1): A system (9.3.1) will be said to be an element in Rep $(\mathcal{O}_n, \mathcal{H})$. It is known that the set of equivalence classes of irreducible representations of $\mathcal{O}_n$ is "too large" to admit a meaningful classification, see [Gli60]; specifically, this set does not have a Borel cross section.

Lemma 9.3.2. *Let $\mathcal{H}_i$, $i = 1, 2$, be complex Hilbert spaces, and let $n \in \mathbb{N}$, $n \geq 2$, be given. Let $(S_i) \in$ Rep $(\mathcal{O}_n, \mathcal{H}_1)$, and let $V_1, \ldots, V_n$ be a system of operators in the Hilbert space $\mathcal{H}_2$. Then the following two conditions are equivalent:*

(i) *the operator*

$$U := \sum_{i=1}^{n} S_i \otimes V_i^* \tag{9.3.2}$$

is unitary in $\mathcal{H} := \mathcal{H}_1 \otimes \mathcal{H}_2$,

and

(ii) $V_i \in$ Rep $(\mathcal{O}_n, \mathcal{H}_2)$.

Proof. Consider arbitrary pairs of vectors $x_i, y_i \in \mathcal{H}_i$, $i = 1, 2$. Using the relations (9.3.1) for the S-system, we find that the unitarity property (i) is equivalent to the following two identities:

$$\langle x_1 \mid y_1 \rangle \Big\langle x_2 \mid \sum_i V_i V_i^* y_2 \Big\rangle = \langle x_1 \mid y_1 \rangle \langle x_2 \mid y_2 \rangle \tag{9.3.3}$$

and

$$\sum_i \sum_j \langle x_1 \mid S_i S_j^* y_1 \rangle \langle x_2 \mid V_i^* V_j y_2 \rangle = \langle x_1 \mid y_1 \rangle \langle x_2 \mid y_2 \rangle \tag{9.3.4}$$

Setting $e(i, j) := S_i S_j^*$, we see that (9.3.1) is a restatement of the familiar matrix identities

$$e(i, j)^* = e(j, i) \tag{9.3.5}$$

and

$$e(i, j) e(k, l) = \delta_{j,k} e(i, l) \tag{9.3.6}$$

for all $i, j, k, l \in \{1, \ldots, n\}$.

If we form the n-by-n block matrix

$$M(V) = \left(V_i^* V_j \right)_{i,j=1}^{n} \in M_n(\mathbb{C}) \otimes B(\mathcal{H}_2) = M_n(B(\mathcal{H}_2)), \tag{9.3.7}$$

the two identities (9.3.3)–(9.3.4) simply state that $M(V)$ is the identity matrix in $M_n(B(\mathcal{H}_2))$, i.e., that

$$V_i^* V_j = \delta_{i,j} I_{\mathcal{H}_2}. \tag{9.3.8}$$

Let trace be the normalized trace on $M_n(\mathbb{C})$, and consider

$$\text{trace} \otimes \text{id}: M_n(\mathbb{C}) \otimes B(\mathcal{H}_2) \to B(\mathcal{H}_2).$$

Applying this to the element $\left(V_i V_j^*\right)_{i,j=1}^n$ in $M_n(\mathbb{C}) \otimes B(\mathcal{H}_2)$, we get $\sum_i V_i V_i^*$. But identity (9.3.2) also yields $(\text{trace} \otimes \text{id}) \left(V_i V_j^*\right) = \mathbb{1}_{\mathcal{H}_2}$. As a result, we get

$$\sum_i V_i V_i^* = \mathbb{1}_{\mathcal{H}_2}. \tag{9.3.9}$$

Combining (9.3.8) and (9.3.9), we get the implication (i) $\Rightarrow$ (ii). Since the converse implication is immediate, the proof is completed.   □

Definition 9.3.3. Let X be a set, and let $R: X \to X$ be an endomorphism. Let $R^{-1}(x) := \{ y \in X \mid R(y) = x \}$ for $x \in X$. We say that R is an *n-fold branch mapping* if R is onto and if

$$\# R^{-1}(x) = n \qquad \text{for all } x \in X. \tag{9.3.10}$$

For a given n-fold branch mapping, we shall select n branches of the inverse, i.e., n distinct mappings

$$\sigma_i: X \to X, \qquad i = 1, \ldots, n, \tag{9.3.11}$$

such that

$$R \circ \sigma_i = \text{id}_X \qquad \text{for all } i = 1, \ldots, n. \tag{9.3.12}$$

Definition 9.3.4. Let $\mathcal{H}$ be a complex Hilbert space, and let $(S_i) \in \text{Rep}(\mathcal{O}_n, \mathcal{H})$ for some $n \in \mathbb{N}$, $n \geq 2$. We say that (S_i) is a *permutative representation*, see [BrJo99a], is each isometry S_i permutes the elements in some orthonormal basis (ONB) for $\mathcal{H}$.

Lemma 9.3.5. *[BrJo99a] Up to unitary equivalence of representations every permutative representation (S_i) of $\mathcal{O}_n$ in a Hilbert space $\mathcal{H}$ has the following form for some set X and some n-fold branch mapping $R: X \to X$.*

Let $\mathcal{H} = \ell^2(X)$, and for $x \in X$, let $|x\rangle$ be the corresponding basis vector in $\mathcal{H}$. If $c: X \to \mathbb{C}$ is in $\ell^2(X)$, then

$$c = \sum_{x \in X} c(x) |x\rangle, \qquad \|c\|^2 = \sum_{x \in X} |c(x)|^2, \tag{9.3.13}$$

and

$$\langle x \mid y \rangle = \delta_{x,y} \qquad \text{for all } x, y \in X. \tag{9.3.14}$$

For a choice of distinct branches σ_i, $i = 1, \ldots, n$, set

$$S_i |x\rangle := |\sigma_i(x)\rangle. \tag{9.3.15}$$

Proof. Let $(S_i) \in \mathrm{Rep}\,(\mathcal{O}_n, \mathcal{H})$ be a permutative representation. Let X be an index set for some ONB which is permuted by the respective isometries S_i. As a result, there are maps $\sigma_i \colon X \to X$ such that

$$S_i \left| x \right\rangle = \left| \sigma_i \left(x \right) \right\rangle \qquad \text{for } i = 1, \ldots, n \text{ and } x \in X. \tag{9.3.16}$$

Using (a) in (9.3.1), we consider that each σ_i is one-to-one, and that

$$\sigma_i \left(X \right) \cap \sigma_j \left(X \right) = \varnothing \qquad \text{if } i \neq j. \tag{9.3.17}$$

Using (9.3.14) and (9.3.16), we derive the formula

$$S_i^* \left| \sigma_j \left(x \right) \right\rangle = \delta_{i,j} \left| x \right\rangle \qquad \text{for } i, j = 1, \ldots, n \text{ and } x \in X, \tag{9.3.18}$$

for the adjoint operators S_i^*, $i = 1, \ldots, n$. When (9.3.18) is substituted into (b) of (9.3.1) we conclude that

$$\bigcup_{i=1}^{n} \sigma_i \left(X \right) = X. \tag{9.3.19}$$

As a result, we may define $R \colon X \to X$ by setting

$$R \left(\sigma_i \left(x \right) \right) = x \qquad \text{for } i = 1, \ldots, n \text{ and } x \in X, \tag{9.3.20}$$

and conclude that R, defined this way, is an n-fold branch mapping. Substituting back into (9.3.18), we conclude that

$$S_i^* \left| x \right\rangle = \chi_{\sigma_i (X)} \left| R \left(x \right) \right\rangle \qquad \text{for } i = 1, \ldots, n \text{ and } x \in X. \qquad \square$$

9.4 Tilings

Let X be a set, and let $n \in \mathbb{N}$, $n \geq 2$, be given. Let $R \colon X \to X$ be an n-fold branch mapping. For $x \in X$ and $p \in \mathbb{N}$, set

$$R^{-p} \left(x \right) := \left\{ y \in X \mid R^p \left(y \right) = x \right\}. \tag{9.4.1}$$

It is convenient to include the case $p = 0$, and set

$$E \left(x, p \right) = \begin{cases} R^{-p} \left(x \right) & \text{if } p \in \mathbb{N}, \\ \{x\} \ \text{(the singleton)} & \text{if } p = 0. \end{cases} \tag{9.4.2}$$

Definition 9.4.1. A subset $\mathcal{A} \subset X \times \mathbb{N}_0$ is said to define a *tiling* of X if

$$\bigcup_{(x,p)\in\mathcal{A}} E \left(x, p \right) = X \tag{9.4.3}$$

and

$$E \left(x, p \right) \cap E \left(x', p' \right) = \varnothing \qquad \text{if } (x, p) \neq (x', p') \text{ in } \mathcal{A}, \tag{9.4.4}$$

i.e., the sets $E \left(x, p \right)$, indexed by distinct points in $\mathcal{A}$, are disjoint.

Examples 9.4.2. In the next three examples we illustrate the use of tensor products as outlined in Lemma 9.3.2. The scaling will be represented by the unitary operator U. One representation (S_i) of $\mathcal{O}_n$ serves to encode subdivision bands, and a second representation is then used in recovering U from (S_i). This leads to a representation (9.3.2) for the operator U. The first representation (S_i) of $\mathcal{O}_n$ will be a "permutative representation," i.e., it will be defined from a permutation of a canonical basis in one of the two tensor factors. Formula (9.2.10) is an example of such a representation, but there are many more; see for example the memoir [BrJo99a]. The second representation (V_i) will be given by a quadrature-mirror filter as in (9.2.12), or more generally filters corresponding to n subbands as given in Chapter 7. The reader is encouraged to work out the two types of representations in Exercises 8.3 and 8.4.

The additional feature in this construction is tensor products of Hilbert spaces. For this part the use of operator theory helps clarify the use of tensor products and setting up a "wavelet transform." We are further relying on Dirac's elegant bra-ket notation: see the conclusion of Chapter 2 for details.

Example 9.4.2.1. Let $X = \mathbb{N}_0$, and set

$$R(2n) = n \quad \text{and} \quad R(2n+1) = n \qquad \text{for } n \in \mathbb{N}_0. \tag{9.4.5}$$

Then for $(n, p) \in X \times \mathbb{N}_0$, we have the identity

$$E(n, p) = [n2^p, (n+1)2^p). \tag{9.4.6}$$

One easily checks that the mapping R in (9.4.5) is a 2-fold branch mapping with branches

$$\sigma_0(n) = 2n, \quad \sigma_1(n) = 2n+1 \qquad \text{for } n \in \mathbb{N}_0. \tag{9.4.7}$$

If $I \in \Omega(p)$, i.e., $I = (i_1, \ldots, i_p)$, then

$$\sigma_I(n) = i_1 + i_2 2 + \cdots + i_p 2^{p-1} + n2^p, \tag{9.4.8}$$

and it follows that the sets $E(n, p)$ are as described in (9.4.6). In conclusion, the possible tilings of $X = \mathbb{N}_0$ associated with R in (9.4.5) are the partitions of $\mathbb{N}_0$ into non-overlapping segments of the form (9.4.6). Here are three distinct types of such tilings.

Case (a): $\mathcal{A} = \{(n, 0) \mid n \in \mathbb{N}_0\}$, and
$$E(n, 0) = \{n\} \text{ (the singleton)} \qquad \text{for } n \in \mathbb{N}_0.$$

Case (b): $\mathcal{A} = \{(0, 0), (1, p) \mid p \in \mathbb{N}_0\}$, and
$$E(1, p) = [2^p, 2^{p+1}) \qquad \text{for } p \in \mathbb{N}_0.$$

Case (c): $\mathcal{A} = \{(0, 2), (1, 2k), (2, 2k), (3, 2k) \mid k \in \mathbb{N}\}$, where now
$$E(0, 2) = \{0, 1, 2, 3\}, \text{ and}$$
$$E(j, 2k) = [j2^{2k}, (j+1)2^{2k}) \qquad \text{for } j = 1, 2, 3 \text{ and } k \in \mathbb{N}.$$

We stress, however, that there are many more types of examples.

Example 9.4.2.2. It would be tempting to define R on $\mathbb{N}_0$ by the following rules,

$$R(2n) = n \quad \text{and} \quad R(2n+3) = n, \tag{9.4.9}$$

by analogy to (9.4.5) in Example 9.4.2.1, but the equation $1 = 2n + 3$ does not have solutions in $\mathbb{N}_0$. One checks that no subset X of $\mathbb{N}_0$ allows the rules (9.4.9) in the definition of a 2-fold branch mapping. Nonetheless, if we take $X = \mathbb{Z}$, then (9.4.9) does define a 2-fold branch mapping.

So there are several differences betwen the two examples 9.4.2.1 and 9.4.2.2. For Example 9.4.2.1, every point is attracted to $\{0\}$ in the sense that if $n \in \mathbb{N}_0$, then there is a p such that $R^P n = 0$. For Example 9.4.2.2, there is no singleton in $X = \mathbb{Z}$ which serves as an attractor. Nonetheless, for every $n \in \mathbb{Z}$, there is a p such that $R^P n \in \{-3, -2, -1, 0\}$. The analogues of the tiling systems (a)–(c) in Example 9.4.2.1 carry over to Example 9.4.2.2 as follows.

Case (a): $\mathcal{A} = \{(n, 0) \mid n \in \mathbb{Z}\}$, and

$E(n, 0) = \{n\}$ (the singleton)   for $n \in \mathbb{Z}$.

Case (b):   This tile system now contains a more varied system of tiles for the set $X = \mathbb{Z}$. The singleton tiles are $E(n, 0) = \{n\}$ for $n = -3, -2, -1, 0$, and in addition there are the following five classes of (non-overlapping) dyadic tiles:

$E(-6, p)$	for all $p \in \mathbb{N}_0$,
$E(-4, p)$	for all $p \in \mathbb{N}_0$,
$E(1, p)$	for all $p \in \mathbb{N}_0$,
$E(3, p)$	for all $p \in \mathbb{N}_0$, and
$E(8, p)$	for all $p \in \mathbb{N}_0$.

Case (c):   We leave this to the reader.

In conclusion, the two examples show how libraries of wavelet bases are constructed from two entirely different families of representations of the Cuntz algebra $\mathcal{O}_n$.

The occurrence of one of the representations (V_i) is not surprising: it is determined by the kind of subband filters familiar from both signal processing and the standard multiresolution approach to wavelet bases. It is the second representation (S_i) of $\mathcal{O}_n$, the permutative representation, that completes formula (9.2.10) for the scaling operator U, encodes our wavelet bases and accounts for the variety of tilings as they arise in Proposition 8.3.2 and Theorem 8.4.4. As in Proposition 8.3.2, we start with an ONB $\{\varphi_n \mid n \in \mathbb{N}_0\}$ as in (8.3.8); we apply suitable powers of U to these functions, creating the functions $U^P \varphi_n$, and then ask which subsets of the double indices yield new ONBs. The same principle applies to more general basis constructions, and Theorem 8.4.4 spells out the tilings that yield bases of wavelet packets.

In the systematic study of permutative representations in [BrJo99a] it is shown that each permutative representation can be understood from a single endomorphism R of the index set. In the next example we introduce R: see formula (9.4.10).

Example 9.4.2.3. In this next example, we use an arbitrary but fixed scaling number $N \in \mathbb{N}$, $N \geq 2$, generalizing Example 9.4.2.1 above. We take $X = \mathbb{N}_0$, and set

$$R(k + Nn) = n \quad \text{for } k = 0, 1, \ldots, N - 1, \text{ and for all } n \in \mathbb{N}_0. \quad (9.4.10)$$

As in Example 9.4.2.1, one checks that this is a branch mapping, in this case an N-fold branch, i.e., there are N distinct branches of the inverse, $\sigma_k(x) := k + Nn$, $k = 0, 1, \ldots, N - 1$. For $(n, p) \in X \times \mathbb{N}_0$, $X = \mathbb{N}_0$, one checks the formula

$$E(n, p) = \left[nN^p, (n + 1) N^p \right). \quad (9.4.11)$$

The three types of tilings (a)–(c) from Example 9.4.2.1 then generalize as follows.

Case (a): $\mathcal{A} = \{ (n, 0) \mid n \in \mathbb{N}_0 \}$, and
   $E(n, 0) = \{n\}$ (the singletons)   for $n \in \mathbb{N}_0$.

Case (b): $\mathcal{A} = \{ (0, 0), (1, p), (2, p), \ldots, (N - 1, p) \mid p \in \mathbb{N}_0 \}$, and
   $E(k, p) = \left[kN^p, (k + 1) N^p \right), k = 0, 1, \ldots, N - 1, \ p \in \mathbb{N}_0$.

Case (c): $\mathcal{A} = \{ (0, 2), (1, Nk), (2, Nk), \ldots, ((N^2 - 1), Nk) \mid k \in \mathbb{N} \}$,
   where now

$$E(0, 2) = \left\{ 0, 1, 2, 3, \ldots, N^2 - 1 \right\}, \text{ and}$$
$$E(j, 2k) = [jN^{2k}, (j + 1) N^{2k})$$
$$\text{for } j = 0, 1, \ldots, N^2 - 1 \text{ and } k \in \mathbb{N}.$$

In the rest of the chapter, we study some more general features of the n-fold branching mapping R which occurred in a special case in Example 9.4.2.3. In our general study of permutative representations in [BrJo99a], we refer to R as the canonical endomorphism. What makes the next theorem different is that it yields an axiomatic approach to libraries of bases in Hilbert space. It applies to the kind of iterated-function-system fractals studied in Chapter 8 above and in more detail in [BrJo99a], and at the same time it generalizes the pyramid approach to bases of wavelet packets; see Proposition 8.3.2, Theorem 8.4.4, and Figure 7.5 (pp. 120–121).

An ONB $\{ \varphi_n \mid n \in \mathbb{N}_0 \}$ as in (8.3.8) yields one index set. The second arises from the scale-similarity inherent in wavelet analysis, scaling by a power of 2 or N, or in several variables by a power of a fixed scaling matrix. The scaling is a unitary operator U in the ambient Hilbert space, which may be $L^2(\mathbb{R}^d)$, and then we create the functions $U^p \varphi_n$, and ask which subsets of the double indices yield new ONBs.

The setting in the next result, Theorem 9.4.3, is maximally flexible in that it allows a completely general ONB and index set X. Once this is given, we may consider the most general permutative representations as in [BrJo99a]. Depending on the application, e.g., an iterated-function-system fractal, a time-series problem from signal processing, or an image-processing algorithm, we are then able to build a unitary operator, a tensor-product representation, and associated tilings and bases of wavelet packets, so generalized libraries of bases of wavelet packets.

A special class of iterated-function-system fractal where this works well is the affine iterated function systems. In Section 9.6, we show how multiresolutions and generalized libraries of bases of wavelet packets may be adapted to these systems. Closing the circle from Chapter 4, we begin with the middle-third Cantor set, and our associated wavelet families are given in Theorem 9.6.1, so-called space-filling wavelet bases. In Section 9.7 we go on to study the wider class of these affine fractals.

Theorem 9.4.3. *Let $R: X \to X$ be an n-fold branch mapping, and let (S_i) be the corresponding permutative representation on $\ell^2(X)$. Let $\mathcal{K}$ be a Hilbert space with orthonormal basis (ONB) $\mathcal{B} = \{|b\rangle\}$, and let $(V_i) \in \text{Rep}(\mathcal{O}_n, \mathcal{K})$. Set $U = \sum_{i=1}^n S_i \otimes V_i^*$, and let $\mathcal{A} \subset X \times \mathbb{N}_0$ be a subset.*
Then the following two conditions are equivalent:

(i) *the vectors $U^p |x \otimes b\rangle$ indexed by $(x, p) \in \mathcal{A}$ and $b \in \mathcal{B}$ form an ONB for $\ell^2(X) \otimes \mathcal{K}$; and*
(ii) *$\mathcal{A}$ defines a tiling of X.*

Proof. Let $\mathbf{n} = \{1, \dots, n\}$, and set $\Omega(p) = \underbrace{\mathbf{n} \times \mathbf{n} \times \cdots \times \mathbf{n}}_{p \text{ times}}$. Then

$$U^p |x \otimes b\rangle = \sum_{I \in \Omega(p)} |S_I x\rangle \otimes |V_I^* b\rangle, \tag{9.4.12}$$

and $S_I x \in E(x, p)$.

(ii) $\Rightarrow$ (i). Assuming (ii), it is clear that the corresponding vectors in (i) form an orthonormal family in $\mathcal{H} := \ell^2(X) \otimes \mathcal{K}$. Let $y \in X$ and $b' \in \mathcal{B}$. Pick $(x, p) \in \mathcal{A}$ such that $y \in E(x, p)$. Then $y = S_I x$ for a unique $I = (i_1, \dots, i_p) \in \Omega(p)$, and

$$|y\rangle \otimes |b'\rangle = U^p |x \otimes V_I b'\rangle, \tag{9.4.13}$$

where we used the identity

$$V_J^* V_I = \delta_{J,I} \qquad \text{for } J, I \in \Omega(p). \tag{9.4.14}$$

A substitution of

$$V_I b' = \sum_{b \in \mathcal{B}} \langle b \mid V_I b' \rangle \tag{9.4.15}$$

into (9.4.13) yields

$$|y\rangle \otimes |b'\rangle = \sum_{b \in \mathcal{B}} \langle b \mid V_I b' \rangle U_p |x \otimes b\rangle. \tag{9.4.16}$$

Since the vectors $|y\rangle \otimes |b'\rangle$ form an ONB for $\mathcal{H}$, we conclude that the family (i) is total in $\mathcal{H}$: the vectors on the right-hand side in (9.4.16) are precisely the vectors listed in (i).

(i) $\Rightarrow$ (ii). We now assume that the vectors in (i) form an ONB in $\mathcal{H}$.

Let (x, p), $(x', p') \in \mathcal{A}$. Then for every $I \in \Omega(p)$ and $I' \in \Omega(p')$, $S_I x \in E(x, p)$ and $S_{I'} x' \in E(x', p')$. Since the vectors $U^p |x \otimes b\rangle$ and $U^{p'} |x' \otimes b'\rangle$ from (i) are orthogonal, we conclude from (9.4.12) that (9.4.4) holds, i.e., that the distinct sets $E(x, p)$ and $E(x', p')$ for (x, p) and (x', p') in $\mathcal{A}$ are disjoint.

If (9.4.3) were not satisfied and $y \in X \setminus \bigcup_{(x,p)\in\mathcal{A}} E(x, p)$, then it follows from (9.4.13) that $|y, b'\rangle$ is in the orthogonal complement of the whole family (i). Hence (i) could not be total. Since we assume that (i) is an ONB, the proof is completed. $\square$

9.5 Applications to wavelets

Let $\mathcal{H}$ be the space $L^2(\mathbb{R})$ of all L^2-functions on $\mathbb{R}$, and let $N \in \mathbb{N}$, $N \geq 2$, be given. Then the scaling operator

$$(Uf)(t) = \sqrt{N} f(Nt), \qquad f \in \mathcal{H}, \ t \in \mathbb{R}, \tag{9.5.1}$$

is clearly unitary. The purpose of this section is to show that every multiresolution wavelet decomposition of $\mathcal{H}$, corresponding to scale number N, gives rise to a tensor factorization of U of the form (9.3.2); specifically, U has the form

$$U = \sum_{i=0}^{N-1} S_i \otimes V_i^*. \tag{9.5.2}$$

Here the tensor factorization in (9.5.2) refers to

$$\mathcal{H} = \ell^2(\mathbb{N}_0) \otimes L^2(\mathbb{T}) \qquad \text{where } \mathbb{T} = \mathbb{R}/\mathbb{Z}, \tag{9.5.3}$$

and where

$$(S_i) \in \text{Rep}\left(\mathcal{O}_N, \ell^2(\mathbb{N}_0)\right) \quad \text{and} \quad (V_i) \in \text{Rep}\left(\mathcal{O}_N, L^2(\mathbb{T})\right). \tag{9.5.4}$$

Furthermore, the two representations in (9.5.4) are specified as follows. The representation (S_i) in (9.5.4) is the permutative representation from Example 9.4.2.3 above. (If $N = 2$, it is the special case in Example 9.4.2.1.)

The representation (V_i) from (9.5.4) is defined from a system of functions $m_0, \ldots, m_{N-1}$ in $L^\infty(\mathbb{T})$ such that the $N \times N$ matrix

$$\begin{pmatrix} m_0(x) & m_0\left(x + \frac{1}{N}\right) & \cdots & m_0\left(x + \frac{N-1}{N}\right) \\ m_1(x) & m_1\left(x + \frac{1}{N}\right) & \cdots & m_1\left(x + \frac{N-1}{N}\right) \\ \vdots & \vdots & \ddots & \vdots \\ m_{N-1}(x) & m_{N-1}\left(x + \frac{1}{N}\right) & \cdots & m_{N-1}\left(x + \frac{N-1}{N}\right) \end{pmatrix} \tag{9.5.5}$$

is unitary a.e. $x \in \mathbb{T}$.

We recall the following two lemmas from [BrJo02b]; see also [Wic94].

Lemma 9.5.1. *Let $m_0, m_1, \ldots, m_{N-1}$ be in $L^\infty(\mathbb{T})$, and set*

$$(V_i f)(x) = \sqrt{N}\, m_i(x)\, f(Nx) \tag{9.5.6}$$

for $f \in L^2(\mathbb{T})$, $x \in \mathbb{R}$, and $i = 0, 1, \ldots, N-1$.

Then $(V_i) \in \mathrm{Rep}\left(\mathcal{O}_N, L^2(\mathbb{T})\right)$ if and only if the matrix (9.5.5) is unitary a.e. $x \in \mathbb{T}$.

The next lemma is also known, but we sketch it for reference.

Lemma 9.5.2. *The Fourier transform*

$$\hat{f}(x) = \int_{-\infty}^{\infty} e^{-i2\pi xt} f(t)\, dt \tag{9.5.7}$$

realizes a unitary isomorphism

$$W: L^2(\mathbb{R}) \cong \ell^2(\mathbb{Z}) \otimes L^2(\mathbb{T}) \tag{9.5.8}$$

as follows:

$$(Wf)(x) := \left(\hat{f}(x+k)\right)_{k \in \mathbb{Z}} \in \ell^2(\mathbb{Z}). \tag{9.5.9}$$

Proof. Initially, $Wf(\cdot)$ is just a function from $\mathbb{R}$ mapping into $\ell^2(\mathbb{Z})$. But an application of Parseval's identity and Fubini's theorem shows that

$$\int_0^1 \sum_{k \in \mathbb{Z}} \left|\hat{f}(x+k)\right|^2 dx = \int_{-\infty}^{\infty} \left|\hat{f}(x)\right|^2 dx = \int_{-\infty}^{\infty} |f(t)|^2\, dt. \tag{9.5.10}$$

Hence the mapping W in (9.5.9) passes to a unitary isomorphism of $L^2(\mathbb{R})$ onto $L^2\left(\mathbb{T}, \ell^2(\mathbb{Z})\right) = \ell^2(\mathbb{Z}) \otimes L^2(\mathbb{T})$. $\qquad\square$

Lemma 9.5.3. *Let $m_0, m_1, \ldots, m_{N-1}$ be in $L^\infty(\mathbb{T})$ and suppose the unitarity condition (9.5.5) is satisfied. Assume in addition that m_0 is Lipschitz near $x = 0$, and that $m_0(0) = \sqrt{N}$.*

(a) *Then there is a sequence $\varphi_0, \varphi_1, \ldots$ in $L^2(\mathbb{R})$ such that*

$$\begin{cases} \hat{\varphi}_{Nn}(Nx) &= m_0(x)\,\hat{\varphi}_n(x), \\ \hat{\varphi}_{Nn+1}(Nx) &= m_1(x)\,\hat{\varphi}_n(x), \\ \quad\vdots & \qquad\vdots \\ \hat{\varphi}_{Nn+N-1}(Nx) &= m_{N-1}(x)\,\hat{\varphi}_n(x), \end{cases} \tag{9.5.11}$$

and

$$\int_{\mathbb{R}} \varphi_0(t)\, dt = 1. \tag{9.5.12}$$

(b) *The following three additional conditions on the functions* $\varphi_0, \varphi_1, \varphi_2, \ldots$ *are mutually equivalent:*

(i) $\displaystyle\int_{\mathbb{R}} |\varphi_0(t)|^2 \, dt = 1,$

(ii) $\displaystyle\sum_{j \in \mathbb{Z}} |\hat{\varphi}_0(x+j)|^2 = 1 \qquad a.e. \ x \in \mathbb{R},$

(iii) $\displaystyle\sum_{j \in \mathbb{Z}} \overline{\hat{\varphi}_n(x+j)} \, \hat{\varphi}_{n'}(x+j) = \delta_{n,n'} \qquad a.e. \ x \in \mathbb{R}.$

Remark 9.5.4. The clearest way to visualize the sequence $\{\varphi_n \mid n \in \mathbb{N}_0\}$ from Lemma 9.5.3(b), see especially (9.5.11), is to picture the functions in the case of $N = 2$, for the Haar wavelet construction. In that case,

$$\begin{cases} \varphi_{2n}(t) = \varphi_n(2t) + \varphi_n(2t-1), \\ \varphi_{2n+1}(t) = \varphi_n(2t) - \varphi_n(2t-1), \\ \varphi_0 = \chi_{[0,1)} \end{cases} \qquad (9.5.13)$$

The first 32 functions in this sequence are reproduced in Figure 7.4 (pp. 118–119) where some features of their construction may be observed, such as the partial symmetry/antisymmetry of φ_n (in the Haar case) at all dyadic scales:

$$\varphi_n(2^{-k} - t) = \pm\varphi_n(t), \qquad n = 0, 1, 2, \ldots, \quad k = 0, 1, 2, \ldots, \quad a.e. \ t \in (0, 2^{-k}).$$

Theorem 9.5.5. *Let* $m_0, m_1, \ldots, m_{N-1}$ *be functions in* $L^\infty(\mathbb{T})$ *which satisfy the conditions in Lemma 9.5.3(b), and let* $\varphi_0, \varphi_1, \varphi_2, \ldots$ *be the corresponding sequence in* $L^2(\mathbb{R})$. *Then the double-indexed family*

$$\{\varphi_n(\cdot - k) \mid n \in \mathbb{N}_0, \ k \in \mathbb{Z}\} \qquad (9.5.14)$$

is an orthonormal basis for $L^2(\mathbb{R})$. *Set*

$$e_k(x) := \exp(-i2\pi kx), \qquad (9.5.15)$$

and let $(V_i)_{i=0}^{N-1}$ *be the representation of* $\mathcal{O}_N$ *defined in Lemma 9.5.1; see* (9.5.6). *Then*

$$\sqrt{N}\,\varphi_n(Nt-k) = \sum_{i=0}^{N-1} \sum_{j \in \mathbb{Z}} \langle V_i e_j \mid e_k \rangle \varphi_{Nn+i}(t-j). \qquad (9.5.16)$$

Proof. The fact that (9.5.14) is an ONB in $L^2(\mathbb{R})$ follows from Lemma 9.5.3(b). When the operators V_i, $i = 0, 1, \ldots, N-1$, are defined from the filter functions m_i, as in (9.5.6), it follows from Lemma 9.5.1 that $(V_i) \in \text{Rep}(\mathcal{O}_N, L^2(\mathbb{T}))$. Hence to prove (9.5.16), it is enough to show that

$$\int_{\mathbb{R}} \overline{\varphi_{Nn+i}(t-j)} \sqrt{N}\,\varphi_n(Nt-k) \, dt = \langle V_i e_j \mid e_k \rangle \qquad (9.5.17)$$

for all $n \in \mathbb{N}_0$, and all $j, k \in \mathbb{Z}$. On the right-hand side of (9.5.17), we use the inner product in $L^2(\mathbb{T})$.

The proof of (9.5.17) is again based on Parseval's identity, and a second application of Lemma 9.5.3(b). Starting with the left-hand side in (9.5.17), we set $n = n_1 + n_2 N + \cdots + n_p N^{p-1}$, where $n_1, n_2, \cdots \in \{0, 1, \ldots, N-1\}$. Then

$$\hat{\varphi}_n (x) = m_{n_1} (x/N) \cdots m_{n_p} (x/N^p) \, \hat{\varphi}_0 (x/N^p) ,$$

and

$$\int_{\mathbb{R}} \overline{\varphi_{Nn+i} (t - j)} \sqrt{N} \, \varphi_n (Nt - k) \, dt$$

$$= \int_{\mathbb{R}} \overline{e_j (x) \, \hat{\varphi}_{Nn+i} (x)} \, N^{-1/2} \hat{\varphi}_n \left(\frac{x}{N} \right) e_k \left(\frac{x}{N} \right) dx$$

$$= \sqrt{N} \int_{\mathbb{R}} \overline{e_j (Nx) \, \hat{\varphi}_{Nn+i} (Nx)} \, \hat{\varphi}_n (x) \, e_k (x) \, dx$$

$$= \sqrt{N} \int_{\mathbb{R}} \overline{e_j (Nx) \, m_i (x)} \, |\hat{\varphi}_n (x)|^2 \, e_k (x) \, dx$$

$$= \sqrt{N} \int_0^1 \overline{e_j (Nx) \, m_i (x)} \, \sum_{l \in \mathbb{Z}} |\hat{\varphi}_n (x + l)|^2 \, e_k (x) \, dx$$

$$= \sqrt{N} \int_0^1 \overline{e_j (Nx) \, m_i (x)} \, e_k (x) \, dx$$

$$= \int_0^1 \overline{e_j (x)} \, \frac{1}{\sqrt{N}} \sum_{l=0}^{N-1} \overline{m_i \left(\frac{x + l}{N} \right)} \, e_k \left(\frac{x + l}{N} \right) dx$$

$$= \int_0^1 \overline{e_j (x)} \, (V_i^* e_k) (x) \, dx$$

$$= \langle e_j \mid V_i^* e_k \rangle = \langle V_i e_j \mid e_k \rangle . \qquad \square$$

Since every system $m_0, \ldots, m_{N-1}$ which satisfies the conditions in Lemma 9.5.3(b) generates functions $\varphi_0, \varphi_1, \ldots$ in $L^2(\mathbb{R})$ such that

$$\{ \varphi_n (\cdot - k) \mid n \in \mathbb{N}_0, \ k \in \mathbb{Z} \}$$

is an ONB in $L^2(\mathbb{R})$, the assignment

$$\varphi_n (\cdot - k) \mapsto |n\rangle \otimes |k\rangle \tag{9.5.18}$$

extends to a unitary isomorphism

$$L^2(\mathbb{R}) \cong \ell^2(\mathbb{N}_0) \otimes \ell^2(\mathbb{Z}) \cong \ell^2(\mathbb{N}_0) \otimes L^2(\mathbb{T}), \tag{9.5.19}$$

where we use the familiar isomorphism $\ell^2(\mathbb{Z}) \cong L^2(\mathbb{T})$ defined by the usual Fourier basis $\{ e_k \mid k \in \mathbb{Z} \}$ introduced in (9.5.15).

Corollary 9.5.6. *Let the functions* $m_0, m_1, \ldots, m_{N-1}$ *satisfy the conditions in Lemma 9.5.3(b), and let*

$$L^2(\mathbb{R}) \cong \ell^2(\mathbb{N}_0) \otimes \ell^2(\mathbb{Z})$$

be the unitary isomorphism defined by the corresponding ONB

$$\{\varphi_n(\cdot - k) \mid n \in \mathbb{N}_0, \ k \in \mathbb{Z}\};$$

see (9.5.19) and (9.5.14).

  Let $(V_i) \in \text{Rep}(\mathcal{O}_n, \ell^2(\mathbb{Z}))$ *be defined from the* (m_i) *system as in Lemma 9.5.1, and wet*

$$S_i \lvert n \rangle = \lvert Nn + i \rangle \qquad for \ i = 0, 1, \ldots, N-1 \ and \ n \in \mathbb{N}_0 \qquad (9.5.20)$$

be the permutative representation of Example 9.4.2.3.

  Then the unitary scaling operator

$$Uf(t) := \sqrt{N} f(Nt) \qquad for \ f \in L^2(\mathbb{R}), \ t \in \mathbb{R} \qquad (9.5.21)$$

has the tensor factorization

$$U = \sum_{i=0}^{N-1} S_i \otimes V_i^*. \qquad (9.5.22)$$

Proof. Once we have identified the isomorphism (9.5.18), the result follows from (9.5.16) in Theorem 9.5.5. Specifically,

$$U\left(\lvert n \rangle \otimes \lvert k \rangle\right) = \sqrt{N}\, \varphi_n(Nt - k)$$

$$= \sum_{i=0}^{N-1} \sum_{j \in \mathbb{Z}} \langle V_i e_j \mid e_k \rangle \varphi_{Nn+i}(t - j)$$

$$= \sum_{i=0}^{N-1} \sum_{j \in \mathbb{Z}} \langle e_j \mid V_i^* e_k \rangle \lvert S_i n \rangle \otimes \lvert e_j \rangle$$

$$= \sum_{i=0}^{N-1} \lvert S_i n \rangle \otimes \lvert V_i^* e_k \rangle$$

$$= \sum_{i=0}^{N-1} S_i \otimes V_i^* \lvert n \rangle \otimes \lvert k \rangle. \qquad \square$$

9.6 An application to fractals

In a paper with D. Dutkay [DuJo06b] we showed that a certain class of fractals admits a multiresolution analysis (MRA). It is the class of fractals which is generated by a finite system of contractive affine mappings in $\mathbb{R}^d$, and it includes the middle-third Cantor set C_3.

Rather than treating the most general case here, we will restrict attention to two examples, C_3 and C_4. The Cantor set C_3 is the unique compact subset of $\mathbb{R}$ (in fact of $[0, 1]$) which satisfies

$$3C_3 = C_3 \cup (C_3 + 2), \tag{9.6.1}$$

and C_4 is the unique compact subset of $\mathbb{R}$ which solves

$$4C_4 = C_4 \cup (C_4 + 2). \tag{9.6.2}$$

Both examples are generated by scaling and subdivision into similar "smaller" replicas, and we define the Hausdorff dimension of the fractals by

$$c := \frac{\log (\text{number of replicas})}{\log (\text{magnification factor})}. \tag{9.6.3}$$

Furthermore, we note that

$$c\,(C_3) = \log_3 (2) = \frac{\ln 2}{\ln 3} \tag{9.6.4}$$

and

$$c\,(C_4) = \log_4 2 = \frac{\ln 2}{\ln 4} = \frac{1}{2}. \tag{9.6.5}$$

Using a standard theorem from geometric measure theory, see, e.g., [Hut81], we observe that there are unique probability measures μ_3 and μ_4 with supports C_3 and C_4 respectively such that

$$\int f\,(t)\,d\mu_3\,(t) = \frac{1}{2} \left(\int f\left(\frac{t}{3}\right) d\mu_3\,(t) + \int f\left(\frac{t+2}{3}\right) d\mu_3\,(t) \right) \tag{9.6.6}$$

and

$$\int f\,(t)\,d\mu_4\,(t) = \frac{1}{2} \left(\int f\left(\frac{t}{4}\right) d\mu_4\,(t) + \int f\left(\frac{t+2}{4}\right) d\mu_4\,(t) \right) \tag{9.6.7}$$

hold for all bounded continuous functions f on $\mathbb{R}$.

Set

$$\mathcal{R}_3 := \left\{ t \in \mathbb{R} \,\middle|\, \exists n \in \mathbb{N}_0,\ t_i \in \{0, 1, 2\} \text{ such that} \right.$$

$$\left. t = \sum_{i=-n}^{\infty} \frac{t_i}{3^i} \text{ and only a finite number of } t_i\text{'s are } 1 \right\}, \tag{9.6.8}$$

and

$$\mathcal{R}_4 := \left\{ t \in \mathbb{R} \,\middle|\, \exists n \in \mathbb{N}_0, \; t_i \in \{0, 1, 2, 3\} \text{ such that} \right.$$

$$\left. t = \sum_{i=-n}^{\infty} \frac{t_i}{4^i} \text{ and only a finite number of } t_i\text{'s are 1 or 3} \right\}. \quad (9.6.9)$$

Using the respective Hausdorff measures $(dt)^c$ on $\mathbb{R}$ we get the following separable Hilbert spaces:

$$\mathcal{H}^{(\log_3 2)} = L^2\left(\mathcal{R}_3, (dt)^{\log_3 2}\right) \quad (9.6.10)$$

and

$$\mathcal{H}^{(1/2)} = L^2\left(\mathcal{R}_4, (dt)^{1/2}\right). \quad (9.6.11)$$

In general, we get unitary scaling operators U in these fractal Hilbert spaces given by the formula

$$(Uf)(t) = \sqrt{\#(\text{replicas})}\, f(Nt) \qquad \text{for } t \in \mathbb{R}, \quad (9.6.12)$$

where $N = $ the magnification factor. Specifically, for $\mathcal{R}_3$,

$$(U_3 f)(t) = \sqrt{2}\, f(3t), \quad (9.6.13)$$

and for $\mathcal{R}_4$,

$$(U_4 f)(t) = \sqrt{2}\, f(4t) \qquad \text{for } t \in \mathbb{R}. \quad (9.6.14)$$

In each example, we have a system of filter functions (m_i) satisfying condition (9.5.5) before Lemma 9.5.1. (Recall that condition (9.5.5) is equivalent to the fact that the operators V_i in (9.5.6) form a representation of the Cuntz algebra $\mathcal{O}_N$.) It follows that the two examples are associated to representations of the respective Cuntz algebras $\mathcal{O}_3$ and $\mathcal{O}_4$ acting on $L^2(\mathbb{T})$.

For $\mathcal{R}_3$, the three functions are

$$\begin{cases} m_0(z) = \dfrac{1}{\sqrt{2}}\left(1 + z^2\right), \\[2mm] m_1(z) = z, \\[2mm] m_2(z) = \dfrac{1}{\sqrt{2}}\left(1 - z^2\right), \end{cases} \quad (9.6.15)$$

where we have set $z = e^{i2\pi x}$.

For $\mathcal{R}_4$, the four functions are

$$\begin{cases} m_0(z) = \dfrac{1}{\sqrt{2}}\left(1 + z^2\right), \\[2mm] m_1(z) = z, \\[2mm] m_2(z) = z^3, \\[2mm] m_3(z) = \dfrac{1}{\sqrt{2}}\left(1 - z^2\right). \end{cases} \quad (9.6.16)$$

Theorem 9.6.1. (a) *There is an orthonormal system (ON) $\varphi_0, \varphi_1, \varphi_2, \ldots$ in* $L^2 \left(\mathcal{R}_3, (dt)^{\log_3 2} \right)$ *which solves the system of equations*

$$\begin{cases} \varphi_{3n}(t) = \varphi_n(3t) + \varphi_n(3t-2), \\ \varphi_{3n+1}(t) = \sqrt{2}\,\varphi_n(3t-1), \\ \varphi_{3n+2}(t) = \varphi_n(3t) - \varphi_n(3t-2), \\ \varphi_0 = \chi_{C_3}. \end{cases} \tag{9.6.17}$$

(b) *The functions*

$$\{ \varphi_n(\cdot - k) \mid n \in \mathbb{N}_0, \ k \in \mathbb{Z} \} \tag{9.6.18}$$

form an ONB for $L^2 \left(\mathcal{R}_3, (dt)^{\log_3 2} \right)$.

(c) *If $(S_i) \in \operatorname{Rep}\left(\mathcal{O}_3, \ell^2(\mathbb{N}_0) \right)$ and $(V_i) \in \operatorname{Rep}\left(\mathcal{O}_3, L^2(\mathbb{T}) \right)$ are the associated representations, see Example 9.4.2.3, $N = 3$, and Lemma 9.5.1, then*

$$U_3 = \sum_{i=0}^{2} S_i \otimes V_i^*. \tag{9.6.19}$$

Theorem 9.6.2. (a) *There is an an orthonormal system $\varphi_0, \varphi_1, \varphi_2, \ldots$ in* $L^2 \left(\mathcal{R}_4, (dt)^{1/2} \right)$ *which solves the system of equations*

$$\begin{cases} \varphi_{4n}(t) = \varphi_n(4t) + \varphi_n(4t-2), \\ \varphi_{4n+1}(t) = \sqrt{2}\,\varphi_n(4t-1), \\ \varphi_{4n+2}(t) = \sqrt{2}\,\varphi_n(4t-3), \\ \varphi_{4n+3}(t) = \varphi_n(4t) - \varphi_n(4t-2), \\ \varphi_0 = \chi_{C_4}. \end{cases} \tag{9.6.20}$$

(b) *The functions*

$$\{ \varphi_n(\cdot - k) \mid n \in \mathbb{N}_0, \ k \in \mathbb{Z} \} \tag{9.6.21}$$

form an ONB for $L^2 \left(\mathcal{R}_4, (dt)^{1/2} \right)$.

(c) *If $(S_i) \in \operatorname{Rep}\left(\mathcal{O}_4, \ell^2(\mathbb{N}_0) \right)$ and $(V_i) \in \operatorname{Rep}\left(\mathcal{O}_4, L^2(\mathbb{T}) \right)$ are the associated representations (see Example 9.4.2.3, $N = 4$, and Lemma 9.5.1), then*

$$U_4 = \sum_{i=0}^{3} S_i \otimes V_i^*. \tag{9.6.22}$$

Proof. We have presented the details in Sections 9.4 and 9.5 so that the proofs of the two theorems follow as an easy application. The main point is the observation that the two recursive systems (9.6.17) and (9.6.20) admit solutions which satisfy the respective orthogonality conditions. But the two Hilbert spaces $L^2 \left(\mathcal{R}_3, (dt)^{\log_3 2} \right)$ and $L^2 \left(\mathcal{R}_4, (dt)^{1/2} \right)$ have been defined so that this becomes clear. To see that the respective orthonormal systems (9.6.18) and (9.6.21) really are total, one may use the MRAs which we introduced in [DuJo06b]. The multiresolutions in the respective fractal Hilbert spaces share the same Hilbert-space geometry with $L^2(\mathbb{R})$ which we presented in Section 9.5 above. In particular, our tensor factorizations (9.6.19) and (9.6.22) for U_3 and U_4 follow from the idea in the proof of Corollary 9.5.6 above.   □

9.7 Phase modulation

The difference between the two examples of fractals in Section 9.6 above has to do with phase modulation, i.e., with the operators of multiplication by

$$e_\lambda(t) := e^{-i2\pi\lambda t} \qquad \text{for } t \in \mathbb{R}. \tag{9.7.1}$$

So far, our wavelet constructions have involved only scaling and translation. The phases (9.7.1) have entered only because of their use in understanding translations via Fourier duality.

Lemma 9.7.1. [JoPe98] *Let $\mathbf{C}_4$ be the quarter Cantor set, and let μ_4 be the corresponding normalized measure supported on $\mathbf{C}_4$ and satisfying (9.6.7). Set*

$$\Lambda = \Lambda_4 = \left\{ \sum_{j\geq 0} n_j 4^j \;\middle|\; \textit{finite sums, } n_j \in \{0,1\} \right\}. \tag{9.7.2}$$

Then the functions $\{e_\lambda \mid \lambda \in \Lambda_4\}$ restricted to $\mathbf{C}_4$ form an orthonormal basis in $L^2(\mathbf{C}_4, \mu_4)$.

Remark 9.7.2. It is known [JoPe98] that there are no more than two orthogonal functions e_λ (for any $\lambda \in \mathbb{R}$) in the Hilbert space $L^2(\mathbf{C}_3, \mu_3)$.

Theorem 9.7.3. *Let $N = 4$, and let $\{\varphi_n \mid n \in \mathbb{N}_0\}$ be the orthonormal sequence in $L^2(\mathcal{R}_4, (dt)^{1/2})$ constructed in Theorem 9.6.2.*
    Then the family

$$\left\{ e_\lambda(t)\,\varphi_j(t-k) \mid \lambda \in \Lambda_4,\ j = 0, 3,\ k \in \mathbb{Z} \right\} \tag{9.7.3}$$

and

$$\left\{ e_\lambda(t/4)\,\varphi_j(t-k) \mid \lambda \in \Lambda_4,\ j = 1, 2,\ k \in \mathbb{Z} \right\} \tag{9.7.4}$$

is an orthonormal basis (ONB) in the Hilbert space $L^2(\mathcal{R}_4, (dt)^{1/2})$.

Proof. The proof follows from a combination of (i) Lemma 9.7.1, (ii) the discussion of the affine fractals in Section 9.6, and (iii) some basic observations of scaling and the Hausdorff measure; see also [DuJo06b] and the following list.
    Several observations are needed:

(1) $\Lambda_4 \subset \mathcal{R}_4$.

(2) Setting $\tau_j(t) = (t+j)/4$, $j = 0, 1, 2, 3$, we note that $C_4 = \tau_0 C_4 \cup \tau_2 C_4$, as a non-overlapping union, and

$$
\begin{cases}
\varphi_0 = \chi_{C_4} = \chi_{\tau_0 C_4} + \chi_{\tau_2 C_4}, \\
\varphi_1 = \sqrt{2}\,\chi_{\tau_1 C_4}, \\
\varphi_2 = \sqrt{2}\,\chi_{\tau_3 C_4}, \\
\varphi_3 = \chi_{\tau_0 C_4} - \chi_{\tau_2 C_4}.
\end{cases}
\tag{9.7.5}
$$

(3) The Hausdorff measure $h^{1/2}$ restricted to C_4 is μ_4.
(4) The integration $(dt)^{1/2}$ in the definition of the Hilbert space refers to $h^{1/2}$.
(5) Borel subsets of $\mathbb{R}$ are $h^{1/2}$-measurable.
(6)

$$
h^{1/2}(B+t) = h^{1/2}(B) \tag{9.7.6}
$$

and

$$
h^{1/2}(cB) = \sqrt{c}\, h^{1/2}(B) \tag{9.7.7}
$$

for all $h^{1/2}$-measurable sets B, all $t \in \mathbb{R}$, and all $c \in \mathbb{R}_+$.

(7)

$$
\int_{\mathcal{R}_4} f(t)\, dh^{1/2}(t) = \frac{1}{2} \int_{\mathcal{R}_4} f(\tau_j(t))\, dh^{1/2}(t) \tag{9.7.8}
$$

holds for all $h^{1/2}$-measurable functions on $\mathcal{R}_4$.

With this, we leave the remaining detailed verifications to the reader.   □

Exercises

9.1. Let $\varphi \in L^2(\mathbb{R})$ and suppose there is some sequence $(a_k)_{k \in \mathbb{Z}}$ such that

$$
\varphi(t) = 2 \sum_{k \in \mathbb{Z}} a_k \varphi(2t - k), \qquad t \in \mathbb{R}. \tag{9E.1}
$$

(a) Show that if $\int_{\mathbb{R}} \varphi(t)\, dt \neq 0$, then

$$
\sum_{k \in \mathbb{Z}} a_k = 1.
$$

(b) Suppose there are constants c_1, c_2 such that $0 < c_1 \leq c_2 < \infty$, and

$$c_1 \sum_{k \in \mathbb{Z}} |\xi_k|^2 \le \left\| \sum_{k \in \mathbb{Z}} \xi_k \varphi \left(\cdot - k \right) \right\|_{L^2(\mathbb{R})}^2 \le c_2 \sum_{k \in \mathbb{Z}} |\xi_k|^2 .$$

Let V_φ $(=: V_0)$ denote the closed linear span of $\{ \varphi \left(\cdot - k \right) \mid k \in \mathbb{Z} \}$. Then show that $W = W_\varphi$ given by

$$W \left(\sum_{k \in \mathbb{Z}} \xi_k \varphi \left(\cdot - k \right) \right) := (\xi_k)_{k \in \mathbb{Z}} \tag{9E.2}$$

defines a bounded linear operator from V_0 into $\ell^2 (\mathbb{Z})$.

(c) Show that the operator W in (b) has zero kernel, i.e., that

$$\{ f \in V_0 \mid Wf = 0 \} = \{0\} .$$

(d) Define an operator S_0 on $\ell^2 (\mathbb{Z})$ by

$$(S_0 \xi)_n = \sqrt{2} \sum_{k \in \mathbb{Z}} a_{n-2k} \xi_k,$$

and let U_2 be the dyadic scaling operator in $L^2 (\mathbb{R})$, i.e.,

$$(U_2 f) (t) = \frac{1}{\sqrt{2}} f \left(\frac{t}{2} \right) .$$

Then show that the following intertwining relation holds:

$$W U_2 = S_0 W \qquad \text{on } V_0. \tag{9E.3}$$

9.2. We continue with the assumptions introduced in Exercise 9.1 above.

(a) Using Exercise 5.7, find a Ruelle operator R which has the function

$$h (x) := \mathrm{Av} \, |\hat{\varphi}|^2 (x) := \sum_{n \in \mathbb{Z}} |\hat{\varphi} (x + n)|^2$$

as eigenfunction, i.e., with $Rh = h$.

(b) Using the function $\sum_{n \in \mathbb{Z}} |\hat{\varphi} (x + n)|^2$ from (a), find an explicit formula for the adjoint operator $W_\varphi^* : \ell^2 (\mathbb{Z}) \to V_0$, when W_φ is the intertwining operator introduced in Exercise 9.1 (see (9E.2)).

9.3. Let the operators W, U_2, and S_0 be as described in Exercise 9.1.

(a) Show that there is a unique isometry $T : V_0 \to \ell^2 (\mathbb{Z})$ such that

$$W = (W W^*)^{1/2} T.$$

(b) Show that the operator T in part (a) satisfies

$$W = T (W^* W)^{1/2} .$$

(c) Show that the operator T in part (a) satisfies

$$W^*W = T^*\left(WW^*\right)T.$$

(d) Show that the operator T in part (a) satisfies

$$TU_2 = S_0 T \qquad \text{on } V_0.$$

Hint for part (d): T is the isometric part of the polar decomposition of W. First use (9E.3) to show that $(W^*W)\,U_2 = U_2\,(W^*W)$. Then use the spectral theorem on W^*W to show that $(W^*W)^{1/2}\,U_2 = U_2\,(W^*W)^{1/2}$; and the conclusion then follows from parts (b) and (c).

9.4. Let (a_k) and (b_k) be two sequences indexed by $\mathbb{Z}$, and define operators S_0 and S_1 in $\ell^2\,(\mathbb{Z})$ by

$$(S_0\xi)_n := \sqrt{2}\sum_{k\in\mathbb{Z}} a_{n-2k}\xi_k$$

and

$$(S_1\xi)_n := \sqrt{2}\sum_{k\in\mathbb{Z}} b_{n-2k}\xi_k.$$

(a) Show that the following (i) and (ii) are equivalent.

(i) The Cuntz relations

$$S_i^* S_j = \delta_{i,j} I \quad \text{and} \quad \sum_{i=0}^{1} S_i S_i^* = I$$

hold.

(ii) The three separate identities

$$2\sum_k \bar{a}_k a_{k+2l} = \delta_{0,l}, \quad 2\sum_k \bar{b}_k b_{k+2l} = \delta_{0,l}, \quad \sum_k \bar{a}_k b_{k+2l} = 0$$

hold.

(b) Suppose $(a_k)_{k\in\mathbb{Z}}$ satisfies

$$2\sum_k \bar{a}_k a_{k+2l} = \delta_{0,l}.$$

Setting $b_k = (-1)^k\,\bar{a}_{1-k}$, show that the two sequences then satisfy the conditions in (ii).

(c) Given two sequences (a_k) and (b_k), define

$$U\,(z) := \sum_{k\in\mathbb{Z}} \begin{pmatrix} a_{2k} & a_{2k+1} \\ b_{2k} & b_{2k+1} \end{pmatrix} z^k.$$

Now show that $U\,(z)$ is unitary for all $z \in \mathbb{T}$ if and only if the conditions in (ii) are satisfied.

9.5. Consider a dyadic wavelet basis in $L^2(\mathbb{R})$ indexed as follows:

$$\psi_{j,k}(t) := 2^{-j/2}\psi\left(2^{-j}t - k\right), \qquad j, k \in \mathbb{Z},$$

and let $W: V_0 \to \ell^2(\mathbb{Z})$ be the intertwining operator from Exercise 9.1. Finally, let $(e_k)_{k\in\mathbb{Z}}$ be the canonical basis in ℓ^2, i.e., $e_k(j) := \delta_{k,j}$. Prove that

$$W(\psi_{j,k}) = S_0^{j-1}S_1 e_k \qquad \text{for all } j = 1, 2, \ldots, \text{ and } k \in \mathbb{Z}.$$

9.6. The discrete wavelet transform

Let $(a_k)_{k\in\mathbb{Z}}$ and $(b_k)_{k\in\mathbb{Z}}$ be sequences satisfying the orthogonality conditions in Exercise 9.4(a). Let $F \cong S_0^*$ and $G \cong S_1^*$ be the corresponding slanted matrices in (7E.2), F defined from (a_k), and G from (b_k). For $x \in \ell^2(\mathbb{Z})$, we say that

$$x = \sum_{j=0}^{\infty}\sum_{k\in\mathbb{Z}} c_{j,k} S_0^j S_1 e_k \tag{9E.4}$$

is the *discrete wavelet transform*.

(a) Show that the wavelet coefficients $c_{j,k}$ in (9E.4) are given by the following matrix multiplication:

$$c_{j,k} = \left(GF^j x\right)_k = \sum_{l\in\mathbb{Z}}\left(GF^j\right)_{k,l} x_l. \tag{9E.5}$$

(b) Carry out the matrix products in (9E.5) in the four-tap case, i.e., when the two sequences have only four non-zero terms, say a_0, a_1, a_2, a_3 and b_0, b_1, b_2, b_3.

(c) In the four-tap case (part (b)) show that each of the finite-dimensional sub-spaces $S_k := \text{span}\{e_{-k}, \ldots, e_{-1}, e_0, e_1, \ldots, e_k\}$, $k \geq 2$, is invariant under matrix multiplication with F and with G.

(d) With assumptions as in part (c), show that multiplication with F and G maps S_{k+1} into S_k for $k \geq 2$.

(e) In the four-tap case, and representing vectors in S_2 as

$$x = \begin{pmatrix} x_{-2} \\ x_{-1} \\ x_0 \\ x_1 \\ x_2 \end{pmatrix},$$

show that $y = Fx$ has the following form, matrix multiplication in the four-tap case, i.e., matrix times column vector:

$$\begin{cases} y_{-2} = \bar{a}_2 x_{-2} + \bar{a}_3 x_{-1}, \\ y_{-1} = \bar{a}_0 x_{-2} + \bar{a}_1 x_{-1} + \bar{a}_2 x_0 + \bar{a}_3 x_1, \\ y_0 = \bar{a}_0 x_0 + \bar{a}_1 x_1 + \bar{a}_2 x_2, \\ y_1 = \bar{a}_0 x_2, \\ y_2 = 0. \end{cases}$$

9.7. Let $\mathcal{H}$ be a complex Hilbert space, and let S_0, S_1 be bounded operators in $\mathcal{H}$. For $j \in \{0, 1, 2, \ldots\}$, set $T_j := S_0^j S_1$. Now show that the following two systems of conditions (i) and (ii) are equivalent.

(i) S_0, S_1 satisfy the $\mathcal{O}_2$-Cuntz relations, and $S_0^{*n} \underset{n\to\infty}{\to} 0$.

(ii) $\{T_j\}_{j\in\mathbb{N}_0}$ satisfy the $\mathcal{O}_\infty$-Cuntz relations, i.e.,

$$\begin{cases} T_j^* T_k = \delta_{j,k} I & \text{for all } j, k \in \mathbb{N}_0, \\ \displaystyle\sum_{j\in\mathbb{N}_0} T_j T_j^* = I. \end{cases}$$

P.S.: The assertions in (i) and (ii) about convergence refer to the *strong operator topology* (SOT) on $B(\mathcal{H})$ = the bounded operators on $\mathcal{H}$. Recall that the neighborhoods of 0 in $B(\mathcal{H})$ are generated by finite sets $\{h_i\}$ of vectors in $\mathcal{H}$ and $\varepsilon \in \mathbb{R}_+$: $\{T \in B(\mathcal{H}) \mid \|Th_i\| < \varepsilon\}$. Specifically, $S_0^{*n} \underset{n\to\infty}{\to} 0$ (SOT) if and only if $\lim_{n\to\infty} \|S_0^{*n} h\| = 0$ for all $h \in \mathcal{H}$.

9.8. Kolmogorov

(a) Let $n \in \mathbb{N}$, and let S_n be some set of cardinality n. Let $(R_n(x, y))$ be a fixed positive definite $n \times n$ matrix, i.e., satisfying

$$\sum_{x\in S_n} \sum_{y\in S_n} \bar{\xi}_x R_n(x, y) \xi_y \geq 0$$

for all $(\xi_x)_{x\in S_n}$ in $\mathbb{C}^n$. Show that there is an n-dimensional Gaussian probability distribution $\nu^{(1,\ldots,n)}$ which has R_n as its covariance matrix, and with mean vector zero.

(b) Let S be an *infinite* set, and let $R: S \times S \to \mathbb{C}$ be a positive definite function, i.e., satisfying

$$\sum_j \sum_k \bar{\xi}_j R(x_j, x_k) \xi_k \geq 0 \qquad \text{(finite sum)}$$

for all $\xi_1, \xi_2, \ldots \in \mathbb{C}$ and all $x_1, x_2, \ldots \in S$.

Prove that there is a probability space $(\Omega, \mathcal{B}, \nu)$ and a function $X: S \to L^2(\Omega, \nu)$ such that

$$\begin{cases} R(x, y) = E_\nu\left(\overline{X(x)} X(y)\right) & \text{for all } x, y \in S, \\ \text{and } E_\nu(X(x)) = 0. \end{cases} \qquad (9E.6)$$

Hint: If $n \in \mathbb{N}$ and $S_n = \{x_1, x_2, \ldots, x_n\}$ is a finite subset of S with $\#(S_n) = n$, then use (a) to pick a Gaussian probability distribution $\nu^{(x_1,\ldots,x_n)}$ of dimension n which has $(R(x_j, x_k))$ as covariance matrix, and with mean vector zero.

(c) If $S \subset S'$ are two finite subsets of S, and ν^S, $\nu^{S'}$ are the corresponding finite-dimensional Gaussian probability distributions from (b), then show that they are consistent in the sense of Kolmogorov; see Lemma 2.5.1.

(d) Set $\Omega := \mathbb{C}^S$ = all functions from S into $\mathbb{C}$. For $x \in S$, set $\pi_x(\omega) := \omega(x)$, $\omega \in \Omega$. Show that there is a smallest σ-algebra $\mathcal{B}$ on Ω for which all the functions $\{\pi_x \mid x \in S\}$ are measurable.

(e) Use Kolmogorov's theorem to conclude that there is a unique probability measure ν on $(\Omega, \mathcal{B})$ such that for all finite subsets S, the marginal distribution of ν is the measure ν^S from (c).

(f) Set $X(x, \omega) := \pi_x(\omega)$ for $x \in S$, and $\omega \in \Omega$. Then show that $X(x, \cdot) \in L^2(\Omega, \nu)$ and that this random process satisfies the conditions (9E.6) in (b).

(g) State a special case of the conclusion in (b), $S = [0, 1]$, which is the converse implication to that of the Karhunen–Loève theorem of Exercise 2.7 (pp. 55–56).

9.9. The following is a corollary to the conclusion in Exercise 9.8. Give a direct and geometric proof independently of Kolmogorov's measure-theoretic construction in Exercise 9.8(b).

Let S be a set, and let $R: S \times S \to \mathbb{C}$ be a positive definite function. Show that there is a Hilbert space $(\mathcal{H}, \langle \cdot \mid \cdot \rangle)$ and a function $X: S \to \mathcal{H}$ such that

$$R(x, y) = \langle X(x) \mid X(y) \rangle \qquad \text{for all } x, y \in S. \tag{9E.7}$$

Hint: Set $X(x) = R(x, \cdot)$, viewing $R(x, \cdot)$ as a function on S for $x \in S$. Then use linear span, quotient, norm-completion, and (9E.7) to finish the argument.

References and remarks

In an earlier textbook [BrJo02b], we consistently lived with the notational convention $m_0(0) = \sqrt{N}$ for the frequency response function m_0; but I noticed when giving lectures about this material to a mixed audience of students in mathematics and in engineering that the alternative convention $m_0(0) = 1$ seems to be less confusing. The idea is that the entire signal is admitted through by the low-pass filter at frequencies near zero, i.e., low frequencies. And the other frequency components of the signal are blocked by the m_0 filter. So in this book we have broken with the convention from [BrJo02b].

Add to that the confusion about a different notational dichotomy, multiplicative vs. additive notation for the torus groups: Frequency 0 in additive notation corresponds to the point $z = 1$ on $\mathbb{T}$ in multiplicative notation. This dichotomy is dictated by the choice of the alternative meanings of the manifolds $\mathbb{T}^d$, $d = 1, 2, \ldots$. Functions on $\mathbb{T}^d$ may be viewed alternately as periodic functions on $\mathbb{R}^d$, or equivalently as functions on the compact torus $\mathbb{T}^d$.

Although the material in the last exercise, Exercise 9.8 above, serves to walk the student through some main ideas of Kolmogorov, this material is also available in more detail in a number of books on probability theory. Here we wish to especially recommend the presentation [PaSc72] by Parthasarathy and Schmidt. But see also Nelson's paper [Nel59].

Appendices: Polyphase matrices and the operator algebra $\mathcal{O}_N$

Born wanted a theory which would generalize these matrices or grids of numbers into something with a continuity comparable to that of the continuous part of the spectrum. The job was a highly technical one, and he counted on me for aid. . . . I had the generalization of matrices already at hand in the form of what is known as operators. Born had a good many qualms about the soundness of my method and kept wondering if Hilbert would approve of my mathematics. Hilbert did, in fact, approve of it, and operators have since remained an essential part of quantum theory. —Norbert Wiener

PREREQUISITES: Curiosity about functions mapping into the group of unitary matrices.

Prelude

The dialog between engineers and mathematicians is hampered by a substantial difference in jargon in the two fields. Often the same idea makes its appearance in the two fields but under a different name. A case in point is the representation of a class of algebras which in the operator-algebraic community is known as the Cuntz algebras, see [Cun77], but which in signal processing is known as a dual system of subband filters yielding a perfect reconstruction in the signal output. The breaking up of a signal (say a speech signal) into a finite number N of filtered and down-sampled subbands is called analysis. There is then a dual operation of up-sampling and filtering. When the result is then merged (added), we call it synthesis. When $N = 2$, the use of filters (high-pass/low-pass) with a perfect reconstruction is called quadrature-mirror (referring to the duality) filters. Even when N is larger than 2, we may on occasion abuse notation and still talk about quadrature-mirror filters.

So even within mathematics, there are separate themes; and analogously for engineering! And it does not become any less confusing by the huge variety of terminology and occasionally inconsistent jargon. In order to help organize the presentation and the mathematics around engineering themes, we have subdivided the discussion into four separate appendices.

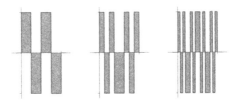

Appendix A: Signals and filters

Our use in this book of signal-processing diagrams such as Figures 7.7 and 7.14 (pp. 124 and 132) summarizes this combined process (analysis and synthesis) very nicely. While the diagrammatic viewpoint in fact originated in the early days of signal processing, the diagrams are much more versatile, and they are now used widely in modern applications such as image processing as well. In our present discussion, for simplicity, we have stressed signal processing. So in the simplest case, a signal (also called a time series) is represented by a sequence $x = (x_n)$ of numbers, with the index n denoting time. For the purpose of devising algorithms, it is natural to introduce generating functions of a complex variable z, i.e., $X(z) := \sum x_n z^n$. We have illustrated some wavelet algorithms based on this approach in Figures 7.8–7.13 (pp. 125–128). One of the advantages of this approach is that a variety of analytic steps which on the face of it appear not to be especially computational get rewritten in a finite sequence of relatively elementary matrix steps. As emphasized in Figures 7.13 and 7.14, when the operations of down- and up-sampling are introduced into filtering models, then the matrices become slanted. Indeed, the slanted nature of the matrices in turn is responsible for a speed-up of the computations, as reflected in the well-known sparseness of the wavelet matrices; see, e.g., [BrRo91, Coh03, Dau92, PaSW99, StNg96]. As a result, the complexity of the steps in a computation is reduced from n^2 to $n \log n$.

In signal processing, it is convenient to restrict the complex variable z to the circle $\mathbb{T}$, i.e., setting $z = \exp(i\omega)$, so that $z^n = \exp(in\omega)$, and we think of ω as frequency, or more generally as the dual variable. Of course, this means that $X(z)$ becomes a Fourier series. Engineers refer to $X(z)$ as the frequency response. If numbers (a_n) are given, the Cauchy product (y_n) of the two sequences (a_n) and (x_n) is called a filter, or a filtering of the signal x, and the function $m(z) := \sum a_n z^n$ is called the frequency-response filter. We will often refer to $m(z)$ itself as the filter, or more precisely the filter function. The reader will easily verify that the associated frequency response $Y(z)$ of the filtered signal is then the pointwise product $Y(z) = m(z)X(z)$. But we shall here use duality much more generally than for the classical duality of time and frequency in time series analysis. The general duality we have in mind is thus a special case of Fourier duality; see, e.g., [Mal98, Waln02].

A main point in this book is to organize the diverse themes (both mathematics and engineering) within the framework of Hilbert-space geometry. While mathematicians tend to create Hilbert spaces of functions, engineers are concerned with computations, and hence with transformations of sequences. The sequences could be indexed by the integers for time, i.e., time series; or they could be organized as matrices with double index (e.g., pixels) as is used for the grayscale numbers for an exposure in a digital camera.

As for the mathematics, the next step is then to break the transformations in sequence spaces into smaller algorithmic steps. That is where matrix tricks become handy. One such matrix trick centers on what engineers call "the polyphase matrix;" see Figures C.1 and C.2 (pp. 214–215). For sequence space we suggest the Hilbert spaces ℓ^2 but we allow flexibility for the indexing.

As we saw in Chapter 7, the selection for a particular problem of a resolution subspace V_0 (and a generating function, a scaling function φ) within an ambient Hilbert space of functions allows us to set up an isometric isomorphism between a chosen V_0 and the Hilbert space ℓ^2 of sequences. Hence we are faced with a correspondence principle. This has been organized into Table C.1.

In the simplest case, we may take $L^2(\mathbb{R}^d)$ to be the ambient Hilbert space, and the subspace V_0 to be the closed linear span of the translates $\{\varphi(\cdot - n) \mid n \in \mathbb{Z}^d\}$, where $\mathbb{Z}^d$ denotes the usual rank-d lattice in $\mathbb{R}^d$. If there are finite positive constants (*frame constants*) A and B such that

$$A \leq \sum_{k \in \mathbb{Z}^d} |\hat{\varphi}(t + k)|^2 \leq B \qquad \text{for all } t \in \mathbb{R}^d,$$

we may then define an operator (a *frame operator*) $W \colon V_0 \to \ell^2(\mathbb{Z}) =: \ell^2$ as follows:

$$W\left(\sum_{n \in \mathbb{Z}^d} x_n \varphi(\cdot - n)\right) := (x_n)_{n \in \mathbb{Z}^d}.$$

The reader can check that W is bounded, and invertible with bounded inverse.

Theorem A.1. *If $U := U^{(A)}$ denotes a chosen scaling operator on $L^2(\mathbb{R}^d)$, for example*

$$\left(U^{(A)} f\right)(x) := |\det A|^{-1/2} f\left(A^{-1}x\right), \qquad x \in \mathbb{R}^d,$$

for some expansive integral $d \times d$ matrix A, then it follows that the frame operator $W \colon V_0 \to \ell^2$ intertwines U with the low-pass synthesis operator $S_0^{(A)}$ on ℓ^2; i.e., that

$$S_0^{(A)} W = W U^{(A)}.$$

Proof. The reader is encourged to work out the details of the argument in Exercises A.1 and A.2 below; see especially part (b) of Exercise A.2. However, note that the exercises only sketch the outline of proof in the special case of a dyadic scaling operator. Nonetheless, one easily sees that the general case follows by the same outline with only minor modifications.   □

Recall that $S_0^{(A)}$ is the first operator in a whole Cuntz system of isometries,

$$\left\{ S_j^{(A)} \;\middle|\; 0 \leq j \leq |\det A| - 1 \right\}.$$

This system (see details in the next appendix) in turn depends on an associated system of subband filters $\left\{ m_j\,(\cdot) \mid 0 \leq j \leq |\det A| - 1 \right\}$, which are now $\mathbb{Z}^d$-periodic, or equivalently functions on the d-torus $\mathbb{T}^d := \mathbb{R}^d / \mathbb{Z}^d$.

While the number N from $\mathcal{O}_N$, the Cuntz algebra, is simply the scaling in the wavelet analysis of functions on the real line $\mathbb{R}$, i.e., in one dimension, it is a little more subtle in higher dimension, i.e., in $\mathbb{R}^d$.

There, a scaling is specified by a choice of a d-by-d matrix A. To be useful in wavelet bases, and in the study of scale-similarity, the matrix A must fulfill two conditions: The entries of A must be integers; and all its eigenvalues λ must satisfy $|\lambda| > 1$. Then $N := |\det A|$ yields the N in $\mathcal{O}_N$. We saw in Chapter 7 that this number N is also the number of frequency bands which is needed in a subband-filter approach to wavelet bases.

Strictly speaking, this is true only if we do wavelet bases on $\mathbb{R}^d$ itself. But if we are working on fractals, then the number of frequency bands will typically be strictly smaller than $|\det A|$.

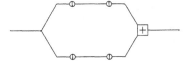

Exercises

A.1. Let $\varphi \in L^2\,(\mathbb{R})$ and suppose that the function

$$S_\varphi\,(t) := \sum_{k \in \mathbb{Z}} \left| \hat{\varphi}\,(t + k) \right|^2$$

is well defined, where $\hat{\varphi}$ denotes the Fourier transform of φ. Suppose in addition that there are finite positive constants A and B such that

$$A \leq \sum_{k \in \mathbb{Z}} \left| \hat{\varphi}\,(t + k) \right|^2 \leq B, \qquad t \in \mathbb{R},$$

holds.

(a) Then show that the ansatz

$$W\left(\sum_{n\in\mathbb{Z}} x_n\varphi\,(\cdot-n)\right):=(x_n)_{n\in\mathbb{Z}}$$

yields a well-defined linear operator on the closed linear span $\mathcal{D}_\varphi$ of the translated-function family $\{\varphi\,(\cdot-n)\mid n\in\mathbb{Z}\}$ in $L^2\,(\mathbb{R})$, and that the following estimate holds:

$$A\sum_{n\in\mathbb{Z}}|x_n|^2\le\left\|\sum_{n\in\mathbb{Z}} x_n\varphi\,(\cdot-n)\right\|_{L^2(\mathbb{R})}^2\le B\sum_{n\in\mathbb{Z}}|x_n|^2.$$

(b) Using the usual ordering for hermitian operators in Hilbert space, show that the estimates in (a) may be rewritten in the following equivalent form:

$$B^{-1}I\le W^*W\le A^{-1}I,$$

where I denotes the identity operator in the closed subspace $\mathcal{D}_\varphi$.

A.2. Let W, φ, and $\mathcal{D}_\varphi$ be as in the previous exercise, with the operator $W\colon\mathcal{D}_\varphi\to\ell^2\,(\mathbb{Z})=:\ell^2$ defined as before.

Suppose in addition that a sequence $(a_k)_{k\in\mathbb{Z}}$ is given and fixed such that an associated operator $S\colon\ell^2\to\ell^2$ is bounded, where

$$(Sx)_n:=\sqrt{2}\sum_{k\in\mathbb{Z}} a_{2k-n}x_k.$$

On $L^2\,(\mathbb{R})$, set $U=U_2$, where

$$(U_2f)\,(t)=\frac{1}{\sqrt{2}}f\left(\frac{t}{2}\right),\qquad f\in L^2\,(\mathbb{R})\,,\ t\in\mathbb{R}.$$

(a) If the function φ satisfies the scaling identity

$$\varphi\,(t)=2\sum_{k\in\mathbb{Z}} a_k\varphi\,(2t-k)\,,$$

then show that the space $\mathcal{D}_\varphi$ is invariant under the dyadic scaling operator U.

(b) Conditions as in (a): Show that the operator-intertwining relation

$$WU_2=SW$$

holds as an identity on the subspace $\mathcal{D}_\varphi$.

A.3. With assumptions as in the previous two exercises, find a formula for the adjoint operator $W^*\colon\ell^2\to\mathcal{D}_\varphi$.

Hint: Up to the Fourier duality from Table C.1, the answer is multiplication by S_φ^{-1} followed by $(x_n)\mapsto\sum_{n\in\mathbb{Z}} x_n\varphi\,(\cdot-n)$.

Appendix B: Hilbert space and systems of operators

Our use of Hilbert space throughout this book facilitates the breaking up of a computation or an algorithm into a set of basic algorithmic steps. In fact, it gives a geometric meaning to these matrix factorizations, as stressed for example in [Jor03]. Hence a signal $x = (x_n)$ will be viewed as a vector in the Hilbert space $\mathcal{H} = \ell^2(\mathbb{Z})$. But by Fourier duality (in this case, Parseval's identity), we will identify $\mathcal{H}$ with the Hilbert space of L^2 functions on $\mathbb{T}$, and it will be clear from the context which meaning $\mathcal{H}$ has. This is the geometric viewpoint used throughout the book, and in particular in Figures 7.8–7.13 (pp. 125–128). When some signal x is broken up into a finite number, say N, of frequency bands, the result is then a vector in the N-fold direct (or orthogonal) sum of $\mathcal{H}$ with itself, denoted $\mathcal{H}_N$; or equivalently the result is a vector-valued function on $\mathbb{T}$. The reader easily checks that the Hilbert norm on $\mathcal{H}_N$ agrees with the natural Hilbert norm on the space of all square-integrable functions from $\mathbb{T}$ into the N-dimensional Hilbert space $\mathbb{C}^N$.

As illustrated in Figures 7.14 and 7.9 (pp. 132 and 126), this operator-theoretic viewpoint can be accomplished with a set of N operators, or subband filters. To take advantage of matrix algebra, we shall view this operator system as a column matrix of operators. As is familiar for scalar matrices, we then note that the Hilbert-space adjoint of a column matrix of operators will be a row matrix of operators, the entries in the row being simply the adjoint operators from the column. And we note that a row operator is conveniently viewed as a single operator from $\mathcal{H}_N$ into $\mathcal{H}$.

When composing several algorithmic steps, we are faced with operators from $\mathcal{H}_N$ into itself, or with a composition of such operators. The introduction of N-by-N matrices with operator entries lets us represent composition of operators on $\mathcal{H}_N$ as matrix multiplication, again facilitating computations. Moreover, the requirement of stability from signal processing leads us to favor unitary operators from $\mathcal{H}_N$ to $\mathcal{H}_N$. But if frequency-response filters are involved, we will (as noted above) be studying matrices of operators where the N^2 individual entry operators are multiplication operators in $\mathcal{H}$. In the literature of signal-processing engineering (see [StNg96], [GaNS01a], [GaNS01b], [GaNS02]), these matrices of functions are called *polyphase matrices* (as in the heading of this group of appendices). So a polyphase matrix is a function F from $\mathbb{T}$ into the algebra of all N-by-N complex matrices. We say that it is unitary if this function F maps $\mathbb{T}$ into the group of N-by-N unitary matrices. (Note that $F(z)$ will only be unitary for z in $\mathbb{T}$, and not for z in the complement of $\mathbb{T}$ within the complex plane $\mathbb{C}$.)

It is the purpose of this appendix to point out that the operator-algebraic framework of Cuntz algebras from Chapter 9 (see also [Cun77] and [BrJo02b]) is especially useful in making the link between the theory of individual filters in a system of frequency bands, and operators on the system of vector functions which makes up the band under discussion. And we will further be stressing the use of this theory in the analysis of the wavelet and fractal algorithms throughout from inside the book.

As noted, the two figures 7.7 and 7.14 (pp. 124 and 132) illustrate the concept of subband filtering from signal processing, but in the more general context adapted here to wavelets and to fractals. In this operator-theoretic approach, we work out algorithmic diagrams starting with N functions, say $m_0, m_1, \ldots, m_{N-1}$ on $\mathbb{T}$; and we build a system of operators

$$S_j = S_{m_j}, \qquad j \in \mathbb{Z}_N = \mathbb{Z}/N\mathbb{Z} \cong \{0, 1, \ldots, N-1\}$$

satisfying the following relations:

$$S_j^* S_k = \delta_{j,k} I, \tag{B.1}$$

$$\sum_j S_j S_j^* = I. \tag{B.2}$$

Definition B.1. If we think of (B.1)–(B.2) as axioms for operators in Hilbert space $\mathcal{H}$, then we arrive at the familiar *Cuntz relations* $\mathcal{O}_N$ [Cun77] from operator-algebra theory; and so subband filtering yields a particular family of representations of $\mathcal{O}_N$; see Table C.1 in the next appendix.

Exercises

B.1. Let $n \in \mathbb{N}$, $n \geq 2$, be given, and let $(S_i)_{i=1}^n$ be a system of operators in a Hilbert space $\mathcal{H}$ which satisfies the Cuntz relations.
  (a) Let $u: \mathcal{H} \to \mathcal{H}$ be a unitary operator, and set

$$S_i' := uS_i.$$

Show that the system $(S_i')_{i=1}^n$ also satisfies the Cuntz relations.
  (b) Let $(S_i)_{i=1}^n$ be as above. Let $(a_{i,j}) \in U_n(\mathbb{C}) =$ the group of all $n \times n$ unitary matrices, and set

$$S_i' = \sum_{j=1}^n a_{i,j} S_j.$$

Show that the system $(S_i')_{i=1}^n$ also satisfies the Cuntz relations.
  (c) Formulate and prove the implications demonstrating that the conditions in (a) and (b) are also necessary.

B.2. Using the formula in Exercise B.1(b), show that the group $U_n(\mathbb{C})$ acts as a transformation group on the C^*-algebra $\mathcal{O}_n$, i.e., as a group of $*$-automorphisms.

Appendix C: A tale of two Hilbert spaces

We now turn to Table C.1, a systematic table which will serve as a graphic dictionary translating between current terminology in mathematics and jargon from signal-processing engineering.

Explanation of Table C.1. The two columns in the table represent the same operators, but in different guises, that of *time series*, and that of *frequency functions*. Each is important, and each has its advantages and its drawbacks. The *sequences* on the left represent time series or *signals* (where time is the discrete integer index), while the associated *functions* on the right carry *frequency* information.

   Organization of the table: In the left-hand-side column, we have sequences and operations/operators on sequences; and then the corresponding functions and operations/operators on functions in the right-hand-side column. Thus, moving down the table, each of the listed operators has a representation in each of the two columns; i.e., each operator has two incarnations (time and frequency), but they will often be denoted with the same symbol. In addition to time/frequency duality, there is a second duality, operator vs. adjoint operator. Specifically, each operator, say S, has an adjoint operator S^*. When S is listed in one line, then the adjoint S^* follows in the next line. Each of the two is important as each has distinct significance in the context of signal processing: The adjoint of up-sampling is down-sampling, the adjoint of right-shift is left-shift, and so on.

   Comments on the adjoints: The adjoint of each operator depends on the inner product of the Hilbert space in question. On the left and the right, respectively, it is

$$\langle x \mid y \rangle = \sum_{n \in \mathbb{Z}} \bar{x}_n y_n \quad \text{and} \quad \langle f \mid g \rangle = \int_{\mathbb{T}} \overline{f(z)} g(z),$$

where the integration is with respect to the Haar measure on $\mathbb{T}$. Note that

$$\lim_{k \to \infty} ⑂^k \xi = \int_{\mathbb{T}} \xi \, d\,\text{Haar}. \tag{C.1}$$

   In fact, we may take (C.1) as a definition of the Haar measure on $\mathbb{T}$. Specifically, one checks independently that the limit in (C.1) exists for all $\xi \in C(\mathbb{T})$. Introducing rotations on $\mathbb{T}$, $\xi_w(z) = \xi(zw)$ for $z, w \in \mathbb{T}$, one checks that

$$\lim_{k \to \infty} ⑂^k \xi = \lim_{k \to \infty} ⑂^k \xi_w,$$

which is the invariance characterizing Haar measure.

   The operation of adjoint (from operator theory) reflects the word "mirror" in *quadrature-mirror filter* from signal processing. Recall, taking the adjoint of S twice gets you back S itself, i.e., we have

$$S^{**} = S,$$

as is immediate from $\langle Sx \mid y \rangle = \langle x \mid S^* y \rangle$.

Table C.1. Operations on two Hilbert spaces: The correspondence principle.

$x \in \ell^2(\mathbb{Z})$	$\xi \in L^2(\mathbb{T})$
Vectors in each space	
time signals $(x_n)_{n \in \mathbb{Z}}$	frequency functions $\xi(z) = \sum\limits_{n \in \mathbb{Z}} x_n z^n,\ z \in \mathbb{T}$
Filters	
• filter by $m(z) = \sum a_n z^n$ $y_n = (F_m x)(n) = \sum\limits_k a_k x_{n-k}$	• multiplication M_m $(M_m \xi)(z) = m(z)\,\xi(z)$
Shift operators	
• shift to the right $(Sx)(n) = x_{n-1},\ n \in \mathbb{Z}$	• multiplication by z $(M_z \xi)(z) = z\xi(z),\ z \in \mathbb{T}$
The adjoint of a shift operator is also a shift:	
• shift to the left $(S^* x)(n) = x_{n+1},\ n \in \mathbb{Z}$	• multiplication by $z^{-1} = \bar{z}$ for $z \in \mathbb{T}$ $(M_z^* \xi)(z) = M_{z^{-1}} \xi(z) = z^{-1} \xi(z)$
Sampling operations (by N)	
$(\textcircled{$\uparrow$} x)(n) = \begin{cases} x_k & \text{if } n = kN \\ 0 & \text{if } N \nmid n \end{cases}$	$(\textcircled{$\uparrow$} \xi)(z) = \xi\left(z^N\right)$
Down-sampling is the adjoint of up-sampling:	
$\textcircled{$\downarrow$} = \textcircled{$\uparrow* $(\textcircled{$\downarrow$} x)(n) = x_{nN},\ n \in \mathbb{Z}$	$\textcircled{$\downarrow$} = \textcircled{$\uparrow* $(\textcircled{$\downarrow$} \xi)(z) = \frac{1}{N} \sum\limits_{\substack{w \in \mathbb{T} \\ w^N = z}} \xi(w)$
Subband-filter operators	
• $(S_m x)(n) = \sqrt{N} \sum\limits_k a_k x_{n-kN}$	• $S_m = \sqrt{N}\, M_m \textcircled{$\uparrow$}$ $(S_m \xi)(z) = \sqrt{N}\, m(z)\, \xi\left(z^N\right)$
The adjoint operators:	
• $(S_m^* x)(n) = \sqrt{N} \sum\limits_k \bar{a}_k x_{k+nN}$	• $S_m^* = \textcircled{$\downarrow$} \sqrt{N}\, M_{\bar{m}}$ $(S_m^* \xi)(z) = \frac{1}{\sqrt{N}} \sum\limits_{w^N = z} \overline{m(w)}\, \xi(w)$

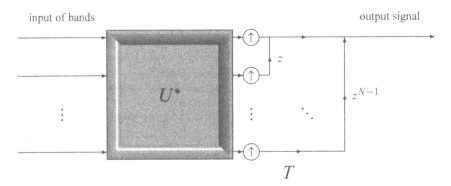

input of bands   output signal

T

Fig. C.1. Representation of $S = TU^*$. This and the next diagram illustrate the use of the operator relations from Appendix C in synthesis of subbands of a signal, or of a subdivision of an image. The two diagrams form a pair. The present first one represents a matrix action transforming one band-configuration into another. This is followed by up-sampling applied to each strand. There is then a system of translations before the strands are merged and added. This diagram is a natural dual version of the next one, Figure C.2, i.e., the analysis step which begins with subdivision, or breaking apart an input signal.

We now resume the discussion of representations of $\mathcal{O}_N$.

For our reference point, we shall use the particular representation $\left(T_j\right)_{j \in \mathbb{Z}_N}$ of $\mathcal{O}_N$ given by

$$(T_j\xi)(z) = z^j \xi\left(z^N\right)$$

$$\text{for } z \in \mathbb{T}, \ j \in \{0, 1, \ldots, N-1\}, \text{ and } \xi \in L^2(\mathbb{T}); \qquad (\text{C.2})$$

and the reader readily checks that the $\mathcal{O}_N$-relations are satisfied, i.e., that

$$T_j^* T_k = \delta_{j,k} I \quad \text{and} \quad \sum_{j=0}^{N-1} T_j T_j^* = I. \qquad (\text{C.3})$$

In this appendix, we show that there is an alternative approach based instead on certain matrix-functions $U = \left(U_{j,k}\right)_{j,k \in \mathbb{Z}_N}$ from $\mathbb{T}$ into the group of all $N \times N$ unitary matrices $=: U_N(\mathbb{C})$.

Introducing operator-valued matrices and adjoints

$$S = (S_0, \ldots, S_{N-1}), \qquad S^* = \begin{pmatrix} S_0^* \\ \vdots \\ S_{N-1}^* \end{pmatrix}, \qquad (\text{C.4})$$

input signal   output of bands

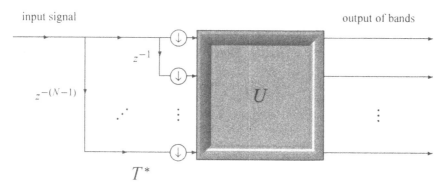

Fig. C.2. Representation of $S^* = UT^*$. The present two figures together, Figures C.1 and C.2, represent equivalent formulations of the respective left-hand and right-hand sides in Figure 7.7 (p. 124). But the present figures in fact represent signal-processing algorithms (or equivalently wavelet algorithms) that are more versatile than the more traditional polyphase matrices: specifically, the matrix functions in our present diagrams may be arbitrary, and be of arbitrary size. The size of a polyphase matrix equals the number of subbands which is used. But we also allow non-unitary matrix functions. Of course, more general choices of matrices in Figures C.1–C.2 will then correspond to more general choices of filters in Figure 7.7. These choices are highly relevant, for example for the algorithms based on lifting, see [DaSw98]. Our present Figures C.1–C.2 are multiband versions of diagrammatic representations of subsampling/subband-filtering algorithms which appear frequently in the signal-processing engineering literature; see for example [WWW1] with text, and [WWW2] and [WWW3] with pictures.

and similarly for $(T_j)_{j \in \mathbb{Z}_N}$, we arrive at the following matrix formulas:

$$S = TU^* \tag{C.5}$$

and

$$S^* = UT^*. \tag{C.6}$$

In signal processing, the representation of these two operator identities takes the diagrammatic form shown in Figures C.1 and C.2, and the operator matrix U is called the *polyphase matrix*.

Specifically, in terms of processing diagrams the operator-theoretic formulas (C.5) and (C.6) turn into Figures C.1 and C.2.

Remark C.1. Our use here of the operator notation S and S^* is reversed from the convention in signal processing. (Conventions: engineers typically set $F = S^*$ and

$F^* = S$.) Our choice of terminology is motivated by the traditions in operator-algebra theory, and by the fact that the individual operators S_j will then be *isometries*, while the S_j^*'s are *co-isometries*. Specifically, $S_j^* S_j = I$ for $j = 0, \ldots, N - 1$; and each operator $S_j S_j^* = E_j$ is a projection. Moreover, the projections $\left(E_j\right)_{j \in \mathbb{Z}_N}$ satisfy

$$E_j E_k = \delta_{j,k} E_j \qquad \text{(orthogonality)}, \tag{C.7}$$

and

$$\sum_{j \in \mathbb{Z}_N} E_j = I. \tag{C.8}$$

EXPLANATION OF PROGRAMMING DIAGRAMS FROM SIGNAL PROCESSING AND THE CORRESPONDING COMPOSITION OF OPERATORS IN HILBERT SPACE: GUIDE TO FIGURES C.1 AND C.2. Caution: in general note that we read figures with input-output flow diagrams from left to right, and this corresponds to an action of operators, but now reading the action of the respective operators from right to left. So the first figure, Figure C.1, represents the following operator factorization: $S = T U^*$. The direction from the left to the right in a diagram corresponds to the flow of the operations performed on signals. Specifically, the diagram in Figure C.1 begins with input of bands into a box for U^* on the left in the figure. This is followed by the diagram for the operator T which involves bands that are assembled into a single output signal. In contrast, the second picture, Figure C.2, is the result of taking the adjoint of the operators from Figure C.1. So it corresponds to the operator factorization of the adjoint operator $S^* = U T^*$, and it begins with the diagram for the operator T^* on the left in Figure C.2. The diagram for T^* is then followed by a box placed to the right-hand side of T^* representing the matrix U. The result of matrix multiplication by U is a vector output representing a system of banded signals. These output signals may then in turn be the input in a new operation representing a new and different matrix. The various matrices are also called "gates" in programming. The unitary matrices correspond to gates which preserve the energy of signals from input to output.

The next appendix is largely concerned with Figures C.1–C.2, their use, their interpretation, and their relationship to both the Cuntz formulas (B.1)–(B.2) and the polyphase-matrix formalism from engineering.

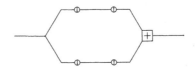

Exercises

C.1. Let $n \in \mathbb{N}$, $n \geq 2$, be given and let $S_1, \ldots, S_n$ be a system of bounded operators in a Hilbert space $\mathcal{H}$. Then show that the following two *a priori* estimates are equivalent:

$$\left\| \sum_{i=1}^{n} S_i u_i \right\|^2 \leq \sum_{i=1}^{n} \|u_i\|^2 \qquad \text{for all } u_i \in \mathcal{H}; \tag{CE.1}$$

and

$$\sum_{i=1}^{n} \left\| S_i^* v \right\|^2 \leq \|v\|^2 \qquad \text{for all } v \in \mathcal{H}. \tag{CE.2}$$

Note: If the estimate (CE.1) holds, then we say that $(S_1, \ldots, S_n)$ is a *row-contraction*.

C.2. Let $n \in \mathbb{N}$, $n \geq 2$, be given, and consider a family of 1-periodic functions $m_1, \ldots, m_n$ on $\mathbb{R}$ which are assumed in L^∞. On the Hilbert space $\mathcal{H} = L^2(0, 1)$ we introduce the system

$$(S_i f)(x) := \sqrt{2}\, m_i(x)\, f(2x), \qquad x \in [0, 1),$$

where $x \mapsto 2x$ is understood mod 1.

(a) Then write a set of necessary and sufficient conditions on the function system $(m_i)_{i=1}^n$ for $(S_1, \ldots, S_n)$ to be a row-contraction.

(b) Spell out how in the case $n = 2$ the conditions in (a) generalize the quadrature-mirror filter condition, i.e., the assumption that the matrix

$$\begin{pmatrix} m_1(x) & m_1\left(x + \frac{1}{2}\right) \\ m_2(x) & m_2\left(x + \frac{1}{2}\right) \end{pmatrix}$$

is in $U_2(\mathbb{C})$ for a.a. x, i.e., is a unitary 2×2 complex matrix.

C.3. Verify the assertions made in Table C.1 about adjoint operators, i.e., the formulas for S_m^*, ⓣ, ⓓ, and the formula ⓛ $=$ ⓣ*.

C.4. Using the identification of Hilbert spaces from Table C.1, $\ell^2(\mathbb{Z}) \cong L^2(\mathbb{T}) \cong L^2(0, 1) \cong L^2(\mathbb{R}/\mathbb{Z})$, return to the operator

$$W: \mathcal{D}_\varphi \to \ell^2$$

from Exercises A.1–A.2; same assumptions.

(a) Then show that when $M := WW^*$ is realized as an operator in $L^2(\mathbb{R}/\mathbb{Z})$, then it is a multiplication operator, i.e., multiplication by a 1-periodic function on $\mathbb{R}$.

(b) Show that $M = WW^*$ from (a) is multiplication by the function

$$\mathbb{R} \ni t \mapsto \sum_{k \in \mathbb{Z}} \left| \hat{\varphi}(t + k) \right|^2.$$

Appendix D: Signal processing, matrices, and programming diagrams

We now turn to the Hilbert-space geometry of the polyphase matrices. If $(S_i)_{i \in \mathbb{Z}_N}$ and $(T_i)_{i \in \mathbb{Z}_N}$ is a *pair of representations* of $\mathcal{O}_N$ in a Hilbert space $\mathcal{H}$, i.e., both satisfying (B.1)–(B.2), then we show that the operator matrix

$$U := \left(S_i^* T_j \right) \tag{D.1}$$

is *unitary*, i.e., U is a unitary operator in the Hilbert space

$$\mathcal{H}_N := \underbrace{\mathcal{H} \oplus \cdots \oplus \mathcal{H}}_{N \text{ times}}.$$

The convention in (D.1) is that U is an $N \times N$ matrix with entries in the algebra $B(\mathcal{H})$ of all bounded linear operators in $\mathcal{H}$, i.e., that $U_{i,j} := S_i^* T_j$ for $(i, j) \in \mathbb{Z}_N \times \mathbb{Z}_N$. The formulas (C.5)–(C.6) are matrix products; specifically,

$$S_j = \sum_k T_k U_{j,k}^*, \qquad j \in \{0, \ldots, N-1\}; \tag{D.2}$$

and

$$S_j^* = \sum_k U_{j,k} T_k^*, \qquad j \in \{0, \ldots, N-1\}. \tag{D.3}$$

But if U is unitary, we also get $T = SU$; or, in matrix form,

$$T_j = \sum_k S_k U_{k,j}, \tag{D.4}$$

keeping in mind that the products on the right-hand side refer to products in the non-abelian algebra $B(\mathcal{H})$ of all bounded linear operators on $\mathcal{H}$. Note further that the matrix representation of formula (D.1) now takes the form

$$U = S^* T, \tag{D.5}$$

where S^* is a column matrix of operators, while T is a row matrix.

Proposition D.1. *Let $(S_i)_{i \in \mathbb{Z}_N}$ be a representation of $\mathcal{O}_N$ in a Hilbert space $\mathcal{H}$, and let U be a bounded operator in the Hilbert space $\mathcal{H}_N = \underbrace{\mathcal{H} \oplus \cdots \oplus \mathcal{H}}_{N \text{ times}}$. Writing S, as before, and $T = (T_0, \ldots, T_{N-1})$ as row matrices of operators, we claim that the following two conditions are equivalent:*

(a) $T = SU$ is a representation of $\mathcal{O}_N$, and
(b) $U = S^* T$ is unitary in $B(\mathcal{H}_N)$.

Proof. (a) $\Rightarrow$ (b). Now the assumption is that both S and T are representations of $\mathcal{O}_N$. To verify (b), we calculate the (i, j) matrix entry of each of the matrix products U^*U and UU^*. Specifically,

$$\left(U^*U\right)_{i,j} = \sum_k T_i^* S_k S_k^* T_j = T_i^* T_j = \delta_{i,j} I$$

and

$$\left(UU^*\right)_{i,j} = \sum_k S_i^* T_k T_k^* S_j = S_i^* S_j = \delta_{i,j} I,$$

showing that U is unitary.

(b) $\Rightarrow$ (a). If (b) holds, we now show that the matrix product $T = SU$ is a representation of $\mathcal{O}_N$. Specifically, we get the two $\mathcal{O}_N$ relations:

$$T_i^* T_j = \sum_k \sum_l U_{k,i}^* \underbrace{S_k^* S_l}_{\delta_{k,l}} U_{l,j} = \sum_k U_{k,i}^* U_{k,j} = \delta_{i,j} I$$

and

$$\sum_i T_i T_i^* = \sum_i \sum_k \sum_l S_k U_{k,i} U_{l,i}^* S_l^*$$
$$= \sum_k \sum_l \delta_{k,l} S_k S_l^*$$
$$= \sum_k S_k S_k^*$$
$$= I. \qquad \square$$

We now return to the setting of signal processing. In this application, we have $\mathcal{H} = L^2(\mathbb{T}) \cong \ell^2(\mathbb{Z})$, and the two operator systems S and T will be as outlined in the formulas

$$S_j = S_{m_j} = \sqrt{N} M_{m_j} \textcircled{\uparrow},$$

or

$$\left(S_j \xi\right)(z) = \sqrt{N} m_j(z) \xi\left(z^N\right),$$

in Table C.1, and in (C.2) for T_j. The representation $\left(S_j\right)$ will be called a *subband representation*, and $\left(T_j\right)$ will be called a *base-point representation*.

Corollary D.2. *Let $\left(m_j\right)_{j \in \mathbb{Z}_N}$ be a family of bounded measurable functions on $\mathbb{T}$, and let*

$$\left(S_j \xi\right)(z) := \sqrt{N} m_j(z) \xi\left(z^N\right), \qquad z \in \mathbb{T}, \ \xi \in L^2(\mathbb{T}), \ j = 0, 1, \ldots, N-1 \tag{D.6}$$

be the corresponding operators in $\mathcal{H} = L^2(\mathbb{T})$.

Then $\left(S_j\right)_{j \in \mathbb{Z}_N}$ defines a representation of $\mathcal{O}_N$ in $\mathcal{H}$ if and only if the N^2 functions

$$U_{i,j}(z) := \frac{1}{\sqrt{N}} \sum_{w^N = z} \overline{m_i(w)}\, w^j, \qquad z \in \mathbb{T}, \tag{D.7}$$

define a unitary matrix for all $z \in \mathbb{T}$, i.e., $z \mapsto (U_{i,j}(z))$ defines a function from $\mathbb{T}$ into the Lie group $U_N(\mathbb{C})$ of all unitary $N \times N$ matrices.

Moreover, in that case,

$$m_i(z) = \frac{1}{\sqrt{N}} \sum_j z^j\, \overline{U_{j,i}(z^N)}, \qquad z \in \mathbb{T},\ i \in \mathbb{Z}_N. \tag{D.8}$$

Proof. The result is immediate from Proposition D.1 once the two formulas (D.7) and (D.8) have been established, subject to the stated assumptions.

Verification of (D.7): We have

$$\begin{aligned}
(S_i^* T_j)\,\xi\,(z) &= \frac{1}{\sqrt{N}} \sum_{w^N = z} \overline{m_i(w)}\, (T_j \xi)\,(w) \\
&= \frac{1}{\sqrt{N}} \sum_{w^N = z} \overline{m_i(w)}\, w^j \xi\,(z) \\
&= U_{i,j}(z)\,\xi\,(z) \qquad \text{for } z \in \mathbb{T},
\end{aligned}$$

proving (D.7).

Verification of (D.8): By Proposition D.1, we have $T = SU$, or

$$T\xi\,(z) = (SU\xi)\,(z) = U\left(z^N\right) S\xi\,(z),$$

for $z \in \mathbb{T}$, so (using unitarity) we get

$$(S\xi)\,(z) = U\left(z^N\right)^* (T\xi)\,(z),$$

or

$$\begin{aligned}
(S_i \xi)\,(z) &= \sum_j \overline{U_{j,i}\left(z^N\right)}\, T_j \xi\,(z) \\
&= \sum_j \overline{U_{j,i}\left(z^N\right)}\, z^j \xi\left(z^N\right) \\
&= \sqrt{N}\, m_i(z)\, \xi\left(z^N\right), \qquad \text{for } z \in \mathbb{T},
\end{aligned}$$

proving the result. $\qquad\qquad\qquad\qquad\qquad\qquad\qquad\qquad\qquad\square$

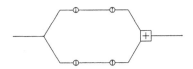

Exercises

D.1. Let $\mathcal{H}$ be a Hilbert space, and let $n \in \mathbb{N}$, $n \geq 2$, be given. Suppose a system of isometries $S_1, \ldots, S_n$ satisfies the Cuntz relations in $\mathcal{H}$. Set $\mathcal{H}^{(n)} := \underbrace{\mathcal{H} \oplus \cdots \oplus \mathcal{H}}_{n \text{ times}}$.

(a) Then show that

$$\mathcal{B}(\mathcal{H}) \ni X \overset{\alpha}{\mapsto} \left(S_i^* X S_j\right) \in \mathcal{B}\left(\mathcal{H}^{(n)}\right)$$

defines an isomorphism of the respective $*$-algebras of all bounded linear operators.

(*Note:* By $*$-isomorphism, we mean that α is bijective, and further satisfies $\alpha(XY) = \alpha(X)\alpha(Y)$ and $\alpha(X^*) = \alpha(X)^*$ for all $X, Y \in \mathcal{B}(\mathcal{H})$.)

(b) Find the inverse

$$\beta = \alpha^{-1} : \mathcal{B}\left(\mathcal{H}^{(n)}\right) \to \mathcal{B}(\mathcal{H}).$$

Hint: If $A = \left(A_{i,j}\right) \in \mathcal{B}\left(\mathcal{H}^{(n)}\right)$, show that

$$\beta(A) = \sum_{i,j} S_i A_{i,j} S_j^*.$$

References and remarks: Systems theory

The reader will notice that our formulation in Proposition D.1 above is "pure" Hilbert space geometry: it is about linear operators in abstract Hilbert space, i.e., it is operator theory. The proposition shows that every system of isometries (S_i) in a Hilbert space $\mathcal{H}$ subject to the Cuntz relations may be rewritten as a single unitary operator U in a direct-sum Hilbert space, i.e., as a unitary operator matrix. By this we mean that the matrix-entries in U are operators in $\mathcal{H}$. Then in Corollary D.2 we specialize to the case when the Cuntz system is of the kind that is used in subband filtering. In this case we note that the corresponding unitaty operator matrix U then has entries which are multiplication operators. So these are special operator matrices, so-called *polyphase matrices*.

But it is worth stressing that the use of systems of isometries (S_i) subject to the Cuntz relations is ubiquitous in the analysis of problems involving some kind of branching, and a feature involving scales, or a notion of similarity which can be couched in terms of operator theory. A case in point is the formulation of scattering theory due to Ralph Phillips and Peter Lax. In that theory, there is a single unitary operator, or a one-parameter group of unitary operators; the parameter is for time. The isometries in the theory then arise by restriction to a chosen pair of subspaces which are invariant forward in time and backward in time, respectively: so-called incoming and outgoing subspaces. As it turns out, the scattering then "takes place" in the ortho-complement of these subspaces. This is "obstacle scattering:" the obstacle is modeled on the ortho-complement of these subspaces. It turns out that the subspaces in the Lax–Phillips theory are examples of the kind of multiresolutions that we have emphasized in the present book.

A number of authors (J.A. Ball, S. Cora, W. Helton, V. Vinnikov, and others; see, e.g., [BaCV05] and [BaVi05]) have extended Lax–Phillips scattering to systems theory, a branch of engineering. Our discussion of the dual pairs of Hilbert spaces in Table C.1 applies to this setting as well. Further, it is interesting to note that the family of isometries used in systems theory may also be modeled on the Cuntz relations, i.e., that they yield different classes of representations of the Cuntz algebra. Hence the general framework of the present appendices applies to this branch of systems theory as well.

It should be noted that our operator systems from Exercises C.1 and C.2 arise in a number of places in mathematics, and have already found many uses. Here we mention only their use in operator theory as row-contractions (see, e.g., [Arv04], [Pop89]) and in wavelet theory (see, e.g., [RoSh97], [She98], and the papers cited there). In the context of [RoSh97] these authors have the functions and the operators from Exercise C.2 as part of what they call the Unitary Extension Principle (UEP). As demonstrated in [RoSh97], the types of generalized wavelets which may be generated via use of the UEP have a number of desirable properties.

Afterword

Comments on signal/image processing terminology

Introduction

A Google search on the word "wavelet" yields 2,650,000 entries, "fractal" 8,530,000, and "signal processing" 45,000,000, as of September 2005. While this may seem staggering, it is wise to keep in mind that by now general ideas in the subject which do originate with wavelets are presently used in many sciences outside of mathematics. While the general subject may be said to have a mathematical core, the vast number of applications and independent tracks followed in the last two decades have lead to an amazing diversity, even when counting only the mathematical trends.

This diversity of ideas is both exciting, but at the same time, it often leaves students confused. Ideas which started with wavelets turned out at the present time to be significant elsewhere, for example in computational mathematics, in engineering and in computer science; in part because of their algorithmic efficiency. Another reason is the prevalence of time-space scale similarity in both science (e.g., in physics of large scale and physics at the quantum level) and in engineering. While the notion of scale-similarity is not always made mathematically precise when it is used outside of mathematics (for example in finance!), it is crystallized especially nicely in wavelet theory through the notion of a "multiresolution," a concept from optics. This scale similarity may explain why wavelets keep getting reinvented outside mathematics.

While the mathematical concept of wavelet dates back (in a special case) almost one hundred years, to Alfred Haar (mathematics) and Oliver Heaviside (signal analysis), the potential of the interaction between mathematics and signal processing was only realized much later. It is only the scientific and engineering developments since the mid-1980s that have accounted for the impressive growth which is now reflected in the gigantic totals we find in typical Google searches.

There are at least three reasons for the resurgence of activity since 1980: one comes from signal processing in engineering (e.g., wireless communication and data mining); another from image processing (e.g., digital cameras, JPEG 2000, finger prints) and medical imaging (vision, optics and more); and a third from statistics and telecommunication (quantization, filtering of noisy signals). While the mathematics of wavelets continues to be both very active and exciting, it is probably all the interdisciplinary connections and developments which account for the bulk of the activity in the general area.

While interdisciplinary developments are wonderful and often take place along parallel tracks, they have a tendency of making it difficult for students, for users such as engineers and computer scientists, and for researchers to get started in the subject, and to get a good sense of the main trends. They are busy and look for friendly introductions to a particular main trend, and each trend has its own scientific culture.

There are several reasons for why it may now be hard for a student to know where to begin: The different disciplines have vastly differing lingo, probably reflecting the fact that they have quite different aims.

For the mathematician who is used to seeing wavelets as a part of function theory, it may be hard to accept that many users in digital signal/image processing and its applications are mainly interested in numbers and in algorithms. Because of the "cultural" differences between the diverse subjects, the connection between the function theory on one side and the practical algorithms which process numbers on the other is not always transparent.

Similarly, we noticed that colleagues from engineering (computer and electrical engineering, industrial engineering, data mining, etc.) find the version of wavelet theory in typical mathematics books on function theory rather forbidding.

While all the diversity of applications is truly impressive, the student from mathematics or from one of the other disciplines involved often has difficulties in getting started. This difficulty is not because of a shortage of books, but rather because of an apparent divergence of the various trends, developments and applications.

In this book we have aimed at remedying some of this. To make the book useful for diverse audiences, we have approached the task from two sides, and we have added a discussion of some key terms below.

On the one hand, each chapter (including exercises) has elements of tutorial, and a practical side as well. On the other hand, we have included separate sections which serve to "translate" between the lingo which is used in the different, and sometimes disparate disciplines. In this endeavor we make an effort to both explain concepts from engineering and statistics to mathematicians, and also to explain the various areas of mathematics to engineers and scientists from the neighboring disciplines.

What follows are two small sections dealing with how ideas and terminology are used differently in mathematics and in its applications: First we discuss technical terms from inside the book and stress how they are used quite differently in engineering and in (relatively) pure mathematics. (While perhaps confusing, this dichotomy is hardly surprising since the two communities have quite different aims.) Mindful that technical lingo is viewed and used differently by engineers and mathematicians, we have tried to present the concepts and ideas evenhandedly from the perspectives of the two communities.

Secondly, we briefly hint at the use of some central themes from the text in "Computational mathematics." This expands on our initial presentation of related ideas in the Glossary (a systematic discussion of terminology in the front matter above, pp. xvii–xxv). Both this "Computational mathematics" section and the Glossary serve to motivate central ideas used in the text.

The Glossary is arranged as a table. In it each underlying idea has up to four incarnations, hence the different terms! We outline item by item how each concept is used in up to four related but different ways; in four contexts: in mathematics, in probability, in engineering, and in physics. We hope to clarify (a little) how the distinct aims of the four subjects are reflected in a variety of ways, for example in the fact that there is often a multitude of names for what is essentially the same term.

JPEG 2000 vs. GIF

We begin with two engineering terms of a more recent vintage; both are from image-processing. They help us to strike a contrast between two themes in our book, wavelets vs. Fourier. Specifically, there are some practical features unique to A-to-D quantization (analog-to-digital) for wavelets (e.g., localization, algorithms, computability, and resolutions) which are absent in analogous Fourier tools. For much more detailed discussions, see, e.g., [JPEG00], [JaMR01] and [Mey05]. There is a huge engineering literature on this, and we only scratch the surface.

JPEG 2000

(Joint Photographics Experts Group)—A new *image coding* which is largely wavelet based. Applications include digital cameras, remote sensing, image archives, scanning, and medical imaging.

It comes in different parts: Part 1 offers both lossless and lossy compression and provides much better image quality at smaller file-sizes. Part 6 is aimed at compressing scanned color documents containing both bi-tonal elements as well as images.

Fundamentally, JPEG 2000 is built much like a certain AI computer-vision model, following closely the biology of "human vision." See [Mar82]: Eye focus, zoom, and scales of detail organized as visual resolutions.

In engineering terms, image-input onto pixels contains information-detail at all scales; the detail levels separate the resolution scales, and this hierarchical structure can be digitized. Analogously, the human eye (as well as digital cameras) processes intensity changes at a variety of resolution scales, much like in the pyramid algorithm used in wavelets (where "intensity changes" are wavelet coefficients). Hence, images are digitized taking advantage of scale-similarity in recursive processing, and using iterated matrix powers, i.e., integral powers of the slanted wavelet matrices outlined in Chapter 7. In this form, the (wavelet) algorithm is thus a recursive matrix algorithm, and it takes advantage of a key feature of wavelet-scales: each degree of scale is a level in the corresponding combinatorial pyramid. Further, it is *localized*, so it does not make the redundant infinite additions that are notorious in Fourier approximations.

JPEG is commonly known as a format for compressing, digitizing and storing color images. It supports a number of colors, in the millions: and it can reduce file sizes to about 5% of their original size with only small amount of lost data, i.e., "small" relative to detection by the human eye. The latest JPEG2000 promises to compress images 200 times with better resulting quality than earlier versions based on Fourier waves. The key technology enabling such improvement involves switching to wavelets, away from the earlier Fourier waves that were used in discrete cosine transform (DCT).

From [JPEG00]:

> The coder is essentially a bit-plane coder, using the same Layered Zero Coding (LZC) techniques which have been employed in a number of embedded Wavelet coders. Key additions are:
>
> - The use of fractional bit-planes, in which the quantization symbols for any given quantization layer (or bit-plane) are coded in a succession of separate passes, rather than just one pass.
> - A simple embedded quad-tree algorithm is used to identify whether or not each of a collection of "subblocks" contains any non-zero (significant) samples at each quantization layer, so that the encoding and decoding algorithms need only visit those samples which lie within subblocks which are known to have significant samples.

GIF

(Graphics Interchange Format)—Largely "Fourier based."

A compressed file format used for storing and transmitting color graphics. The GIF model is older, and it is more widely used (up to now!), but at the same time it is more restricted in capabilities than JPEG 2000; more limited with respect to the number of colors (a few hundred) and compression degree.

With the latest advances with wavelets in digital image processing I imagine new titles in the next generation of horror films, such as:

- *He Came at Breakfast Time and Left at 8:30 p.m.*
- *Marooned in Space with a Digital Camera Fanatic*
- *Digital Photographers from Deneb*
- *Revolt of the Memory Sticks*
- *Countdown to .jpeg*
- *Digital Downloads/Uploads from Hell*

Grayscale

This is a notion from digital image analysis. In image processing, for a given image, a value is assigned to each subdivision square (called "pixel"). It is a certain sample number: A single number for each pixel!

In general, the displayed images themselves are typically composed of shades of gray, varying from black at the weakest intensity to white at the strongest. For color images, each of the three primary colors is assigned pixel intensities in the same way. This amounts to an encoding of various colors with different intensities. A mixing then becomes part of the digital processing. Grayscale images are distinct from black-and-white images, which in the context of computer imaging are images with only two colors; grayscale images have many shades of gray in between.

Quadrature-mirror filter

"Quadrature-mirror filter" is engineering jargon, and signal-processing engineers aren't exactly poets. [From the online Oxford English Dictionary [OED]: "quadrature. (a). Math– The action or process of squaring; spec. the expression of an area bounded by a curve, esp. a circle, by means of an equivalent square. More widely, the calculation of the area bounded by, or lying under, a curve. (b). 1942 H. M. BACON –Differential & Integral Calculus: The desire was to find a square equal in area to the area bounded by the given curve (in this case, a circle). For this reason the problem has been called the problem of quadrature."]

Signal-processing engineers noticed early in the subject that the conditions imposed on each of the two filter functions, say m_0 and m_1 that are used in the analysis/synthesis of speech signals into two subbands (see Figure 7.14, p. 132) involve sums of squares. Similarly the functions themselves m_0 and m_1 satisfy a sum-square rule; or you could say, a circle-rule.

These quadratic conditions are summarized in the text around (9.2.12). Of course this is also what allows us to get the unitary matrix functions (of the Appendices) into the game. Or equivalently, the representations of the Cuntz relations from Chapter 9 serve to create a geometric framework for the popular pyramid algorithms of wavelet/fractal subdivision algorithms.

The essential conclusion in the Appendices above is that the so-called "quadrature conditions" from signal processing, or equivalently from wavelet filters, take a simple equivalent form in terms of unitary matrices. See also [Jor03]. Each instance of a sum-of-squares rule suggests a circle law, and that is perhaps the root of this engineering terminology. Actually for the engineers, it is the finite set of numbers (also called masking, or wavelet coefficients) that go into the filters that are of more immediate interest, and the sum-of-squares rule for the filter functions merely reflects a quadratic system of equations for the wavelet coefficients, see (1.3.20). They are the frequency response to the system (1.3.20). The related condition (1.3.21) refers to the low-pass condition which characterizes the first signal-processing filter in a subband system. For example the four numbers (alias, the four taps) that define the Daubechies wavelet (see Chapter 1, Example 1.3.3, and (7.6.6)) result as one of the solutions to this quadratic system of equations.

Additional discussion of the engineering term "quadrature-mirror filter" and its relation to "mirror" can be found on the website [WWW4]. It explains the quadrature part differently; i.e., in the following sense of "quadrature:" It is the frequency point $\pi/2$, the "quadrature point" that divides the circle into four parts.

What is a *frame?*

To the mathematics student:

It is a generalization of an orthonormal basis (ONB)! Let (b_i), i in some index set, be an orthonormal basis for a Hilbert space. To understand the generalization, begin with Parseval's familiar identity for an ONB:

$$\|x\|^2 = \sum_i |\langle b_i \mid x \rangle|^2. \qquad (*)$$

More generally, if a system of vectors (b_i) satisfies $(*)$, it is said to form a tight frame, or a Parseval frame. But it need not be an ONB: You might have $\|b_i\| < 1$, i.e., the norm is "too small." And redundancy in the system will then smear out orthogonality.

Or it could be even worse: If instead of an identity in $(*)$, you only have estimates, with two positive constants A, and B: The term $A \|x\|^2$ as a lower bound, and $B \|x\|^2$ as an upper bound for $\sum_i |\langle b_i \mid x \rangle|^2$; then you talk about a general *frame* with A and B as frame bounds.

It is easy to rewrite all of this in terms of *dilations* from operator theory: Frames (b_i) in a Hilbert space $\mathcal{H}$ are all of the form $b_i = T(c_i)$ where (c_i) is an ONB in an expanded Hilbert space $\mathcal{K}$, and $T: \mathcal{K} \to \mathcal{H}$ a bounded invertible linear operator.

The Parseval frames, for example, correspond to the case when this operator T is the projection of $\mathcal{K}$ onto $\mathcal{H}$.

So the notion of a "frame" arises from relaxing the standard requirement on a "basis." While at first this particular term "frame" might appear somewhat as a mathematical technicality or a mere curiosity, in fact we have seen in the past decade that the subject "frames" emerging in leaps and bounds as a substantial mathematical discipline in its own right: one with a real presence both in the book literature (see, e.g., [Chr03] and the papers cited there) and in research journals. Mathematically there are good reasons to relax the more stringent axioms that have previously been used for bases in infinite-dimensional function spaces; and much of this has been motivated by needs dictated by wavelets. Other motivations are drawn from engineering.

It turns out that it is much easier to generate "wavelet bases" which are only frames, as opposed to orthonormal bases (ONBs). Moreover, a number of wavelet problems in numerical analysis rely on easy and readily available libraries of wavelet bases. For this, the "library" of ONB wavelets is too small! Some of the frame wavelets have been known in applied mathematics for a generation or more under the name of "splines;" see [Chr03] for details. Add to this the fact that now, both in wavelet mathematics and in telecommunications engineering, it has proved practical to give up the stringent and restrictive axiom of ONBs. What is needed is a notion of "basis" which accommodates some degree of redundancy in the process of synthesis. (By *synthesis* we mean the expansion of a vector in a (frame) "basis;" i.e., reconstructing the vector from its base coefficients.) Our Chapter 6 above illustrates this point by example, and for the simplest wavelet of them all. The issue in its general form is closely tied into the role played by scale-similarity.

To an engineer:

Frames are used by signal-processing engineers, and they are motivated by practical concerns regarding transmission and measurement in telecommunication. Many of the non-trivial engineering applications and uses take place in finite dimensions.

The name *frame* has to do with measurements within a visual "frame," referring to an instrument. For mathematical reasons, we know that an "honest" basis, or an ONB, would escape "out of" the frame!

Alias (aliasing)

Engineering:

(1) In signal processing, the effect that causes different continuous signals to create multiplicities or to become indistinguishable (or aliases of one another) when sampled.

(2) In computing, the indirect (usually unexpected) effect on other data when a variable or reference is changed; typically referring to multiplicities of the original data.

Mathematics:

This notion of "aliasing" from signal processing is also current in such areas of mathematics as operator theory and harmonic analysis. It is used in connection with problems in a Hilbert space, say $\mathcal{H}$, when a super-structure is constructed in the form of an ambient dilated Hilbert space $\mathcal{K}$, and an isometry embedding $\mathcal{H}$ into $\mathcal{K}$. Then aliasing is seen as the effect on an initial signal resulting from oversampling. The signal could be a vector in $\mathcal{H}$, or a frame basis for $L^2\left(\mathbb{R}^d\right)$.

We introduced the term *sampling* in Chapter 1 above. The sampling could be done with a selection of points on a lattice in $\mathbb{R}^d$ (i.e., a rank-d discrete subgroup in $\mathbb{R}^d$), and *oversampling* then refers to sampling points in a bigger lattice.

When oversampling is applied to a continuous signal (realized in $\mathcal{H}$), it creates one or more different signals (aliases, or multiplicities) indistinguishable from the original signal; and it is then possible to realize the aliases in the dilated Hilbert space $\mathcal{K}$. Hence some of our results in Chapter 6 and in [DuJo06c] make aliasing precise via a super-structure. This is a dilated Hilbert space, and it arises, for example, in the context of affine wavelet frames in $L^2\left(\mathbb{R}^d\right)$.

In this setting, there is a procedure in which sampling in an initial frame for $L^2\left(\mathbb{R}^d\right)$ yields a dilated Hilbert space $\mathcal{K}$ and a super-frame in $\mathcal{K}$. Thus, in a sense "nothing is lost" in oversampling: The oversampled frame is a corner of a third frame, a super-structure, or an associated super-frame. The sampling setting in [DuJo06c] admits a concrete representation of the Hilbert space $\mathcal{K}$ as a direct sum of a finite number of copies of $L^2\left(\mathbb{R}^d\right)$, the number of copies depending on the amount of oversampling.

Computational mathematics

On a personal note, after teaching some of the present material in courses, this author has come to appreciate the usefulness of Hilbert-space geometry and operator theory in addressing even such practical problems of calculating wavelet coefficients with iterative and fast matrix multiplication algorithms.

In fact, I have become much more optimistic than I used to be about the practical and the computational usefulness of relying on even singular wavelet filters of one kind or the other, in computation.

One of the things coming out from Chapter 7, the Appendices above, from my teaching of wavelets, and from my work with engineers is the usefulness of Hilbert-space geometry for iterative algorithms. Thus, once we agree to stay in a fixed resolution subspace in $L^2\left(\mathbb{R}^n\right)$, then we can do wavelet expansions without ever having to calculate wavelet coefficients the slow way, i.e., by integrating over $\mathbb{R}^n$, or over a subset of it. The trick is to compute wavelet coefficients instead with the use of suitable matrix iterations, and then using slanted matrices (see Figure 7.13, p. 128) which are computationally much faster. For more detail, we refer the reader to the series of figures in Chapter 7, see especially Figures 7.7, 7.8, and 7.9 (pp. 124–126), and Figure 7.13. At first, I was not sure that it is possible to avoid integration, but it is!

In concrete cases of image processing, we note that all the pictures you come across on the web showing iterative image processing of Lena or of some other digital image (see, e.g., [WWW3]) are done precisely with the standard matrix iteration algorithm for wavelets. "Computers can't integrate!"

What further emerges by a closer scrutiny of these iterative algorithms is that Cuntz (or Cuntz-like) relations are just perfect for this; see the discussion in the Appendices above, especially (B.1)–(B.2) and Table C.1. Of course, with hindsight, we now know that these relations have their root in old ideas from signal processing; see [Jor03].

The only technical modification needed for all of these iterative schemes to work for such singular filters that are used in fractals of one kind or the other (Chapters 7–8) is that the slanted matrices might now become infinite, but their slanted nature makes this infinity only a mild nuisance. Engineers are good at devising threshold schemes for truncating the infinite, as long as it is under control; and as we saw, it is for this purpose.

Epigraphs

Quotation from John von Neumann on page vii above the Preface: This quote is popular on web pages about von Neumann, and about computing and mathematics generally. It is apparently not from a published work of von Neumann's, but Franz L. Alt recalls it as a remark made from the podium by von Neumann as keynote speaker at the first national meeting of the Association for Computing Machinery in 1947. The exchange at that meeting is described at the end of Alt's brief article *Archaeology of computers: Reminiscences, 1945–1947*, Communications of the ACM, vol. 15, issue 7, July 1972, special issue: *Twenty-fifth anniversary of the Association for Computing Machinery*, p. 694. Alt recalls that von Neumann "mentioned the 'new programming method' for ENIAC and explained that its seemingly small vocabulary was in fact ample: that future computers, then in the design stage, would get along on a dozen instruction types, and this was known to be adequate for expressing all of mathematics.... Von Neumann went on to say that one need not be surprised at this small number, since about 1,000 words were known to be adequate for most situations of real life, and mathematics was only a small part of life, and a very simple part at that. This caused some hilarity in the audience, which provoked von Neumann to say: 'If people do not believe that mathematics is simple, it is only because they do not realize how complicated life is.' "

Quotation from David Mumford on page xv: David Mumford, *The dawning of the age of stochasticity*, Atti della Accademia Nazionale dei Lincei, Classe di Scienze Fisiche, Matematiche e Naturali, Rendiconti Lincei, Serie IX, Matematica e Applicazioni, vol. XI, 2000, special issue: *Mathematics Towards the Third Millennium* (Papers from the International Conference held in Rome, May 27–29, 1999), p. 107. This is quoted from the beginning of Mumford's article, which offers a fascinating and refreshing view on thinking as Bayesian inference, and the use of probability spaces in image processing.

In the "Getting started" section of the front matter, on page xv, we "sort of quote" from G.H. Hardy, *A Mathematician's Apology*, Canto, Cambridge University Press, Cambridge, 1992, with a foreword by C.P. Snow (first edition 1940, and latest edition 1992), in which sixty-six years ago Hardy so eloquently apologized to the World for mathematics. Back then Hardy, the Platonic puritan he was, had in mind pure mathematics: at the time, some parts of applied mathematics had been used in an unpopular war. In my opening paragraph of the present "Getting started" section, I could not help wondering if in the meantime the winds could have changed; wondering whether perhaps now a mathematics author who trespasses into engineering topics and other applied domains might not be expected to apologize; at least if he/she has in mind mathematics students as his primary audience. Aside from this, Hardy's lovely little book has become a paradigm for mathematical apologies, and any apologetic mathematician ought to at least mention Hardy's *A Mathematician's Apology* in her credits.

Quotation from Lewis Carroll on page xvii: Lewis Carroll, *Through the Looking-Glass*, *The Complete Illustrated Lewis Carroll*, Wordsworth Editions, 1991, page 196.

Quotation from Søren Kierkegaard on page xxxvii in the "Getting started" section of the front matter: Søren Kierkegaard, *Journalen* JJ:167 (1843), *Søren Kierkegaards Skrifter*, Søren Kierkegaard Research Center, Copenhagen, 1997–, vol. 18, p. 306. Thanks to Karsten Kynde, Søren Kierkegaard Forskningscenteret, web page http://www.sk.ku.dk/citater/, for the Danish text of the quotation and directions to its location in print. The English translation of the long quote is my own. The Danish short form is due to Julia Watkin; see the web page http://www.utas.edu.au/docs/humsoc/kierkegaard/resources/Kierkquotes.html .

Quotation from Stephen Hawking on page xliii in the Acknowledgments: The quote here is from page ix in Stephen Hawking's book *On the Shoulders of Giants: The Great Works of Physics and Astronomy*, Running Press, Philadelphia, 2002. This book in turn is a collection of reprints of original classics in the sciences. The book title "On the shoulders of giants" is a quote from Isaac Newton.

Quotation from Edward B. Burger and Michael Starbird on page 1: Edward B. Burger and Michael Starbird, *Coincidences, Chaos, and All That Math Jazz: Making Light of Weighty Ideas*, W.W. Norton & Company, 2005. Quoted from the *Front matter*: Opening thoughts.

Quotation from Lewis Carroll on page 9: Lewis Carroll, *Through the Looking-Glass*, Chapter 3, *The Complete Illustrated Lewis Carroll*, Wordsworth Editions, 1991.

Quotation from C.M. Brislawn on page 22: C.M. Brislawn, *Fingerprints go digital*, Notices of the American Mathematical Society, vol. 42, 1995, p. 1278.

Quotation from Piet Hein on page 27: Piet Hein, "Problems," *Grooks*, Borgens Forlag, Copenhagen, Denmark, The MIT Press, Cambridge, MA, 1966; *Grooks 1*, Doubleday & Company Inc., Garden City, NY, General Publishing Company Limited, Toronto, 1969; *Collected Grooks I*, Borgens Forlag, Copenhagen, Denmark, 2002.

Quotation from Lewis Carroll on page 39: Lewis Carroll, *Alice's Adventures in Wonderland*, Chapter VI, *The Complete Illustrated Lewis Carroll*, Wordsworth Editions, 1991.

Quotation from P.A.M. Dirac on page 58: *The Development of Quantum Theory (J. Robert Oppenheimer Memorial Prize Acceptance Speech)*, Gordon and Breach Publishers, New York, 1971, pp. 20–24. The quote used an an epigraph on p. 2 in *Operator Commutation Relations* by Palle E.T. Jorgensen and Robert T. Moore, D. Reidel, Dordrecht, Boston, 1984, is an abridgement of the above passage. A longer excerpt (with the curious substitution of "commutation" for "noncommutation" where it first appears) is presented as an epigraph in the announcement of a "Program on Noncommutative Algebra" at the Mathematical Sciences Research Institute, http://www.msri.org/activities/programs/9900/noncomm/.

Back when I thought about what to put into *Operator Commutation Relations*, I relied a lot on *The Historical Development of Quantum Theory* by Jagdish Mehra and Helmut Rechenberg, Springer-Verlag, New York, 1982– . I was also impressed by how well re-searched this lovely book-set is. The two authors, Mehra and Rechenberg, did long inter-views over the span of time when they worked on their book set. They had known Bohr, and they had many meetings with Heisenberg, Pauli, Dirac, and many more, and as I re-member, much material in the book set results directly from these interviews. It is good that the two coauthors had the interviews, as these giants in quantum theory passed on shortly after the book set was completed. I think the book set is a treasure of information on quantum theory (especially the mathematical part of it) and on the architects of the theory. Late in life, Dirac would always tell the physicists at conferences to look to the *math* for clues to the deep questions in physics, and he liked to use his (Dirac) equation for the electron as an example, stressing that he was led to it by paying attention to the beauty of the math, more than to the physics experiments. He was alive when I was working on *Operator Commutation Relations*, and I talked to him a few times. He told me that he was happy to be quoted. He used to visit his son Gabriel Dirac (graph theory) who was my colleague in Aarhus.

Quotation from A.N. Kolmogorov on page 59: A.N. Kolmogorov, *Foundations of the Theory of Probability*, 2d English ed., translation edited by Nathan Morrison, Chelsea, New York, 1956, p. 1; for the German original see [Kol77].

Quotation from Benoit B. Mandelbrot on page 69: Benoit B. Mandelbrot, *Multifractals and 1/f noise: Wild self-affinity in physics* (1963–1976), Selecta Volume N, Selected Works of Benoit B. Mandelbrot, Springer- Verlag, New York, 1999, p. 9.

Quotation from Albert Einstein on page 83: These two quotes by A. Einstein are from pages 228–9 in *The New Quotable Einstein*, collected from Einstein's archives and edited by Alice Calaprice, Princeton University Press, 2005. In their original, they are from conver-sations, the second one with Einstein and Valentine Bargmann, meaning that God makes us believe we have understood something that in reality we are far from understanding.

Quotation from Percy Bysshe Shelley on page 91: Percy Bysshe Shelley, "Queen Mab: A Philosophical Poem, with Notes," published by the author, London, 1813.

Quotation from Douglas Adams on page 99: Quoted from the front matter in Douglas Adams, *Hitchhiker's Guide to the Galaxy (Mostly Harmless)*, Del Rey, Ballantine Books, New York, 2005.

Quotation from Yves Meyer on page 109: Yves Meyer, *Wavelets and functions with bounded variation from image processing to pure mathematics*, Atti della Accademia Nazionale dei Lincei, Classe di Scienze Fisiche, Matematiche e Naturali, Rendiconti Lincei, Serie IX, Matematica e Applicazioni, vol. XI, 2000, special issue: *Mathematics Towards the Third Millennium* (Papers from the International Conference held in Rome, May 27–29, 1999), p. 95.

Quotation from Oliver Heaviside on page 157: Oliver Heaviside, *On operators in physical mathematics, part II*, Proceedings of the Royal Society of London, vol. 54, 1893, p. 121.

Quotation from Max Born on page 176: Jagdish Mehra and Helmut Rechenberg, *The Historical Development of Quantum Theory, vol. 3: The Formulation of Matrix Mechanics and Its Modifications, 1925–1926*, Springer-Verlag, New York, 1982, p. 129, footnote 146.

Quotation from Werner Heisenberg on page 179: Jagdish Mehra and Helmut Rechenberg, *The Historical Development of Quantum Theory, vol. 3: The Formulation of Matrix Mechanics and Its Modifications, 1925–1926*, Springer-Verlag, New York, 1982, p. 94.

Quotation from Norbert Wiener on page 205: Norbert Wiener, *I Am a Mathematician*, Doubleday, Garden City, NY, 1956; Victor Gollancz, London, 1956; The MIT Press, Cambridge, MA, 1964, pp. 108–109.

References

Explanation: The list below includes both books and journal articles, listed alpha-
betically by author. The type style and punctuation are generated by BibTeX, and we
follow a well established AMS prescription. One general rule applies to all different
types of sources cited (books, journals, monographs, memoirs, edited volumes, web
sources): The *title of the work cited* is in italic type. This makes it easy for readers to
identify at a glance what is being cited. Thus "longer works" such as books are not
given the special status of being in italic. This BibTeX styling makes it clear which
item is a book and which a paper: entries for journal articles end with the volume
number in bold, the year in parentheses, and the page range, while entries for books
end with the publisher's name and address, and the year not in parentheses. Articles
published in books such as proceedings volumes have the same book information
near the end of the entry, but it is followed by the abbreviation "pp." and the page
range of the article within the book.

Comments on our citations of a variety of websites: In general, websites might not
have well-defined authors, and well-defined year of "publication," so we cite them as
[WWW1], [WWW2], etc. Readers should keep in mind that we cite these URLs only
as supplements to issues covered inside the book; and we hope that they will inspire
readers to follow up on the themes covered in the book and in the various URLs.

[AgKu04a]   B. Agard and A. Kusiak, *A data-mining based methodology for the design
            of product families*, International Journal of Production Research **42** (2004),
            no. 15, 2955–2969.

[AgKu04b]   B. Agard and A. Kusiak, *Data mining for subassembly selection*, ASME
            Transactions: Journal of Manufacturing Science and Engineering **126** (2004),
            no. 3, 627–631.

[ACM04]   A. Aldroubi, C.A. Cabrelli, and U.M. Molter, *How to construct wavelet frames
            on irregular grids and arbitrary dilations in* $\mathbb{R}^d$, Wavelets, Frames and Opera-
            tor Theory (College Park, MD, 2003) (C. Heil, P.E.T. Jorgensen, and D.R. Lar-
            son, eds.), Contemp. Math., vol. 345, American Mathematical Society, Provi-
            dence, 2004, pp. 1–9.

[AlGr01]   A. Aldroubi and K. Gröchenig, *Nonuniform sampling and reconstruction in shift-invariant spaces*, SIAM Rev. **43** (2001), 585–620.

[Arv04]   W. Arveson, *The free cover of a row contraction*, Doc. Math. **9** (2004), 137–161.

[Ash90]   R.B. Ash, *Information Theory*, Dover, New York, 1990, corrected reprint of the original 1965 Interscience/Wiley edition.

[AyTa03]   A. Ayache and M.S. Taqqu, *Rate optimality of wavelet series approximations of fractional Brownian motion*, J. Fourier Anal. Appl. **9** (2003), 451–471.

[BaCM02]   L.W. Baggett, J.E. Courter, and K.D. Merrill, *The construction of wavelets from generalized conjugate mirror filters in $L^2(\mathbb{R}^n)$*, Appl. Comput. Harmon. Anal. **13** (2002), 201–223.

[BaJMP04] L.W. Baggett, P.E.T. Jorgensen, K.D. Merrill, and J.A. Packer, *An analogue of Bratteli-Jorgensen loop group actions for GMRA's*, Wavelets, Frames, and Operator Theory (College Park, MD, 2003) (C. Heil, P.E.T. Jorgensen, and D.R. Larson, eds.), Contemp. Math., vol. 345, American Mathematical Society, Providence, 2004, pp. 11–25.

[BaJMP05] L.W. Baggett, P.E.T. Jorgensen, K.D. Merrill, and J.A. Packer, *Construction of Parseval wavelets from redundant filter systems*, J. Math. Phys. **46** (2005), no. 8, 083502, 28 pp., doi:10.1063/1.1982768.

[BaJMP06] L.W. Baggett, P.E.T. Jorgensen, K.D. Merrill, and J.A. Packer, *A non-MRA C^r frame wavelet with rapid decay*, Acta Appl. Math. **89** (2006), 251–270, doi:10.1007/s10440-005-9011-4.

[BaMM99]   L.W. Baggett, H.A. Medina, and K.D. Merrill, *Generalized multi-resolution analyses and a construction procedure for all wavelet sets in $\mathbf{R}^n$*, J. Fourier Anal. Appl. **5** (1999), 563–573.

[BaMe99]   L.W. Baggett and K.D. Merrill, *Abstract harmonic analysis and wavelets in $\mathbf{R}^n$*, The Functional and Harmonic Analysis of Wavelets and Frames (San Antonio, 1999) (L.W. Baggett and D.R. Larson, eds.), Contemp. Math., vol. 247, American Mathematical Society, Providence, 1999, pp. 17–27.

[Bal00]   V. Baladi, *Positive Transfer Operators and Decay of Correlations*, World Scientific, River Edge, NJ, Singapore, 2000.

[BaCV05]   J.A. Ball, C. Sadosky, and V. Vinnikov, *Conservative input-state-output systems with evolution on a multidimensional integer lattice*, Multidimens. Syst. Signal Process. **16** (2005), no. 2, 133–198.

[BaVi05]   J.A. Ball and V. Vinnikov, *Lax–Phillips Scattering and Conservative Linear Systems: A Cuntz-Algebra Multidimensional Setting*, Mem. Amer. Math. Soc. **178** (2005), no. 837.

[BaNi70]   M.N. Barber and B.W. Ninham, *Random and Restricted Walks: Theory and Applications*, Gordon and Breach, New York, 1970.

[Bas95]   R.F. Bass, *Probabilistic Techniques in Analysis*, Probability and Its Applications, Springer-Verlag, New York, 1995.

[Bas03]   R.F. Bass, *Stochastic differential equations driven by symmetric stable processes*, Séminaire de Probabilités, XXXVI (J. Azéma, M. Émery, M. Ledoux, and M. Yor, eds.), Lecture Notes in Math., vol. 1801, Springer-Verlag, Berlin, 2003, pp. 302–313.

[Bat87]   G. Battle, *A block spin construction of ondelettes, I: Lemarié functions*, Comm. Math. Phys. **110** (1987), 601–615.

[Bea91]   A.F. Beardon, *Iteration of Rational Functions: Complex Analytic Dynamical Systems*, Graduate Texts in Mathematics, vol. 132, Springer-Verlag, New York, 1991.

[BeBe95]   J.J. Benedetto and E.G. Bernstein, *Pyramidal Riesz products associated with subband coding and self-similarity*, Wavelet Applications II (H.H. Szu, ed.), Proceedings of SPIE, vol. 2491, SPIE, Bellingham, WA, 1995, pp. 212–221.

[BeBK05]   J.J. Benedetto, E. Bernstein, and I. Konstantinidis, *Multiscale Riesz products and their support properties*, Acta Appl. Math. **88** (2005), no. 2, 201–227.

[Bil99]   P. Billingsley, *Convergence of Probability Measures*, second ed., Wiley Series in Probability and Statistics, Wiley-Interscience, New York, 1999.

[BoNe03]   E. Bondarenko and V.V. Nekrashevych, *Post-critically finite self-similar groups*, Algebra Discrete Math. **2003**, 21–32.

[BrEJ00]   O. Bratteli, D.E. Evans, and P.E.T. Jorgensen, *Compactly supported wavelets and representations of the Cuntz relations*, Appl. Comput. Harmon. Anal. **8** (2000), 166–196.

[BrJo97]   O. Bratteli and P.E.T. Jorgensen, *Isometries, shifts, Cuntz algebras and multiresolution wavelet analysis of scale N*, Integral Equations Operator Theory **28** (1997), 382–443.

[BrJo99a]   O. Bratteli and P.E.T. Jorgensen, *Iterated function systems and permutation representations of the Cuntz algebra*, Mem. Amer. Math. Soc. **139** (1999), no. 663.

[BrJo99b]   O. Bratteli and P.E.T. Jorgensen, *Convergence of the cascade algorithm at irregular scaling functions*, The Functional and Harmonic Analysis of Wavelets and Frames (San Antonio, 1999) (L.W. Baggett and D.R. Larson, eds.), Contemp. Math., vol. 247, American Mathematical Society, Providence, 1999, pp. 93–130.

[BrJo02a]   O. Bratteli and P.E.T. Jorgensen, *Wavelet filters and infinite-dimensional unitary groups*, Wavelet Analysis and Applications (Guangzhou, China, 1999) (D. Deng, D. Huang, R.-Q. Jia, W. Lin, and J. Wang, eds.), AMS/IP Studies in Advanced Mathematics, vol. 25, American Mathematical Society, Providence, International Press, Boston, 2002, pp. 35–65.

[BrJo02b]   O. Bratteli and P.E.T. Jorgensen, *Wavelets through a Looking Glass: The World of the Spectrum*, Applied and Numerical Harmonic Analysis, Birkhäuser, Boston, 2002.

[BrJKW00]   O. Bratteli, P.E.T. Jorgensen, A. Kishimoto, and R. Werner, *Pure states on $\mathcal{O}_d$*, J. Operator Theory **43** (2000), 97–143.

[BrJO04]   O. Bratteli, P.E.T. Jorgensen, and V. Ostrovs'kyĭ, *Representation Theory and Numerical AF-invariants: The Representations and Centralizers of Certain States on $\mathcal{O}_d$*, Mem. Amer. Math. Soc. **168** (2004), no. 797.

[BrJP96]   O. Bratteli, P.E.T. Jorgensen, and G.L. Price, *Endomorphisms of $\mathcal{B}(\mathcal{H})$*, Quantization, Nonlinear Partial Differential Equations, and Operator Algebra (W. Arveson, T. Branson, and I. Segal, eds.), Proc. Sympos. Pure Math., vol. 59, American Mathematical Society, Providence, 1996, pp. 93–138.

[Bri95]   C. Brislawn, *Fingerprints go digital*, Notices Amer. Math. Soc. **42** (1995), 1278–1283.

[BrRo91]   C. Brislawn and I.G. Rosen, *Wavelet based approximation in the optimal control of distributed parameter systems*, Numer. Funct. Anal. Optim. **12** (1991), 33–77.

[BrMo75]   G. Brown and W. Moran, *Products of random variables and Kakutani's criterion for orthogonality of product measures*, J. London Math. Soc. (2) **10** (1975), no. part 4, 401–405.

[CaHM04]   C.A. Cabrelli, C. Heil, and U.M. Molter, *Self-similarity and multiwavelets in higher dimensions*, Mem. Amer. Math. Soc. **170** (2004), no. 807.

[Chr03]   O. Christensen, *An Introduction to Frames and Riesz Bases*, Applied and Numerical Harmonic Analysis, Birkhäuser, Boston, 2003.

[Coh90]   A. Cohen, *Ondelettes, analyses multirésolutions et filtres miroirs en quadrature*, Ann. Inst. H. Poincaré Anal. Non Linéaire **7** (1990), 439–459.

[Coh03]   A. Cohen, *Numerical Analysis of Wavelet Methods*, Studies in Mathematics and Its Applications, vol. 32, North-Holland, Amsterdam, 2003.

[CoMW95]   R.R. Coifman, Y. Meyer, and V. Wickerhauser, *Numerical harmonic analysis*, Essays on Fourier Analysis in Honor of Elias M. Stein (Princeton, 1991) (C. Fefferman, R. Fefferman, and S. Wainger, eds.), Princeton Mathematical Series, vol. 42, Princeton University Press, Princeton, NJ, 1995, pp. 162–174.

[CoWi93]   R.R. Coifman and M.V. Wickerhauser, *Wavelets and adapted waveform analysis: A toolkit for signal processing and numerical analysis*, Different Perspectives on Wavelets (San Antonio, TX, 1993) (I. Daubechies, ed.), Proc. Sympos. Appl. Math., vol. 47, American Mathematical Society, Providence, 1993, pp. 119–153.

[CoHR97]   J.-P. Conze, L. Hervé, and A. Raugi, *Pavages auto-affines, opérateurs de transfert et critères de réseau dans $\mathbb{R}^d$*, Bol. Soc. Brasil. Mat. (N.S.) **28** (1997), 1–42.

[CoRa90]   J.-P. Conze and A. Raugi, *Fonctions harmoniques pour un opérateur de transition et applications*, Bull. Soc. Math. France **118** (1990), 273–310.

[Cun77]   J. Cuntz, *Simple C^*-algebras generated by isometries*, Comm. Math. Phys. **57** (1977), 173–185.

[DaSw98]   I. Daubechies and W. Sweldens, *Factoring wavelet transforms into lifting steps*, J. Fourier Anal. Appl. **4** (1998), 247–269.

[CvSS85]   P. Cvitanović, B. Shraiman, and B. Söderberg, *Scaling laws for mode lockings in circle maps*, Phys. Scripta **32** (1985), 263–270.

[Dau92]   I. Daubechies, *Ten Lectures on Wavelets*, CBMS-NSF Regional Conf. Ser. in Appl. Math., vol. 61, SIAM, Philadelphia, 1992.

[DaHRS03]   I. Daubechies, B. Han, A. Ron, and Z. Shen, *Framelets: MRA-based constructions of wavelet frames*, Appl. Comput. Harmon. Anal. **14** (2003), 1–46.

[Dav96]   K.R. Davidson, *C^*-algebras by Example*, Fields Institute Monographs, vol. 6, American Mathematical Society, Providence, 1996.

[DaKS01]   K.R. Davidson, D.W. Kribs, and M.E. Shpigel, *Isometric dilations of non-commuting finite rank n-tuples*, Canad. J. Math. **53** (2001), 506–545, http://arxiv.org/abs/math.OA/0411521.

[DeSh04]   V. Deaconu and F. Shultz, *C*-algebras associated with interval maps*, Trans. Amer. Math. Soc., to appear, math.OA/0405469 .

[Dev92]   R.L. Devaney, *A First Course in Chaotic Dynamical Systems: Theory and Experiment*, Addison-Wesley Studies in Nonlinearity, Addison-Wesley Advanced Book Program, Reading, MA, 1992, with a separately available computer disk.

[DiFr99]   P. Diaconis and D. Freedman, *Iterated random functions*, SIAM Rev. **41** (1999), 45–76, graphical supplement 77–82.

[DoGH00]   V. Dobrić, R. Gundy, and P. Hitczenko, *Characterizations of orthonormal scale functions: A probabilistic approach*, J. Geom. Anal. **10** (2000), 417–434.

[DoJo94]   D.L. Donoho and I.M. Johnstone, *Ideal denoising in an orthonormal basis chosen from a library of bases*, C. R. Acad. Sci. Paris Sér. I Math. **319** (1994), 1317–1322.

[DoMSS03]   D.L. Donoho, S. Mallat, R. von Sachs, and Y. Samuelides, *Locally stationary covariance and signal estimation with macrotiles*, IEEE Trans. Signal Process. **51** (2003), 614–627.

[Doo94]   J.L. Doob, *Measure Theory*, Graduate Texts in Mathematics, vol. 143, Springer-Verlag, New York, 1994.

[Doo01]   J.L. Doob, *Classical Potential Theory and Its Probabilistic Counterpart*, Classics in Mathematics, Springer-Verlag, Berlin, 2001, reprint of the 1984 edition.

[Dut02]   D.E. Dutkay, *Harmonic analysis of signed Ruelle transfer operators*, J. Math. Anal. Appl. **273** (2002), 590–617.

[Dut04a]   D.E. Dutkay, *The local trace function for super-wavelets*, Wavelets, Frames, and Operator Theory (Focused Research Group Workshop, College Park, Maryland, January 15–21, 2003) (C. Heil, P.E.T. Jorgensen, and D. Larson, eds.), Contemp. Math., vol. 345, American Mathematical Society, Providence, 2004, pp. 115–136.

[Dut04b]   D.E. Dutkay, *Positive definite maps, representations and frames*, Rev. Math. Phys. **16** (2004), no. 4, 451–477.

[DuJo05a]   D.E. Dutkay and P.E.T. Jorgensen, *Wavelet constructions in non-linear dynamics*, Electron. Res. Announc. Amer. Math. Soc. **11** (2005), 21–33, http://www.ams.org/era/2005-11-03/S1079-6762-05-00143-5/home.html.

[DuJo05b]   D.E. Dutkay and P.E.T. Jorgensen, *Hilbert spaces of martingales supporting certain substitution-dynamical systems*, Conform. Geom. Dyn. **9** (2005), 24–45, http://www.ams.org/ecgd/2005-09-02/S1088-4173-05-00135-9/home.html.

[DuJo06a]   D.E. Dutkay and P.E.T. Jorgensen, *Martingales, endomorphisms, and covariant systems of operators in Hilbert space*, J. Operator Theory, to appear (in galley proof 2006, pp. 101–145), http://arXiv.org/abs/math.CA/0407330.

[DuJo06b]   D.E. Dutkay and P.E.T. Jorgensen, *Wavelets on fractals*, Rev. Mat. Iberoamericana **22** (2006), 131–180.

[DuJo06c]   D.E. Dutkay and P.E.T. Jorgensen, *Oversampling generates super-wavelets*, Proc. Amer. Math. Soc., to appear, http://arxiv.org/abs/math.FA/0511399.

[Edw01]   H.M. Edwards, *Riemann's Zeta Function*, Dover, Mineola, NY, 2001, reprint of the 1974 original [Academic Press, New York].

[Fal85]   K.J. Falconer, *The Geometry of Fractal Sets*, Cambridge Tracts in Mathematics, vol. 85, Cambridge University Press, Cambridge, 1985.

[Fal90]   K. Falconer, *Fractal Geometry: Mathematical Foundations and Applications*, Wiley, Chichester, 1990.

[FaLa99]   A.H. Fan and K.-S. Lau, *Iterated function system and Ruelle operator*, J. Math. Anal. Appl. **231** (1999), 319–344.

[Fel71]   W. Feller, *An Introduction to Probability Theory and Its Applications*, 3rd ed., vol. 2, Wiley, New York, 1971.

[FeLa02]   D.-J. Feng and K.-S. Lau, *The pressure function for products of non-negative matrices*, Math. Res. Lett. **9** (2002), 363–378.

[FiEs61]   M.E. Fisher and J.W. Essam, *Some cluster size and percolation problems*, J. Math. Phys. **2** (1961), 609–619.

[FrLM83]   A. Freire, A. Lopes, and R. Mañé, *An invariant measure for rational maps*, Bol. Soc. Brasil. Mat. **14** (1983), 45–62.

[Fug74]   B. Fuglede, *Commuting self-adjoint partial differential operators and a group theoretic problem*, J. Funct. Anal. **16** (1974), 101–121.

[GaNa98b]   J.-P. Gabardo and M.Z. Nashed, *Nonuniform multiresolution analyses and spectral pairs*, J. Funct. Anal. **158** (1998), no. 1, 209–241.

[GaYu05]   J.-P. Gabardo and X. Yu, *Wavelets associated with nonuniform multiresolution analyses and one-dimensional spectral pairs*, preprint 2005, McMaster University.

[GaNS01a]   X.Q. Gao, T.Q. Nguyen, and G. Strang, *Theory and lattice structure of complex paraunitary filterbanks with filters of (Hermitian-) symmetry/antisymmetry properties*, IEEE Trans. Signal Process. **49** (2001), 1028–1043.

[GaNS01b]   X.Q. Gao, T.Q. Nguyen, and G. Strang, *On factorization of M-channel paraunitary filterbanks*, IEEE Trans. Signal Process. **49** (2001), 1433–1446.

[GaNS02]   X.Q. Gao, T.Q. Nguyen, and G. Strang, *A study of two-channel complex-valued filterbanks and wavelets with orthogonality and symmetry properties*, IEEE Trans. Signal Process. **50** (2002), 824–833.

[GlZu80]   M.L. Glasser and I.J. Zucker, *Lattice sums*, Theor. Chem. Adv. Perspect. **5** (1980), 67–139.

[Gli60]   J. Glimm, *On a certain class of operator algebras*, Trans. Amer. Math. Soc. **95** (1960), 318–340.

[GrMa92]   K. Gröchenig and W.R. Madych, *Multiresolution analysis, Haar bases, and self-similar tilings of $\mathbf{R}^n$*, IEEE Trans. Inform. Theory **38** (1992), 556–568.

[Gro01]   K. Gröchenig, *Foundations of Time-Frequency Analysis*, Applied and Numerical Harmonic Analysis, Birkhäuser, Boston, 2001.

[GrMo84]   A. Grossmann and J. Morlet, *Decomposition of Hardy functions into square integrable wavelets of constant shape*, SIAM J. Math. Anal. **15** (1984), 723–736.

[Gun00]   R.F. Gundy, *Low-pass filters, martingales, and multiresolution analyses*, Appl. Comput. Harmon. Anal. **9** (2000), 204–219.

[Gun66]   R.F. Gundy, *Martingale theory and pointwise convergence of certain orthogonal series*, Trans. Amer. Math. Soc. **124** (1966), 228–248.

[Gun99]   R.F. Gundy, *Two remarks concerning wavelets: Cohen's criterion for low-pass filters and Meyer's theorem on linear independence*, The Functional and Harmonic Analysis of Wavelets and Frames (San Antonio, 1999) (L.W. Baggett and D.R. Larson, eds.), Contemp. Math., vol. 247, American Mathematical Society, Providence, 1999, pp. 249–258.

[Gun04]   R.F. Gundy, *Wavelets and probability*, preprint, Rutgers University, material presented during the author's lecture at the workshop "Wavelets and Applications", Barcelona, Spain, July 1–6, 2002, http://www.imub.ub.es/wavelets/Gundy.pdf.

[GuKa00]   R.F. Gundy and K. Kazarian, *Stopping times and local convergence for spline wavelet expansions*, SIAM J. Math. Anal. **31** (2000), 561–573.

[Haa10]   A. Haar, *Zur Theorie der orthogonalen Funktionensysteme*, Math. Ann. **69** (1910), 331–371.

[Hal83]   F.D.M. Haldane, *Fractional quantization of the Hall effect: A hierarchy of incompressible quantum fluid states*, Phys. Rev. Lett. **51** (1983), 605–608.

[Hal67]   P.R. Halmos, *A Hilbert Space Problem Book*, D. Van Nostrand, Princeton, Toronto, London, 1967, Springer, 2nd edition, 1982, Graduate Texts in Mathematics.

[HeJL04]   C. Heil, P.E.T. Jorgensen, and D.R. Larson (eds.), *Wavelets, Frames, and Operator Theory: Papers from the Focused Research Group Workshop held at the University of Maryland, College Park, MD, January 15–21, 2003*, Contemp. Math., vol. 345, American Mathematical Society, Providence, 2004.

[HeWe96]   E. Hernández and G. Weiss, *A First Course on Wavelets*, Studies in Advanced Mathematics, CRC Press, Boca Raton, Florida, 1996.

[HuTK05]   C.-C. Huang, T.-L. Tseng, and A. Kusiak, *XML-based modeling of corporate memory*, IEEE Transactions on Systems, Man, and Cybernetics, Part A **35** (2005), no. 5, 629–640.

[Hug95]   B.D. Hughes, *Random Walks and Random Environments, Vol. 1: Random Walks*, Oxford Science Publications, Clarendon Press, Oxford University Press, Oxford, New York, 1995.

[HuMS82]   B.D. Hughes, E.W. Montroll, and M.F. Shlesinger, *Fractal random walks*, J. Statist. Phys. **28** (1982), 111–126.

[HuSM81]   B.D. Hughes, M.F. Shlesinger, and E.W. Montroll, *Random walks with self-similar clusters*, Proc. Nat. Acad. Sci. U.S.A. **78** (1981), 3287–3291.

[Hut81]   J.E. Hutchinson, *Fractals and self similarity*, Indiana Univ. Math. J. **30** (1981), 713–747.

[IoMa50]   C.T. Ionescu Tulcea and G. Marinescu, *Théorie ergodique pour des classes d'opérations non complètement continues*, Ann. of Math. (2) **52** (1950), 140–147.

[Jaf05]   S. Jaffard, *Beyond Besov spaces, II: Oscillation spaces*, Constr. Approx. **21** (2005), 29–61.

[JaMe96]   S. Jaffard and Y. Meyer, *Wavelet Methods for Pointwise Regularity and Local Oscillations of Functions*, Mem. Amer. Math. Soc. **123** (1996), no. 587.

[JaMR01]   S. Jaffard, Y. Meyer, and R.D. Ryan, *Wavelets: Tools for Science & Technology*, revised ed., SIAM, Philadelphia, 2001.

[Jam64]   B. Jamison, *Asymptotic behavior of successive iterates of continuous functions under a Markov operator*, J. Math. Anal. Appl. **9** (1964), 203–214.

[JiJS01]   R.-Q. Jia, Q. Jiang, and Z. Shen, *Convergence of cascade algorithms associated with nonhomogeneous refinement equations*, Proc. Amer. Math. Soc. **129** (2001), 415–427.

[JiSh99]   Q. Jiang and Z. Shen, *On existence and weak stability of matrix refinable functions*, Constr. Approx. **15** (1999), 337–353.

[Jor99]   P.E.T. Jorgensen, *A geometric approach to the cascade approximation operator for wavelets*, Integral Equations Operator Theory **35** (1999), 125–171.

[Jor01a]   P.E.T. Jorgensen, *Ruelle Operators: Functions Which Are Harmonic with Respect to a Transfer Operator*, Mem. Amer. Math. Soc. **152** (2001), no. 720.

[Jor01b]   P.E.T. Jorgensen, *Minimality of the data in wavelet filters*, Adv. Math. **159** (2001), 143–228.

[Jor01c]   P.E.T. Jorgensen, *Representations of Cuntz algebras, loop groups and wavelets*, XIIIth International Congress on Mathematical Physics (London, 2000) (A. Fokas, A. Grigoryan, T. Kibble, and B. Zegarlinski, eds.), International Press, Boston, 2001, pp. 327–332.

[Jor03]   P.E.T. Jorgensen, *Matrix factorizations, algorithms, wavelets*, Notices Amer. Math. Soc. **50** (2003), 880–894, http://www.ams.org/notices/200308/200308-toc.html.

[Jor04a]   P.E.T. Jorgensen, *Iterated function systems, representations, and Hilbert space*, Internat. J. Math. **15** (2004), 813–832.

[Jor04b]   P.E.T. Jorgensen, *Use of operator algebras in the analysis of measures from wavelets and iterated function systems*, accepted for Operator Theory, Operator Algebras, and Applications (Deguang Han, Palle Jorgensen, and David R. Larson, eds.), Contemp. Math., American Mathematical Society, Providence, to appear 2006. http://arxiv.org/abs/math.OA/0509360.

[Jor05]   P.E.T. Jorgensen, *Measures in wavelet decompositions*, Adv. Appl. Math. **34** (2005), 561–590.

[JoKr03]   P.E.T. Jorgensen and D.W. Kribs, *Wavelet representations and Fock space on positive matrices*, J. Funct. Anal. **197** (2003), 526–559.

[JoPe92]   P.E.T. Jorgensen and S. Pedersen, *Spectral theory for Borel sets in $\mathbb{R}^n$ of finite measure*, J. Funct. Anal. **107** (1992), 72–104.

[JoPe93]   P.E.T. Jorgensen and S. Pedersen, *Group-theoretic and geometric properties of multivariable Fourier series*, Exposition. Math. **11** (1993), 309–329.

[JoPe96]   P.E.T. Jorgensen and S. Pedersen, *Harmonic analysis of fractal measures*, Constr. Approx. **12** (1996), 1–30.

[JoPe98]   P.E.T. Jorgensen and S. Pedersen, *Dense analytic subspaces in fractal L^2-spaces*, J. Analyse Math. **75** (1998), 185–228.

[JoSW95]   P.E.T. Jorgensen, L.M. Schmitt, and R.F. Werner, *Positive representations of general commutation relations allowing Wick ordering*, J. Funct. Anal. **134** (1995), 33–99.

[JPEG00]   *The JPEG2000 resource webpage*, http://stargate.ecn.purdue.edu/~ips/tutorials/j2k/#What-is.

[Kak48]   S. Kakutani, *On equivalence of infinite product measures*, Ann. of Math. (2) **49** (1948), 214–224.

[Kat87]   Y. Katznelson, *Intégrales de produits de Riesz*, C. R. Acad. Sci. Paris Sér. I Math. **305** (1987), 67–69.

[Kea72]   M. Keane, *Strongly mixing g-measures*, Invent. Math. **16** (1972), 309–324.

[Kig01]   J. Kigami, *Analysis on Fractals*, Cambridge Tracts in Mathematics, vol. 143, Cambridge University Press, Cambridge, 2001.

[Knu81]   D.E. Knuth, *The Art of Computer Programming: Vol. 2: Seminumerical Algorithms*, 2nd ed., Addison-Wesley Series in Computer Science and Information Processing, Addison-Wesley, Reading, Mass., 1981.

[Knu84]   D.E. Knuth, *An algorithm for Brownian zeroes*, Computing **33** (1984), 89–94.

[Kol77]   A.N. Kolmogorov, *Grundbegriffe der Wahrscheinlichkeitsrechnung*, Springer-Verlag, Berlin–New York, 1977, reprint of the 1933 original; English translation: *Foundations of the Theory of Probability*, Chelsea, 1950.

[KoSp04]   C. Köstler and R. Speicher, *On the structure of non-commutative white noises*, http://arxiv.org/abs/math.OA/0411519.

[KuDS05]   A. Kusiak, B. Dixon, and S. Shah, *Predicting survival time for kidney dialysis patients: A data mining approach*, Computers in Biology and Medicine **35** (2005), no. 4, 311–327.

[Kus01]   A. Kusiak, *Feature transformation methods in data mining*, IEEE Transactions on Electronics Packaging Manufacturing **24** (2001), no. 3, 214–221.

[Kus02]   A. Kusiak, *A data mining approach for generation of control signatures*, ASME Transactions: Journal of Manufacturing Science and Engineering **124** (2002), no. 4, 923–926.

[Kus05]   A. Kusiak, *Selection of invariant objects with a data mining approach*, IEEE Transactions on Electronics Packaging Manufacturing **28** (2005), no. 2, 187–196.

[KuBu05]   A. Kusiak and A. Burns, *Mining temporal data: A coal-fired boiler case study*, Knowledge-Based Intelligent Information and Engineering Systems, Proceedings of the 9th International Conference, KES 2005, Melbourne, Australia, September 14–16, 2005, Vol. III (R. Khosla, R.J. Howlett, and L.C. Jain, eds.), Lecture Notes in Artificial Intelligence, vol. 3683, Springer, Heidelberg, 2005, pp. 953–958.

[KuLD01]   A. Kusiak, I.H. Law, and M.D. Dick, *The G-algorithm for extraction of robust decision rules: Children's postoperative intra-atrial arrhythmia case study*, IEEE Transactions on Information Technology in Biomedicine **5** (2001), no. 3, 225–235.

[ŁaWa02]   I. Łaba and Y. Wang, *On spectral Cantor measures*, J. Funct. Anal. **193** (2002), 409–420.

[LaNg98]   K.-S. Lau and S.-M. Ngai, *L^q-spectrum of the Bernoulli convolution associated with the golden ratio*, Studia Math. **131** (1998), 225–251.

[LaNR01]   K.-S. Lau, S.-M. Ngai, and H. Rao, *Iterated function systems with overlaps and self-similar measures*, J. London Math. Soc. (2) **63** (2001), 99–116.

[LaRe91]   W.M. Lawton and H.L. Resnikoff, *Multidimensional wavelet bases*, Report AD910130, AWARE, Inc., Cambridge, MA, 1991.

[Law91a]   W.M. Lawton, *Necessary and sufficient conditions for constructing orthonormal wavelet bases*, J. Math. Phys. **32** (1991), 57–61.

[Law91b]   W.M. Lawton, *Multiresolution properties of the wavelet Galerkin operator*, J. Math. Phys. **32** (1991), 1440–1443.

[LaLS96]   W.M. Lawton, S.L. Lee, and Z. Shen, *An algorithm for matrix extension and wavelet construction*, Math. Comp. **65** (1996), no. 214, 723–737.

[LaLS98]   W.M. Lawton, S.L. Lee, and Z. Shen, *Convergence of multidimensional cascade algorithm*, Numer. Math. **78** (1998), 427–438.

[LySt03]   R. Lyons and J.E. Steif, *Stationary determinantal processes: phase multiplicity, Bernoullicity, entropy, and domination*, Duke Math. J. **120** (2003), 515–575.

[Mal89]   S.G. Mallat, *Multiresolution approximations and wavelet orthonormal bases of* $L^2(\mathbf{R})$, Trans. Amer. Math. Soc. **315** (1989), 69–87.

[Mal98]   S.G. Mallat, *A Wavelet Tour of Signal Processing*, Academic Press, San Diego, 1998.

[Mar82]   D. Marr, *Vision: A Computational Investigation into the Human Representation and Processing of Visual Information*, W.H. Freeman, San Francisco, 1982.

[May91]   D.H. Mayer, *Continued fractions and related transformations*, Ergodic Theory, Symbolic Dynamics, and Hyperbolic Spaces (Trieste, 1989) (T. Bedford, M. Keane, and C. Series, eds.), Oxford Science Publications, The Clarendon Press, Oxford University Press, New York, 1991, pp. 175–222.

[Mey79]   Y. Meyer, *Produits de Riesz généralisés*, Séminaire d'Analyse Harmonique, 1978–1979, Publications Mathématiques d'Orsay 79, vol. 7, Université de Paris-Sud, Faculté des Sciences-Mathématiques, Orsay, 1979, pp. 38–48.

[Mey89]   Y. Meyer, *Wavelets and operators*, Analysis at Urbana, Vol. I: Analysis in Function Spaces (Urbana, IL, 1986–1987) (E. Berkson and T. Peck, eds.), London Math. Soc. Lecture Note Ser., vol. 137, Cambridge University Press, Cambridge, 1989, pp. 256–365.

[Mey97]   Y. Meyer, *Wavelets and fast numerical algorithms*, Handbook of Numerical Analysis, Vol. V: Techniques of Scientific Computing, Part 2 (P.G. Ciarlet and J.L. Lions, eds.), North-Holland, Amsterdam, 1997, pp. 639–713.

[Mey05]   Y. Meyer, *Compression des images fixes*, Gaz. Math. (2005), no. 103, 9–23.

[MeCo97]   Y. Meyer and R. Coifman, *Wavelets: Calderón-Zygmund and Multilinear Operators*, Cambridge Studies in Advanced Mathematics, vol. 48, Cambridge University Press, Cambridge, 1997, translated from the 1990 and 1991 French originals by David Salinger.

[Mon64]   E.W. Montroll, *Random walks on lattices*, Stochastic Processes in Mathematical Physics and Engineering (R. Bellman, ed.), Proceedings of Symposia in Applied Mathematics, vol. 16, American Mathematical Society, Providence, 1964, reprinted 1980, pp. 193–220.

[Nek04]   V.V. Nekrashevych, *Cuntz-pimsner algebras of group actions*, J. Operator Theory **52** (2004), 223–249.

[Nel59]   E. Nelson, *Regular probability measures on function space*, Ann. of Math. (2) **69** (1959), 630–643.

[Nel64]   E. Nelson, *Feynman integrals and the Schrödinger equation*, J. Math. Phys. **5** (1964), 332–343.

[Nel67]   E. Nelson, *Dynamical Theories of Brownian Motion*, Princeton University Press, Princeton, NJ, 1967.

[Nel69]   E. Nelson, *Topics in Dynamics, I: Flows*, Mathematical Notes, Princeton University Press, Princeton, NJ, 1969.

[Nel73]   E. Nelson, *Construction of quantum fields from Markoff fields*, J. Funct. Anal. **12** (1973), 97–112.

[Nev65]   J. Neveu, *Mathematical Foundations of the Calculus of Probability*, Holden-Day Series in Probability and Statistics, Holden-Day, San Francisco, 1965, translated from the French by A. Feinstein.

[Nev75]   J. Neveu, *Discrete-Parameter Martingales*, revised ed., North-Holland Mathematical Library, vol. 10, North-Holland, Amsterdam, 1975, translated from the French by T. P. Speed.

[OED]   *Oxford English Dictionary*, second ed., Oxford University Press, Oxford, 1989.

[PaSW99]   M. Papadakis, H. Šikić, and G. Weiss, *The characterization of low pass filters and some basic properties of wavelets, scaling functions and related concepts*, J. Fourier Anal. Appl. **5** (1999), 495–521.

[PaPo90]   W. Parry and M. Pollicott, *Zeta functions and the periodic orbit structure of hyperbolic dynamics*, Astérisque, vol. 187–188, Société Mathématique de France, Paris, 1990.

[PaSc72]   K. R. Parthasarathy and K. Schmidt, *Positive Definite Kernels, Continuous Tensor Products, and Central Limit Theorems of Probability Theory*, Lecture Notes in Mathematics, vol. 272, Springer-Verlag, Berlin-New York, 1972.

[Per07]   O. Perron, *Zur Theorie der Matrizen*, Math. Ann. **64** (1907), 248–263.

[Pop89]   G. Popescu, *Isometric dilations for infinite sequences of non-commuting operators*, Trans. Amer. Math. Soc. **316** (1989), 523–536.

[PoSt70]   R.T. Powers and E. Størmer, *Free states of the canonical anti-commutation relations*, Comm. Math. Phys. **16** (1970), 1–33.

[Rad99]   C. Radin, *Miles of tiles*, Student Mathematical Library, vol. 1, American Mathematical Society, Providence, 1999.

[Rev84]   D. Revuz, *Markov Chains*, second ed., North-Holland Mathematical Library, vol. 11, North-Holland, Amsterdam, 1984.

[RiSh00]   S.D. Riemenschneider and Z. Shen, *Interpolatory wavelet packets*, Appl. Comput. Harmon. Anal. **8** (2000), 320–324.

[Rie18]   F. Riesz, *Über die Fourierkoeffizienten einer stetigen Funktion von beschränkter Schwankung*, Math. Z. **2** (1918), 312–315.

[Rit79]   G. Ritter, *On Kakutani's dichotomy theorem for infinite products of not necessarily independent functions*, Math. Ann. **239** (1979), 35–53.

[RoWi00]   L.C.G. Rogers and D. Williams, *Diffusions, Markov processes, and martingales, Vol. 1: Foundations*, Cambridge Mathematical Library, Cambridge University Press, Cambridge, 2000, reprint of the second ed., Wiley, Chichester, 1994.

[RoSh97]   A. Ron and Z. Shen, *Affine systems in $L_2(\mathbf{R}^d)$: the analysis of the analysis operator*, J. Funct. Anal. **148** (1997), 408–447.

[RoSh98]   A. Ron and Z. Shen, *Compactly supported tight affine spline frames in $L_2(\mathbf{R}^d)$*, Math. Comp. **67** (1998), 191–207.

[RoSh00]   A. Ron and Z. Shen, *The Sobolev regularity of refinable functions*, J. Approx. Theory **106** (2000), 185–225.

[RoSh03]   A. Ron and Z. Shen, *The wavelet dimension function is the trace function of a shift-invariant system*, Proc. Amer. Math. Soc. **131** (2003), 1385–1398.

[RST01]   A. Ron, Z. Shen, and K.-C. Toh, *Computing the Sobolev regularity of refinable functions by the Arnoldi method*, SIAM J. Matrix Anal. Appl. **23** (2001), 57–76.

[Rud87]   W. Rudin, *Real and Complex Analysis*, third ed., McGraw-Hill, New York, 1987.

[Rue69]   D. Ruelle, *Statistical Mechanics: Rigorous Results*, W. A. Benjamin, Inc., New York-Amsterdam, 1969.

[Rue89]   D. Ruelle, *The thermodynamic formalism for expanding maps*, Comm. Math. Phys. **125** (1989), no. 2, 239–262.

[Rue94]   D. Ruelle, *Dynamical Zeta Functions for Piecewise Monotone Maps of the Interval*, CRM Monograph Series, vol. 4, American Mathematical Society, Providence, 1994.

[Rue02]   D. Ruelle, *Dynamical zeta functions and transfer operators*, Notices Amer. Math. Soc. **49** (2002), 887–895.

[Sat99]   K.-I. Sato, *Lévy Processes and Infinitely Divisible Distributions*, Cambridge Studies in Advanced Mathematics, vol. 68, Cambridge University Press, Cambridge, 1999, translated from the 1990 Japanese original, revised by the author.

[SchCC]   Phil Schniter, *Two-branch quadvalue mirror filterbank (QMF)*, see [WWW4].

[Sch1871]   E. Schröder, *Über iterirte Functionen*, Math. Ann. **3** (1871), 296–322.

[SeCh67]   A. Selberg and S. Chowla, *On Epstein's zeta-function*, J. Reine Angew. Math. **227** (1967), 86–110.

[ShKu04]   S.C. Shah and A. Kusiak, *Data mining and genetic programming based gene/SNP selection*, Artificial Intelligence in Medicine **31** (2004), no. 3, 183–196.

[Sha49]   C.E. Shannon, *Communication in the presence of noise*, Proc. Inst. Radio Engineers **37** (1949), 10–21.

[She98]   Z. Shen, *Refinable function vectors*, SIAM J. Math. Anal. **29** (1998), 235–250.

[StHS+99]   V. Strela, P.N. Heller, G. Strang, P. Topiwala, and C. Heil, *The application of multiwavelet filterbanks to image processing*, IEEE Transactions on Image Processing **8** (1999), 548–563.

[Shu04]   F. Shultz, *Dimension groups for interval maps II: The transitive case*, preprint, math.DS/0405467.

[Shu05]   F. Shultz, *Dimension groups for interval maps*, New York J. Math. **11** (2005), 477–517.

[Sim79]   B. Simon, *Functional Integration and Quantum Physics*, Pure and Applied Mathematics, vol. 86, Academic Press, New York, 1979.

[Sko61]   A.V. Skorokhod, *Issledovaniya po teorii sluchainykh protsessov (Stokhasticheskie differentsialnye uravneniya i predelnye teoremy dlya protsessov Markova)*, Izdat. Kiev. Univ., Kiev, 1961.

[Sko65]   A.V. Skorokhod, *Studies in the Theory of Random Processes*, Addison-Wesley, Reading, Mass., 1965, Translated from the Russian by Scripta Technica.

[Song05]   M.-S. Song, *Wavelet image compression*, Ph.D. thesis, The University of Iowa, 2005.

[Song05a]   M.-S. Song, *Wavelet image decomposition*, http://www.biblethumper.org/˜msong/Images/waveletdec.html.

[Song05b]   M.-S. Song, http://www.biblethumper.org/˜msong/Images/.

[Spi76]   F. Spitzer, *Principles of Random Walk*, second ed., Graduate Texts in Mathematics, vol. 34, Springer-Verlag, New York, 1976, first softcover printing, 2001.

[StNg96]   G. Strang and T. Nguyen, *Wavelets and Filter Banks*, Wellesley-Cambridge Press, Wellesley, Massachusetts, 1996.

[Str98]   R.S. Strichartz, *Remarks on: "Dense analytic subspaces in fractal L^2-spaces" [J. Analyse Math. 75 (1998), 185–228] by P.E.T. Jorgensen and S. Pedersen*, J. Analyse Math. **75** (1998), 229–231.

[Str00]   R.S. Strichartz, *Mock Fourier series and transforms associated with certain Cantor measures*, J. Anal. Math. **81** (2000), 209–238.

[Str05]   R.S. Strichartz, *Convergence of Mock Fourier series*, preprint, Cornell University.

[Stro96]   D.W. Stroock, *Gaussian measures in traditional and not so traditional settings*, Bull. Amer. Math. Soc. (N.S.) **33** (1996), 135–155.

[Stro00]   D.W. Stroock, *An Introduction to the Analysis of Paths on a Riemannian Manifold*, Mathematical Surveys and Monographs, vol. 74, American Mathematical Society, Providence, RI, 2000.

[Stro05]   D.W. Stroock, *An Introduction to Markov Processes*, Graduate Texts in Mathematics, vol. 230, Springer, Berlin, 2005.

[Tao96]   T. Tao, *On the almost everywhere convergence of wavelet summation methods*, Appl. Comput. Harmon. Anal. **3** (1996), no. 4, 384–387.

[Vai93]   P.P. Vaidyanathan, *Multirate Systems and Filter Banks*, Prentice-Hall Signal Processing Series, Prentice Hall, Englewood Cliffs, NJ, 1993.

[VaAk01]   P.P. Vaidyanathan and S. Akkarakaran, *A review of the theory and applications of optimal subband and transform coders*, Appl. Comput. Harmon. Anal. **10** (2001), no. 3, 254–289.

[VeKo95]   M. Vetterli and J. Kovačević, *Wavelets and Subband Coding*, Prentice-Hall Signal Processing Series, Prentice Hall PTR, Englewood Cliffs, NJ, 1995.

[ViMu95]   B. Vidakovic and P. Mueller, *Wavelets for kids: A tutorial introduction*, preprint, 1995, Duke University, Institute of Statistics and Decision Sciences, and [WWW/wiki].

[VoDN92]   D.V. Voiculescu, K.J. Dykema, and A. Nica, *Free Random Variables: A Noncommutative Probability Approach to Free Products with Applications to Random Mmatrices, Operator Algebras and Harmonic Analysis on Free Groups*, American Mathematical Society, Providence, 1992.

[Waln02]   D.F. Walnut, *An Introduction to Wavelet Analysis*, Applied and Numerical Harmonic Analysis, Birkhäuser, Boston, 2002.

[Wal01]   P. Walters, *Convergence of the Ruelle operator for a function satisfying Bowen's condition*, Trans. Amer. Math. Soc. **353** (2001), 327–347.

[Wic93]   M.V. Wickerhauser, *Best-adapted wavelet packet bases*, Different Perspectives on Wavelets (San Antonio, TX, 1993) (I. Daubechies, ed.), Proc. Sympos. Appl. Math., vol. 47, American Mathematical Society, Providence, 1993, pp. 155–171.

[Wic94]   M.V. Wickerhauser, *Adapted Wavelet Analysis from Theory to Software*, IEEE Press, New York, A.K. Peters, Wellesley, MA, 1994.

[Wil91]   D. Williams, *Probability with Martingales*, Cambridge Mathematical Textbooks, Cambridge University Press, Cambridge, 1991.

[WWW1]   *Lifting-scheme-based wavelet transform*, http://www.electronicsletters.com/papers/example/paper.html; [WWW2] and [WWW3] are Figures 5 and 6, respectively.

[WWW2]   http://www.electronicsletters.com/papers/example/Psubsampletransform.gif; Figure 5 in [WWW1].

[WWW3]   http://www.electronicsletters.com/papers/example/Pinversetransform.gif; Figure 6 in [WWW1].

[WWW4]   Phil Schniter, *Two-branch quadvalue mirror filterbank (QMF)*, http://cnx.rice.edu/content/m10426/latest/, *Connexions* module.

[WWW5]   Ma Yi, *Basic image processing demos (for EECS20)*, http://robotics.eecs.berkeley.edu/~mayi/imgproc/.

[WWW/wiki]   http://en.wikipedia.org/wiki/Wavelet.

[YaHK97]   M. Yamaguti, M. Hata, and J. Kigami, *Mathematics of Fractals*, Translations of Mathematical Monographs, vol. 167, American Mathematical Society, Providence, 1997, translated from the 1993 Japanese original by Kiki Hudson.

[YiCC]   Ma Yi, *Basic image processing demos (for EECS20)*, see [WWW5].

[Zyg32]   A. Zygmund, *On lacunary trigonometric series*, Trans. Amer. Math. Soc. **34** (1932), 435–446.

Symbols

Reminder: In the symbol list and in the chapters, function spaces are defined with respect to various integrability conditions. For a function f on a space X, absolute integrability refers to $|f|$, i.e., to the absolute value of f, and to a prescribed (standard) measure on X. This measure on X is often implicitly understood, as is its σ-algebra of measurable sets. Examples: If the space X is $\mathbb{R}^d$, the measure will be the standard d-dimensional Lebesgue measure; for the one-torus $\mathbb{T}$ (i.e., the circle group), it will be normalized Haar measure, and similarly for the d-torus $\mathbb{T}^d$; for $X = \mathbb{Z}$, the measure will simply be counting measure; and for X_3 (the middle-third Cantor set), the measure will be the corresponding Hausdorff measure h_s of fractal dimension $s = \log_3(2)$. In each case, we introduce Hilbert spaces of L^2-functions, and the measure will be understood to be the standard one. Same convention for the other L^p-spaces!

∨ : lattice operation applied to closed
subspaces in a Hilbert space: the
lim sup lattice operation
169, 181

∧ : lattice operation applied to closed
subspaces in a Hilbert space: the
lim inf lattice operation
169, 181

∅ : empty set
171, 172, 185,

$\bar{E}$: closure of a set E
44, 172

$\hat{\varphi}$: Fourier transform (of the scaling
function φ)
10, 114, 111

≼ : relatively absolutely continuous
(relation between measures)
50, 53

⬆ : up-sampling
124, 132, 213, 214

⬇ : down-sampling
124–128, 132, 133, 212, 213, 215

⊕ : direct (orthogonal) sum
112, 172, 218

⊗ : tensor product
139, 158, 161–163, 165, 170–172,
180–183, 189, 190, 193, 194, 197

⊖ : relative orthogonal complement
169

× : Cartesian product
11, 43, 49, 52, 88, 117, 130, 164,
166, 185, 188, 218

: counting function
6, 41, 72, 101, 159, 184, 196

⟨ · | · ⟩ : inner product
16, 75, 77, 79, 104, 114, 140

| · ⟩ : Dirac vector
160–163, 171, 182, 184, 185, 189,
193, 194

[· , ·) : interval closed to the left and
open to the right
41, 61, 63, 65, 136–138, 165, 166,
167, 192

[· , ·) : segment of $\mathbb{N}_0$
165–167, 186, 188

[· , ·] : interval closed at both ends
7, 11, 13, 16–18, 47, 62–66, 71, 77,
84, 89–92, 102, 105, 112, 125,
130, 135–139, 195

Index

Comments on the use of the index: Some terms in the index may appear in the text in a slight variant, or variation of the actual index-term itself. For example, we will have terms in the index referring to "theorem so and so." But when we use the Stone–Weierstraß *theorem*, I just say Stone–Weierstraß. The word "theorem" will be suppressed. It is implicitly understood.

Similarly, I often just say, "by domination" (or some variant thereof), when I mean, "by an application of the dominated convergence theorem," or more fully: "By Lebesgue's dominated convergence theorem." It will be the same theorem whether the name is abbreviated or not.

For Fubini, the word "theorem" may be implicitly understood. Guido Weiss has made a verb out of it: "Fubinate" means "to exchange the order of two integrals."

Similarly, the name Fatou often is used to mean "Fatou's lemma" (the one about lim inf). For some reason poor Fatou only got credit for a lemma. But I do not mind upgrading him to a theorem, although "Fatou's theorem" usually refers to the one about existence a.e. of boundary values of bounded harmonic functions. I usually call that one "the Fatou-Primalov theorem."

Graduate Texts in Mathematics

(continued from p. ii)